World Scientific
Series in Advanced
Manufacturing

Volume 3: Augmented, Virtual and Mixed Reality Applications in Advanced Manufacturing

Manufacturing in the Era of 4th Industrial Revolution

A World Scientific Reference

World Scientific Series in Advanced Manufacturing

Print ISSN: 2717-5901
Online ISSN: 2717-591X

Editor-in-Chief: Prof. Satyandra K. Gupta *(University of Southern California)*

The World Scientific Series in Advanced Manufacturing aims to disseminate the new knowledge being created in the area of advanced manufacturing. Books in this series are expected to serve as a reference for practicing engineers and textbooks for new courses. This series has a broad scope and will cover all potential areas related to Advanced Manufacturing technologies.

Published

Manufacturing in the Era of 4th Industrial Revolution — A World Scientific Reference (in 3 Volumes)

Volume 1: Recent Advances in Additive Manufacturing
edited by Hugh A. Bruck, Yong Chen, and Satyandra K. Gupta

Volume 2: Recent Advances in Industrial Robotics
edited by Satyandra K. Gupta, Venkat N. Krovi, and Craig Schlenoff

Volume 3: Augmented, Virtual and Mixed Reality Applications in Advanced Manufacturing
edited by Monica Bordegoni, Satyandra K. Gupta, and James Ritchie

Editor-in-chief: **Satyandra K Gupta**

World Scientific
Series in Advanced
Manufacturing

Volume 3: Augmented, Virtual and Mixed Reality Applications in Advanced Manufacturing

Manufacturing in the Era of 4th Industrial Revolution

A World Scientific Reference

editors

Monica Bordegoni
Politecnico di Milano, Italy

Satyandra K Gupta
University of Southern California, USA

James Ritchie
Heriot-Watt University, UK

NEW JERSEY · LONDON · SINGAPORE · BEIJING · SHANGHAI · HONG KONG · TAIPEI · CHENNAI · TOKYO

Published by

World Scientific Publishing Co. Pte. Ltd.

5 Toh Tuck Link, Singapore 596224

USA office: 27 Warren Street, Suite 401-402, Hackensack, NJ 07601

UK office: 57 Shelton Street, Covent Garden, London WC2H 9HE

Library of Congress Cataloging-in-Publication Data
Names: Gupta, Satyandra K, editor.
Title: Manufacturing in the era of 4th industrial revolution / editor-in-chief, Satyandra K Gupta.
Other titles: Manufacturing in the era of fourth industrial revolution
Description: Hackensack, NJ : World Scientific, 2020. | Series: A World Scientific reference |
    Includes bibliographical references and index. | Contents: volume 1. Recent advances in
    additive manufacturing / editors, Hugh Bruck, University of Maryland, College Park, USA, Yong Chen,
    University of Southern California, USA, Satyandra K Gupta, University of Southern California, USA --
    volume 2. Recent advances in industrial robotics / editors, Satyandra K Gupta,
    University of Southern California, USA, Venkat N Krovi, Clemson University, USA,
    Craig Schlenoff, National Institute of Standards and Technology, USA --
    volume 3. Augmented, virtual and mixed reality applications in advanced manufacturing /
    editors, Monica Bordegoni, Politecnico di Milano, Italy, Satyandra K Gupta,
    University of Southern California, USA, James Ritchie, Heriot-Watt University, UK.
Identifiers: LCCN 2020034693 | ISBN 9789811222818 (v. 1 ; hardcover) |
    ISBN 9789811222832 (v. 2 ; hardcover) | ISBN 9789811222856 (v. 3 ; hardcover) |
    ISBN 9789811222788 (hardcover ; set) | ISBN 9789811222825 (v. 1 ; ebook for institutions) |
    ISBN 9789811222849 (v. 2 ; ebook for institutions) | ISBN 9789811222863 (v. 3 ; ebook for institutions) |
    ISBN 9789811222801 (ebook for individuals) | ISBN 9789811222795 (ebook for institutions ; set)
Subjects: LCSH: Manufacturing processes--Technological innovations.
Classification: LCC TS183 .M353 2020 | DDC 670--dc23
LC record available at https://lccn.loc.gov/2020034693

British Library Cataloguing-in-Publication Data
A catalogue record for this book is available from the British Library.

For any available supplementary material, please visit
https://www.worldscientific.com/worldscibooks/10.1142/11898#t=suppl

Printed in Singapore

Contents

About the Editors   vii

About the Contributors   ix

1. Introduction   1
    Monica Bordegoni, Satyandra K. Gupta, and James Ritchie

2. Collaborative VR-CAD for Industrial Product Design: CAD Parameter 17
    Modification with 3D Interaction on Heterogeneous Immersive Platforms
    Yujiro Okuya, Nicolas Ladevèze, Olivier Gladin, Cédric Fleury,
    and Patrick Bourdot

3. Improving Maintenance Services through Virtual Reality   49
    Nicola Riboldi, Giulia Wally Scurati, Francesco Ferrise,
    Monica Bordegoni, and Simone Pedrini

4. An Augmented Reality System Model for Integration with   73
    Maintenance Information Systems
    Iñigo Fernández del Amo, John Erkoyuncu, and Rajkumar Roy

5. Manufacturing Assembly Simulations in Virtual and Augmented Reality 103
    Wenjin Tao, Ze-Hao Lai, and Ming C. Leu

6. Virtual Environment Applications for Front-End Design and   131
    Manufacturing Planning Applications
    James Ritchie, Theodore Lim, Aparajithan Sivanathan, Avery Read,
    Sam Harper, Scott Mcgibbon, Hugo I. Medellin-Castillo,
    and Germanico Gonzalez-Badillo

7. Virtual Reality Applications for Computer-Aided Design and   179
    Advanced Manufacture of Medical Devices
    Hugo I. Medellin-Castillo, Jorge Zaragoza-Siqueiros, Eder H. Govea-
    Valladares, James Ritchie, Theodore Lim, and Aparajithan Sivanathan

8. Augmented Reality Applications in Industrial Robots   213
    Jingsong Chu, Ariyan Kabir, William Rose, Dennis Wang,
    Mingjun Yao, and Satyandra K. Gupta

9. Anti-Fragility in Design Engineering Procedures Embedded in   237
    Hybrid Multiple Realms and Blended Environments —
    The Physical Real of Reality
    Robert E. Wendrich

About the Editors

Monica Bordegoni

Monica Bordegoni is Full Professor in Virtual and Physical Prototyping at the School of Design of Politecnico di Milano. Her research interests concern methods and tools for products development, methods and technologies for Virtual Prototyping of industrial products, experience design, olfactory displays.

Satyandra K. Gupta

Dr. Satyandra K. Gupta is Smith International Professor in the Department of Aerospace and Mechanical Engineering and Department of Computer Science in Viterbi School of Engineering at the University of Southern California. He served as a program director for the National Robotics Initiative at the National Science Foundation from September 2012 to September 2014. Dr. Gupta's interests are in the area of physics-aware decision making to facilitate and advance the state of automation. He has published more than 350 technical articles. He is a fellow of the American Society of Mechanical Engineers (ASME), Institute of Electrical and Electronics Engineers (IEEE), and Society of Manufacturing Engineers (SME). He serves as editor of the *ASME Journal of Computing and Information Science in Engineering*. Dr. Gupta has received numerous honors and awards for his scholarly contributions. Representative examples include a Young Investigator Award from the Office of Naval Research in 2000, Robert W. Galvin Outstanding Young Manufacturing Engineer Award from the Society of Manufacturing Engineers in 2001, CAREER Award from the National Science Foundation in 2001, Presidential Early Career Award for Scientists and Engineers in 2001, Invention of the Year Award at the University of Maryland in 2007, Kos Ishii-Toshiba Award from ASME in 2011, Excellence in Research Award from ASME Computers and Information in Engineering Division in 2013, and Distinguished Alumnus Award from Indian Institute of Technology, Roorkee in 2014. He has also received ten best paper awards at international conferences.

James Ritchie

Professor James M. Ritchie is a Professor Emeritus of Heriot-Watt University, Edinburgh. He is a Chartered Engineer and a Fellow of the Institution of Mechanical Engineers, previously holding senior academic positions as Professor of Mechanical Engineering, Head of Mechanical Engineering, Founder and Head of the Mechanical, Process and Energy Engineering Research Institute and Dean of the University. Through a range of UK/EU funded projects, his primary research focus has been on design, manufacture and manufacturing management using digital engineering methods, including virtual reality, with an emphasis in product design, production/project/ process planning, manufacturing process mapping and associated knowledge capture. With over 180 technical publications, other associated research interests have included design process analysis, SME supply chain management, laser machining, quality methods in the food industry, critical railway component finite element analysis, serious games in engineering and virtual surgical planning.

About the Contributors

1. Introduction

Monica Bordegoni

Monica Bordegoni is Full Professor in Virtual and Physical Prototyping at the School of Design of Politecnico di Milano. Her research interests concern methods and tools for products development, methods and technologies for Virtual Prototyping of industrial products, experience design, olfactory displays.

Satyandra K. Gupta

Dr. Satyandra K. Gupta is Smith International Professor in the Department of Aerospace and Mechanical Engineering and Department of Computer Science in Viterbi School of Engineering at the University of Southern California. He served as a program director for the National Robotics Initiative at the National Science Foundation from September 2012 to September 2014. Dr. Gupta's interests are in the area of physics-aware decision making to facilitate and advance the state of automation. He has published more than three hundred fifty technical articles. He is a fellow of the American Society of Mechanical Engineers (ASME), Institute of Electrical and Electronics Engineers (IEEE), and Society of Manufacturing Engineers (SME). He serves as editor of the *ASME Journal of Computing and Information Science in Engineering*. Dr. Gupta has received numerous honors and awards for his scholarly contributions. Representative examples include a Young Investigator Award from the Office of Naval Research in 2000, Robert W. Galvin Outstanding Young Manufacturing Engineer Award from the Society of Manufacturing Engineers in 2001, CAREER Award from the National Science Foundation in 2001, Presidential Early Career Award for Scientists and Engineers in 2001, Invention of the Year Award at the University of Maryland in 2007, Kos Ishii-Toshiba Award from ASME in 2011, Excellence in Research Award from ASME Computers and Information in Engineering Division in 2013, and Distinguished Alumnus Award from Indian Institute of Technology, Roorkee in 2014. He has also received ten best paper awards at international conferences.

James Ritchie

Professor James M. Ritchie is a Professor Emeritus of Heriot-Watt University, Edinburgh. He is a Chartered Engineer and a Fellow of the Institution of Mechanical Engineers, previously holding senior academic positions as Professor of Mechanical Engineering, Head of Mechanical Engineering, Founder and Head of the Mechanical, Process and Energy Engineering Research Institute and Dean of the University. Through a range of UK/EU funded projects, his primary research focus has been on design, manufacture and manufacturing management using digital engineering methods, including virtual reality, with an emphasis in product design, production/project/ process planning, manufacturing process mapping and associated knowledge capture. With over 180 technical publications, other associated research interests have included design process analysis, SME supply chain management, laser machining, quality methods in the food industry, critical railway component finite element analysis, serious games in engineering and virtual surgical planning.

2. *Collaborative VR-CAD for Industrial Product Design: CAD Parameter Modification with 3D Interaction on Heterogeneous Immersive Platforms*

Yujiro Okuya

Dr. Yujiro Okuya is a postdoctoral research fellow at LIMSI-CNRS. He received his BS and MS degrees in Engineering from Tokyo Metropolitan University in 2012 and 2015, respectively. He then moved to University Paris-Saclay, where he completed his PhD in Computer science in 2019. His PhD thesis focused on CAD data modification techniques for design reviews on heterogeneous interactive systems. His research interests include 3D user interaction techniques in immersive systems and remote collaboration.

Nicolas Ladeveze

Nicolas Ladeveze is CNRS Research Engineer in charge of Virtual Reality systems of the Laboratoire d'Informatique pour la Mécanique et les Sciences de l'Ingénieur of Université Paris-Saclay, CNRS-LIMSI since 2016. He obtained his PhD in 2010 on the collaboration between automatic path planners and human users through visuo-haptic rendering to enhance industrial process simulation in virtual reality environments. His interest lies in the field of Human Computer Interaction, in particular Virtual Reality, signal processing, robotics and automation. He is a specialist of multimodal interactions on all type of applications from education to industrial simulations. He has published more than 15 international conference and scientific journals papers.

Olivier Gladin

Olivier Gladin is a graduate of the Yvelines Institute of Science and Technology, University of Versailles Saint-Quentin-en-Yvelines (UVSQ). He is Research Engineer in the experimentation and development team at Inria Saclay – Île-de-France where he works with Computer Human Interaction labs on ultra high-resolution wall-sized displays, VR and AR devices. He is a member of the steering and technical committee of the Digiscope project, a network of high-performance platforms for interactive visualization of large datasets and complex computation distributed throughout the University of Paris-Saclay. He worked for ten years in the video game industry where he was in charge of the Research and Development department of Vivendi Games Mobile and contributed on dozens of console, mobile, and web games.

Cédric Fleury

Dr. Cédric Fleury is assistant professor in Computer Science at Université Paris-Saclay (France) since 2013. He teaches computer science, including human-computer interaction and virtual reality, at the engineering school Polytech Paris-Saclay. He is part of the HCC (Human-Centered Computing) research team at the LRI laboratory and a member of the ex-situ project-team of Inria Saclay. Previously, he was a postdoctoral fellow at the University of North Carolina at Chapel Hill, U.S. and a visiting researcher at the Nanyang Technological University in Singapore as part of the BeingThere Center. He obtained a PhD in Computer Science from INSA Rennes (France) in 2012. His current research interests include human-computer interaction, remote collaboration in interactive systems, telepresence, collaborative virtual environment, 3D interaction, and 3D reconstruction. He has published his research work both in the human-computer interaction community (e.g. ACM CHI, INTERACT) and in the virtual reality community (e.g. ACM VRST, EuroVR, 3DCVE).

Patrick Bourdot

Dr. Patrick Bourdot is Research Director at CNRS, the French National Centre for Scientific Research, and head of VENISE team, the Virtual & Augmented Reality (V&AR) research group he has created in 2001 at CNRS/LIMSI lab (University Paris-Saclay). Architect graduated in 1986, he received his PhD in Computer Sciences at the University of Aix-Marseille in 1992. His main research focuses are: levels of detail, control of virtual navigations, 3D reconstruction, multimodal and collaborative V&AR interactions, and the related issues for users' perception and cognition. Regarding application fields, he has a special interest for Design and Engineering, Bioinformatics, CFD, Education of Sciences, and ASD. Founding secretary of AFRV, the French association of V&AR, he co-chaired its 5th conference. Program co-chair of the Equipex DIGISCOPE funded by the French government, a network of high-performance platforms for interactive visualization of large datasets and complex computation, he is the scientific leader of one of these platforms, namely the EVE system, an innovative multi-sensorimotor, multiuser and reconfigurable CAVE-like setup. Coordinator of the CNRS Labs involved in the INTUITION network on VR/AR of the 6th IST European framework (2004-2008), he is founding member of EuroVR. Member of the Executive Committee of EuroVR from its creation (2009), and currently its Vice-president "Academic Issues & Conferences" since 2016, he is or has been Conference or Program Co-chair of many international conferences organized under the umbrella of this association. Dr. Bourdot has a large number of international publications in V&AR and HCI journals (*Presence*, JVRB, *Frontiers in Robot AI*, *Journal of Multimodal User Interfaces*, *Virtual Reality*) or related to the application he is targeting (e.g. *Journal of Computer-Aided Design*, *Journal of Integrative Bioinformatics*), and in important conferences of his research fields (CHI, INTERACT, IEEE VR, ACM VRST, IEEE 3DUI, EGVE, 3DCVE,). He is Editor of several LNCS of Springer, Guest Associate Editor of *Frontiers in Virtual Environments*, and associate editor of *Frontiers in Technologies for VR*.

3. *Improving Maintenance Services through Virtual Reality*

Nicola Riboldi

Nicola Riboldi is mechanical engineer at OCRIM S.P.A. He received his MS degree in Mechanical Engineering from Politecnico di Milano in 2018, with a thesis concerning the use of Virtual Reality for supporting maintenance services.

Giulia Wally Scurati

Giulia Wally Scurati is a PhD candidate in Mechanical Engineering at Politecnico di Milano. Her research interests include methods and tools for product development, in particular, she focuses on supporting sustainable users' behavior using virtual prototyping techniques. Her research also concerns the use of Virtual and Augmented Reality for Industry 4.0, including industrial maintenance and training.

Francesco Ferrise

Francesco Ferrise is Associate Professor in the Department of Mechanical Engineering at Politecnico di Milano. His research has focused on the use of Augmented, Virtual and Mixed Reality technologies, as tools to support certain industrial processes, such as maintenance.

Monica Bordegoni

Monica Bordegoni is Full Professor in Virtual and Physical Prototyping at the School of Design of Politecnico di Milano. Her research interests concern methods and tools for product development, methods and technologies for Virtual Prototyping of industrial products, experience design, and olfactory displays.

Simone Pedrini

Simone Pedrini is manager at the Mechanical Department at OCRIM S.P.A. He graduated in Aerospace Engineering at Politecnico di Milano in 2002. He has been tutor of M.Sc theses on the usage of Virtual Reality as support for maintenance services and for the training of maintenance technicians.

4. *An Augmented Reality System Model for Integration with Maintenance Information Systems*

Iñigo Fernández del Amo

Iñigo Fernández del Amo started as a PhD student in Cranfield University in November 2016 with a scholarship from Babcock International. He focuses his research in the use of Augmented Reality (AR) and Semantic Web (SW) for knowledge capture in maintenance diagnosis. Iñigo's primary interest is to study innovative software methods to capture maintenance experts' knowledge and reduce cost of AR's industrial implementation. Besides his PhD research, Iñigo has co-supervised various MSc thesis and group projects that involve the implementation of AR and Digital Twins in industrial workplaces using SW technologies. As result of his research, Iñigo has published over 12 journal and conference papers. His overall aim is to enable the transformation of operative roles into a source of valuable information for through-life engineering services using innovative visualisation and data-structuring technologies. Iñigo graduated in 2016 with a double-degree in Industrial Engineer and Manufacturing Consultancy between the Polytechnic University of Madrid (UPM) and Cranfield

University. He won the Cranfield Vice-Chancellor's Prize 2017 for the most outstanding MS student.

John Erkoyuncu

Dr. John Erkoyuncu is the Director of the Through-life Engineering Services Centre at Cranfield University. John is a Senior Lecturer in Digital Service Engineering. John's research interests include: digital twins, augmented reality, digitalization of degradation assessment, AI and simulation of complex manufacturing and maintenance procedures. John has published over 90 journal and conference papers. Dr. Erkoyuncu works closely with organizations including BABCOCK International, Rolls-Royce, BAE Systems, Bombardier, MoD, MTT, Siemens, Curtis-Wright, and Fisher Bio Services. John is the Course Director for the MS in Through-life System Sustainment. Dr. Erkoyuncu is currently co-supervising eight PhD projects; six of which are co-funded by industry. John has supervised over 80 MSc projects. John is a Chartered Engineer, Fellow of the Higher Education Association, Former Chair of the CIRP Research Affiliates, and a Member of IET.

Rajkumar Roy

Professor Rajkumar Roy joined City from Cranfield University, where he was Director of Manufacturing. Professor Roy holds a PhD in Computing from the University of Plymouth (UK) and BEng and MEng degrees in Production Engineering from Jadavpur University in India. He started his career as an engineer at Tata Motors; pioneered research in Through-life Engineering Services (TES) with Rolls-Royce, BAE Systems, Bombardier Transportation, the Ministry of Defence and Babcock International; and established an internationally known TES Centre. Professor Roy's cost engineering and obsolescence research has transformed contemporary understanding of the engineering effort required to design, make and support high-value products, resulting in tools used by BAE Systems, Airbus, the Ministry of Defence, Rolls-Royce, and Ford Motor Company. He is a Founding Editor-in-Chief of the Elsevier Applied Soft Computing journal and a Fellow of the CIRP (International Academy for Production Engineers), the Institute of Engineering Designers (IED), and the Higher Education Academy (HEA). Professor Roy has advocated creative thinking in higher education and has started several new initiatives over the last twenty years. An initiative was to set up a new Centre for Competitive Creative Design (C4D), this is around £5.5m investment from HEFCE, Cranfield University, UAL and EEDA. The Centre aims to embed design thinking across enterprises to improve their creativity and make them more competitive. This is an initiative to link design with science, technology, and management.

5. *Manufacturing Assembly Simulations in Virtual and Augmented Reality*

Wenjin Tao

Wenjin Tao is currently completing his PhD in Mechanical Engineering in the Department of Mechanical and Aerospace Engineering at Missouri University of Science and Technology, advised by Prof. Ming C. Leu, and expects to defend by May 2020. As a graduate researcher of the Innovative Smart & Additive Manufacturing Laboratory, his research interests lie at the intersection of Advanced Manufacturing and Industrial Artificial Intelligence, including but not limited to cyber-physical manufacturing, worker behavior understanding, human-computer/robot interaction, AI-driven intelligent manufacturing such as data-driven prognostics and predictive maintenance, design optimization for additive manufacturing, and Virtual Reality/Augmented Reality for Smart Manufacturing. He has authored and co-authored nine journal papers, eight peer- reviewed conference papers, one book, two book chapters, and four patents. He received the Best Paper Award in IISE Annual conference, 2018.

Ze-Hao Lai

Ze-Hao "Jack" Lai currently works as a process engineer in Quanta Manufacturing Nashville, aiming at cloud computing unit production for web services. His responsibility mainly includes providing digital support in assembly, process improvement and data analysis. In addition, he has the experience in aerospace manufacturing and electronics industry. He earned his MS degree in Manufacturing Engineering at Missouri University of Science and Technology under supervision of Dr. Ming C. Leu and BS in Bio-Mechatronics Engineering at National Chung Hsing University in Taichung, Taiwan.

Ming C. Leu

Dr. Ming C. Leu is the Keith and Pat Bailey Distinguished Professor in the Department of Mechanical and Aerospace Engineering, Missouri University of Science and Technology. Prior to joining Missouri S&T in 1999, he was a Program Director at the National Science Foundation (1996 to 1999), the State Chair Professor in Manufacturing Productivity at the New Jersey Institute of Technology (1987 to 1996), and a faculty member at Cornell University (1981 to 1987). Professor Leu obtained his PhD in 1981 from the University of California at

Berkeley, his MS degree in 1977 from the Pennsylvania State University, and his BS degree in 1972 from the National Taiwan University, all in Mechanical Engineering. Dr. Leu's research interests include additive manufacturing, 3D printing, intelligent robotics & amp; automation, and cyber-physical manufacturing. He has published over 460 papers in refereed journals and conference proceedings, one e-book, 11 book chapters, and five U.S. patents. He has received numerous professional awards including, among others, the ASME Milton C. Shaw Manufacturing Research Medal (2018), University of Missouri President's Leadership Award (2017), ASME Blackall Machine Tool and Gage Award (2014), ISFA Hideo Hanafusa Outstanding Investigator Award (2008), ASME Distinguished Service Award (2004), SME University Lead Award (1994), NJIT Harlan J. Perlis Research Award (1993), NSF Presidential Young Investigator Award (1985), SAE Ralph R. Teetor Education Award (1985), as well as several best paper awards. He was elected to SME Fellow in 2018, CIRP Fellow in 2008, and ASME Fellow in 1993.

6. *Virtual Environment Applications for Front-End Design and Manufacturing Planning Applications*

James Ritchie

Professor James M. Ritchie is a Professor Emeritus of Heriot-Watt University, Edinburgh. He is a Chartered Engineer and a Fellow of the Institution of Mechanical Engineers, previously holding senior academic positions as Professor of Mechanical Engineering, Head of Mechanical Engineering, Founder and Head of the Mechanical, Process and Energy Engineering Research Institute and Dean of the University. Through a range of UK/EU funded projects, his primary research focus has been on design, manufacture and manufacturing management using digital engineering methods, including virtual reality, with an emphasis in product design, production/project/process planning, manufacturing process mapping and associated knowledge capture. With over 180 technical publications, other associated research interests have included design process analysis, SME supply chain management, laser machining, quality methods in the food industry, critical railway component finite element analysis, serious games in engineering and virtual surgical planning.

Theodore Lim

Dr. Theodore Lim is an Associate Professor at Heriot-Watt University and leads the Intelligent Manufacturing, Technology, and Systems Theme with a focus on Digital Tools. His research spans developing and profiling non-conventional interfaces and applications for virtual environments and systems to engineering and manufacturing. He has been instrumental in the research, analysis, and development of mixed reality engineering environments in a variety of product engineering domains emphasizing on knowledge engineering. In 2015, he jointly received the Emerald Literati Network Award for Excellence on haptics simulation, and in 2018 with Becker Group jointly received the Lanner industrial award on Industry 4.0 processes. With over 100 international publications, a book, and the successful commercialization of his novel algorithms, he is now applying his knowledge and expertise to the domain of serious games, game ware, and computational biometrics for next generation engineering applications. The developments have seen applications to other sectors such as Medical and Oil & Gas.

Aparajithan Sivanathan

Dr Aparajithan Sivanathan is a technical fellow heading up the digital manufacturing theme at AMRC North-West, University of Sheffield. Sivanathan comes from a multidisciplinary background of manufacturing, electronics, and computing. He received an MSc in Mechatronics engineering from King's College London and a PhD from Heriot-Watt University. The Ubiquitous Integration and Temporal Synchronisation (UbiITS) Framework for ultra-low latency applications developed through his PhD and post-doctoral research has been implemented in systems from various domains such as Smart Manufacturing, Digital Construction, Surgical Training, Race Driving, Neurocybernetics, Cognitive rehabilitation, and Gaming. Before entering the research career, he worked as an R&D engineer in electronics manufacturing industry. His current research interests generally fall into the area of manufacturing informatics, industrial 5G connectivity for industries, real-time human-in-the-loop systems, knowledge capture, shared virtual spaces, and industrial enterprise data bases.

Avery Read

Avery Read has a Master of Engineering Degree from Heriot-Watt University and is currently a PhD student in Mechanical Engineering at the same University. He is researching the use of virtual reality for the interactive, real time analysis of product design for assembly (DFA). Through the application of a number of mechanical product case studies, his novel research has demonstrated that immersive head mounted display virtual reality combined with a novel combination of real time Boothroyd and Dewhurst DFA analysis, 3D sketching and virtual assembly planning can provide an intuitive environment with minimal interrupts to support the effective redesign of mechanical products.

Sam Harper

Sam Harper is currently a PhD student at Heriot-Watt University where his research is exploring the use of mixed reality for educational, medical and manufacturing purposes. He was a Research Assistant on the University's EU-funded BEACONING project researching intuitive learning technologies using a Microsoft HoloLens by developing a key novel application to assist with the teaching of stonemasonry; the application itself being developed in Unity3D and written in C#. Other responsibilities include on-site demonstrations and further research into other intuitive input technologies

Scott McGibbon

Scott McGibbon, a stonemason to trade, whose career spans over some 30 years working as a construction consultant/contractor/educationalist. Currently he is CEO and founder of Pivotal Consultancy, an independent consultancy, based in Scotland, who provides specialist advice on digital innovation and integrative solutions for construction industry practice and training. His current areas of research interest include Process Innovation, Digital Construction, Technical Vocational Education and Training (TVET), STEM, Technology Enhanced Practice, Learning and Training. Working with a number of high profile Industry and Academic organisations, he explores how digital innovation in practice and training can reduce costs, mitigate risk, improve integration, augment performance and enhance quality, whilst fundamentally supporting businesses' move towards more flexible ways of working and learning, through building responsive business and educational processes. He is a Fellow of Institute for Innovation and Knowledge Exchange (FIKE), a member of the Chartered Institute of Building (CIOB), and the Comité International de Photogrammétrie Architecturale (CIPA). He has published a number of technical articles on the potential of digitization and its associated technologies for Construction Project Management (PM) "process management and improvement" and is currently in the final stages of his PhD whereby the output is the development of a common structured collaborative digitized process-standard (CrOsS) framework. He combines this with being the Scottish Qualification Authority (SQA) UK and International Depute Lead

Verifier and Senior External Qualification Verifier for Construction Technician professionals as well as a Qualification Verifier and Writer for various international training institutions.

Hugo I. Medellin-Castillo

Dr. Hugo I. Medellín-Castillo is a Full-time Professor in the Mechanical and Electrical Engineering department and Research Coordinator at Universidad Autonoma de San Luis Potosí. He completed his undergraduate studies in Mechanical and Electrical Engineering in 1999 at Universidad Autónoma de San Luis Potosí, Mexico. Later, he received his Master's degree in Mechanical Engineering in 2001 at Universidad de Guanajuato, Mexico. After concluding his master studies, he joined Comisión Federal de Electricidad as a design engineer before receiving a Doctorate Scholarship. He completed his PhD studies in Mechanical Engineering in 2005 at Heriot-Watt University, Scotland, UK. Since 2006 he has been working as full time lecturer and researcher in Mechanical Engineering at Universidad Autonóma de San Luis Potosí, Mexico. During this time, he has made several research internships abroad, published more than 150 research papers, graduated more than 20 postgraduate students, conducted several research and industrial projects, and founded the Advanced Design and Manufacturing Laboratory. He is member of the National System of Researchers (SNI) in México. His research interests include virtual design and manufacturing, analysis and computational modeling of manufacturing processes, metal forming, design for additive manufacturing, design of prosthesis and implants, human biomechanics, soft tissue and organ computational modeling, and virtual surgery.

Germanico Gonzalez-Badillo

Dr. Germanico Gonzalez-Badillo is a Full-Time Lecturer, and currently coordinator, of the Mechatronics Engineering Program at the Multidisciplinary Academic Unit of the Middle Zone (UAMZM) of the Autonomous University of San Luis Potosí (UASLP). His areas of interest mainly focus on advanced manufacturing systems such as virtual reality and 3D printing in process planning and training. Dr. Germanico has published in various journals with international impact as well as national and international conferences. One of his works was recognized as a "Highly Commended Article" in 2014 by the emerald publishing group. He is an active member of the American Society of Mechanical Engineers (ASME) and the Mexican Society of Mechanical Engineers (SOMIM). Since 2017 serves as topic co-organizer at ASME International Mechanical Engineering Congress (ASME IMECE) in the Advanced Manufacturing track. In 2014 completed his PhD studies in Mechanical Engineering with an emphasis on mechatronic systems at the Research and Postgraduate Studies Center (CIEP) of the Faculty of Engineering of UASLP. From 2006 to 2009 he participated as a research assistant in the Automotive Mechatronics Research Center (CIMA) of the Monterrey Institute of Technology and Higher Education (ITESM), Toluca campus, where he studied for a master's degree in Automotive Engineering. Dr. Germánico has a major degree as Mechanical Administrator Engineer by Faculty of Engineering of UASLP in 2003. From 2003 to 2006 he worked as a project advisor and branch manager for the company Automation S.A. de C.V.

7. *Virtual Reality Applications for Computer-Aided Design and Advanced Manufacture of Medical Devices*

Hugo I. Medellin-Castillo

Dr. Hugo I. Medellín-Castillo is a Full-time Professor in the Mechanical and Electrical Engineering department and Research Coordinator at Universidad Autonoma de San Luis Potosí. He completed his undergraduate studies in Mechanical and Electrical Engineering in 1999 at Universidad Autónoma de San Luis Potosí, Mexico. Later, he received his Master's degree in Mechanical Engineering in 2001 at Universidad de Guanajuato, Mexico. After concluding his master studies, he joined Comisión Federal de Electricidad as a design engineer before receiving a Doctorate Scholarship. He completed his PhD studies in Mechanical Engineering in 2005 at Heriot-Watt University, Scotland, UK. Since 2006 he has been working as full time lecturer and researcher in Mechanical Engineering at Universidad Autonóma de San Luis Potosí, Mexico. During this time, he has made several research internships abroad, published more than 150 research papers, graduated more than 20 postgraduate students, conducted several research and industrial projects, and founded the Advanced Design and Manufacturing Laboratory. He is member of the National System of Researchers (SNI) in México. His research interests includes virtual design and manufacturing, analysis and computational modeling of manufacturing processes, metal forming, design for additive manufacturing, design of prosthesis and implants, human biomechanics, soft tissue and organ computational modeling, and virtual surgery.

Jorge Zaragoza-Siqueiros

Dr. Jorge Zaragoza-Siqueiros is part-time professor in the Mechanical and Electrical Department of the Engineering College of the Autonomous University of San Luis Potosi, Mexico. Since 2012, He has served in the Mechanical Engineering teaching program, oriented to Computer Numerical Control manufacture and Advanced Topics in Manufacture. In 2014 Zaragoza-Siqueiros got his Master's degree, which focused in Additive Manufacturing (AM). In his investigation regarding AM, Dr. Jorge proposed guidelines oriented to parts manufactured by diverse AM techniques published in American Society of Mechanical Engineering (ASME) and international journals. In 2019, He achieved the PhD degree in Mechanical Engineering partnership work with the virtual reality lab of the Mechanical Engineering program of Heriot-Watt University, generating a virtual system for the maxillary surgery planning and simulation using haptic technologies. Jorge has contributed in the multinational sheet metal fabrication industry, proposing new assembly standards focused on increasing the production productivity.

Eder H. Govea-Valladares

Dr. Eder H. Govea-Valladares graduated as a mechanical engineer in 2006 at Instituto Tecnológico de San Luis Potosi. In 2007, he joined the master in science program at Universidad Autónoma de Querétaro, and graduated in 2009. He started his PhD studies in Mechanical Engineering at Universidad Autónoma de San Luis Potosí, and obtained his PhD degree in 2015. Since 2015, he has worked as part-time lecturer and as a chief engineer in the industry.

8. *Augmented Reality Applications in Industrial Robots*

Jingsong Chu

Jingsong Chu received a Bachelor Science degree in Mechanical Engineering from the University of California, Berkeley and a Master Science degree in Mechanical Engineering from the University of Southern California. While pursuing his Master's degree, he was actively involved with research in robotics and control. In particular, he worked at the Center for Advanced Manufacturing to develop an Augmented Reality interface for development for Industrial Robotic Arm Control to implement what he has learned to build a real product.

Ariyan M. Kabir

Dr. Ariyan Kabir is the co-founder and CEO of GrayMatter Robotics. Before that, he was a Postdoctoral Researcher at the University of Southern California (USC). He completed his PhD from USC with a research focus on artificial intelligence for robotics. His interests are in planning and learning algorithms for high degrees of freedom robotic systems. He is developing algorithmic foundations to find near-optimal solutions for computationally hard problems in real-time. He led the USC team to the finals of the 2017 KUKA Innovation Award and showcased robotic finishing technology at the Hannover Messe. Ariyan has won one best paper award and two best poster awards.

Dennis Wang

Dennis Wang received a Bachelor Science degree in Electrical Engineering and Computer Sciences from the University of California, Berkeley and a Master Science degree in Computer Engineering from the University of Southern California. While pursuing his Master's degree, he was actively involved with research. In particular, he worked at the Center for Advanced Manufacturing to develop an Augmented Reality interface for development for Industrial Robotic Arm Control. He also worked on embedded system development for communication between robots. In addition, he has many years of hardware and software experience from industries where he has worked in Xilinx, Marvell, Niche Biomedical, and Ravenswood Solutions.

William Rose

William Rose is a Design Engineer at GE Aviation working on a variety of commercial and military aerospace projects with the purpose of inventing the future of flight. His work focusses on mechanical component design, additive manufacturing, and LEAN integration of the supply chain. Prior to GE Aviation, he received a Bachelor of Science in Ocean Engineering from the United States Naval Academy and served as an officer in the United States Marine Corps where he worked with advanced electro-mechanical systems and led multiple teams in dynamic and challenging environments. He received a Master of Science in Mechanical Engineering and a Master of Business for Veterans from the University of Southern California, before joining GE Aviation through the Junior Officer Leadership Program which focuses on developing future business leaders by leveraging prior leadership experience.

Mingjun Yao

Mingjun Yao received a Bachelor Science degree in Mechanical Engineering from the Shanghai Jiao Tong University and a Master Science degree in Mechanical Engineering from the University of Southern California. While pursuing his Master's degree, he was actively involved with research in robotics and additive manufacturing. He worked at the Center for Advanced Manufacturing to develop an Augmented Reality interface for development for Industrial Robotic Arm Control and a Soft Robotic Hand.

Satyandra K. Gupta

Dr. Satyandra K. Gupta is Smith International Professor in the Department of Aerospace and Mechanical Engineering and Department of Computer Science in Viterbi School of Engineering at the University of Southern California. He served as a program director for the National Robotics Initiative at the National Science Foundation from September 2012 to September 2014. Dr. Gupta's interests are in the area of physics-aware decision making to facilitate and advance the state of automation. He has published more than three hundred fifty technical articles. He is a fellow of the American Society of Mechanical Engineers (ASME), Institute of Electrical and Electronics Engineers (IEEE), and Society of Manufacturing Engineers (SME). He serves as editor of the *ASME Journal of Computing and Information Science in Engineering*. Dr. Gupta has received numerous honors and awards for his scholarly contributions. Representative examples include a Young Investigator Award from the Office of Naval Research in 2000, Robert W. Galvin Outstanding Young Manufacturing Engineer Award from the Society of Manufacturing Engineers in 2001, CAREER Award from the National Science Foundation in 2001, Presidential Early Career Award for Scientists and Engineers in 2001, Invention of the Year Award at the University of Maryland in 2007, Kos Ishii-Toshiba Award from ASME in 2011, Excellence in Research Award from ASME Computers and Information in Engineering Division in 2013, and Distinguished Alumnus Award from Indian Institute of Technology, Roorkee in 2014. He has also received ten best paper awards at international conferences.

9. *Anti-Fragility in Design Engineering Procedures Embedded in Hybrid Multiple Realms and Blended Environments — The Physical Real of Reality*

Robert E. Wendrich

Dr Robert Wendrich is an assistant professor and researcher in the Design, Production and Management Department (DPM) from the Engineering Technology (ET) faculty within the University of Twente. His main research focuses on human/cyborg /robot-machine interaction, idea development, conceptual design, product development processes and design tools. He is the founder of Rawshaping Technology (RST) a research laboratory (2008) in which hybrid (XR / VR / AR / MR) computational interactive design tools are designed, build, tested and developed. As a researcher and scientist, with considerable industrial experience, he has numerous products, systems, hybrid and virtual environments analyzed, researched and developed. Current research is directed at the development of creative AI (CAI) imbued in computational support tools and anti-fragile robust interaction design (AfxD). Dr. Wendrich contributed more than 55 international publications, several book chapters and deployed successful commercialization of products and systems. He is a member of the American Society of Mechanical Engineers (ASME), the Design Society (DS), and special interest groups (SIGs) such as; EuroVR VETE SIG, Emotional Engineering SIG and biom* SIG. His knowledge and expertise are currently focused on the domain of cyber-physical systems, artificial intelligence, gamification and spontaneous creativity development for hybrid computer-controlled applications. Over the years he has received several national and international design awards, best paper/ poster awards and institutional education awards.

Chapter 1

Introduction

Monica Bordegoni, Satyandra K. Gupta, and James M. Ritchie

Virtual and Augmented Reality technologies are being leveraged by the manufacturing community to improve operations in a wide variety of ways. Opportunities arise from multiple manufacturing engineering research areas which can potentially enable such technologies to provide both innovative support and solutions to improve product design, planning, manufacturing and support throughout the product life cycle. These not only extend to the manufacturing domain itself but also to other areas where engineering-type virtual manufacturing approaches are relevant to the tools and skill sets required in other domains, such as healthcare, health and safety, ergonomics and education and training, to name but a few. Such solutions and technologies must be considered from the point-of-view of both the individual engineer and their needs as well as team-based engineering when collaborative working, design reviews and data/information provenance are necessary. All of the capabilities of real time engineering interaction must be considered when interfacing with VR/AR models and associated data; this will facilitate rapid product development, agile manufacturing and product support. With careful virtual manufacturing system planning and development – including front-end design – this will enable the effective generation of downstream data and information as well as upstream feedback. These capabilities will be critical for the engineering of products through a range of contemporary concepts now very much relevant to manufacturing applications, such as digital twins, Industry4.0, intelligent asset management, etc.

This chapter presents basic terminology and major applications areas where these technologies are being used to significantly improve manufacturing while providing some insight into potential future research and development.

1.1 Definitions

1.1.1 *What is a Virtual Reality?*

Virtual environment can be defined as a computer-generated environment used to simulate the real world. Many different types of virtual environments are possible. On the one hand, these environments can be as simple as a semi-immersive computer-based environment. On the other hand, these environments can be completely immersive, three-dimensional interactive experiences utilizing sound and force feedback to simulate a real environment. Virtual environments can be created that are completely photorealistic, called the image-based rendering method, or they can be created from 3D solid models, called the model-based rendering method. Typically, virtual environments created using image-based rendering are less interactive. Because they are image-based textures applied to the environment, they typically only allow movement through the scene and no manipulation of objects. On the other hand, virtual environments created using model-based rendering contain less visual realism because the scenes and objects are computer-generated, but they allow for manipulation of the environment. One method is not necessarily better than the other. They each have their role depending upon user objectives and the applications needs. In general, image-based rendering methods are used in game applications and model-based rendering methods are used in technical applications.

Virtual Reality (VR) is a specific form of a virtual environment which provides the user with a feeling of presence. Immersion offers the conditions which promote the feeling of presence. Immersion can be produced by feeding the user a continuous stream of realistic visual, audio, and touch stimuli and by enabling the user to naturally interact with virtual objects in the environment. It is not necessary to stimulate all three senses for immersion. Often the right combination of stereoscopic images and good user tracking can produce a sufficient level of immersion and a feeling of presence.

1.1.2 *What is Augmented Reality?*

While Virtual Reality allows a full immersion in virtual spaces, Augmented Reality (AR) adds digital information to the reality. Augmented Reality has been around since a while. It has the potential of a huge technological innovation, with impact on all of us. We can find applications of AR in our daily life, at work, on sport. AR effectiveness is based on the fact that we look at the physical world and we can get digital information on it. Many examples can be found in several areas. In addition to the first applications developed in the military sector, today there are screen ups for aircraft and cars augmenting the landscape with useful digital items of information, real games augmented with lines and scores, surgical set-ups augmenting what the surgeon is looking at with digital information on how to do the procedure. The technology enabling AR applications includes popular personal devices, as tablets and mobile phones, and more emerging technology, like 3D holograms. Hardware is combined with pieces of software based on computer graphics, computer vision and machine learning. The user interface is also evolving from keyboard and mouse to more natural interaction modalities as speech and gesture, and even thought in the years to come. Companies are paying a lot of attention to AR, perceiving its potential. It is possible to experience future products, machines, buildings, and pieces of furniture, co-located in real environments. The future of repair, maintenance, and manufacturing is AR supporting operators in walking through procedures. AR can also better connect people, and collaboration is expected to be more effective through AR. It is not that long that our colleagues and friends will appear to us rendered in AR.

1.2 Components of Virtual Environments

1.2.1 *Displays*

One of the key components of virtual environments is the stereo display of objects in the virtual environment, which aids the user in the feeling of immersion. There are generally two methods for obtaining stereo display. One of them is the use of head mounted displays. The other method is based on the projection of images onto a surface.

Head mounted displays (HMDs) are visualization devices that the user wears on top of the head and receives two streams of slightly different images of a scene through the two eyepieces. One set of images is slightly offset laterally from the other, simulating the interpupillary distance between the two eyes. By eliminating all outside light sources, HMDs are highly effective at presenting a user with a completely virtual environment without occluding the view with any real objects that may be present in the vicinity.

Projection-based displays employ a similar set of two-image streams projected onto a surface by multiple projectors. Users normally wear lightweight shutter glasses that filter out projected images for a particular eye. This way, one projection can only be seen by the right eye while another projection can only be seen by the left eye. The shutter glasses are normally synchronized with the projectors to block and unblock vision for each eye at a high rate. Although multiple users may observe the same 3D scene with a projection-based display method, only one user receives the most accurate stereoscopic view – the user being tracked by the system.

1.2.2 *User Tracking*

Another key component of many virtual environments is the tracking system used to monitor the movements of the user in order to properly update the virtual environment. Tracking systems generally fall in one of the following categories: magnetic, inertial, optical, and acoustic. Magnetic trackers generally involve a remote transmitter and a set of receivers worn on the user's body. Optical tracking systems generally involve the use of at least two cameras to track either active or passive markers worn by the user. The optical tracking systems use triangulation to determine the user's position. Inertial trackers are devices worn by the user which generally use a set of gyroscopes, accelerometers, and magnetometers to keep track of all six degrees of freedom. Such devices are often subject to accumulating errors, called drift, over long periods of time. Acoustic trackers are similar to magnetic trackers and use sound as the signal.

1.2.3 *Haptics*

Haptic feedback is another common component of a virtual environment. Haptic feedback can promote the feeling of immersion and presence by stimulating the user's sense of touch or by providing realistic force feedback to convey forces simulated inside the virtual environment. One of the most common methods of providing haptic feedback is via vibration that is activated in the device held by the user or within the glove worn by the user. Another common method of giving the user haptic feedback is through force exerted on the user's hands. Forces on the user can be exerted with simple inexpensive devices like joysticks and with more advanced devices like gloves.

1.2.4 *3D Sound*

Three-dimensional sound is another possible component of a virtual environment. Unlike stereo sound, which feels like the sound is originating inside the user's head and moves with the user when used with headphones, devices which produce real 3D sound using headphones make it seem like the sound is coming from an external source and stays in the same place as the user rotates his or her head. A potential method for generating 3D sound is by using headphones with devices called convolvotrons. Three-dimensional sound devices which employ convolvotrons use the position and orientation of the user's head reported by the tracking system to perform computations and synthesize sound for each of the two headphones.

1.3 Visualization During Design

Front-end product design and development involves a wide range of iterative activities early on in the product life cycle such as creativity, innovation, ideation, product requirements definition and design itself incorporating prototyping and testing. This must be grounded through a deep understanding of the customers' requirements as well as a strong awareness of the market and find a balance amongst the aesthetic, functional, ergonomic, cost, manufacturing, supply chain and sustainability requirements of the product. Product design also acts as a foundation for the rest of the life cycle by informing and driving these requirements throughout as the product itself takes shape from conceptualization and design, through planning, manufacture and delivery to eventual disposal. During such virtual engineering, important data and information can be captured, even simply by recording sessions; however, huge opportunities arise using virtual environments to do constructive analyses of communications, user interactions and decision making activities which can enhance the downstream formalization and understanding of both customer requirements and product functionality. If done in a structured way this can provide a foundation for the semi-/fully automated capture of time-phased data, information and knowledge along with its associated provenance, allowing the detailed monitoring and formalization of product history, ownership, location and, most importantly, decision making throughout the whole product life cycle. Not only individual uses of virtual environments should be considered: team-based engineering support systems are also crucial to this technology's application in future creative engineering processes as well as the integration of more traditional technologies such as computer aided design (CAD) and computer aided engineering (CAE).

Conceptual design is one of the most challenging areas in which to apply virtual technologies. Many of the earlier applications of what was termed "conceptual design" tended to be walkthroughs or simply visualization at a stage of the product development process which included early 3D models of some kind (usually quite late in the conceptual design phase). The challenge is to provide interactive tools at the earliest stage of the product development process with the capability to allow conceptual sketching from the off as quickly and efficiently as using a simple paper and pencil. Nowadays, there are virtual tools and associated interfaces available on the market that provide engineers with the ability to sketch conceptually, very rapidly providing them with the capability to conceive and create 3D models in real time without necessarily interrupting the creative process. A great deal of conceptual "design" takes place during manufacturing planning, simulation, factory/process design, etc. and engineers should look at the tools being developed and used at this stage of product design to identify where similar productivity gains can be made elsewhere in the product life cycle.

These conceptual design issues also highlight some important general aspects of virtual interfaces that should be considered when developing virtual reality solutions within the manufacturing environment, particularly the need to support the cognitive and creative processes of engineers through their natural human factors capabilities, providing user-friendly devices and interfaces that supplement their ingenuity. These should be matched with and take full advantage of the engineer's ergonomic requirements as well as their psychological and intellectual needs. Another important aspect is that applying VR/AR in this way tends to give people a more relaxed, positive and enjoyable experience. However, further understanding of the human behavioral and psychological impact of VR/AR in engineering (along with other computerized tools), as well as the social and collaborative aspects of engineering itself, will provide new and exciting opportunities for research into how products are engineered and how virtual technologies should evolve. Supporting solutions for such studies could include human factors, biometrics, neurometrics and game theory.

Another key requirement of such systems is the seamless bi-directional transfer of model data throughout the product life cycle and the ability to engage in sketching to enhance product design concepts. This will include, of course, the capability to carry our manufacturability and assemblability analyses and free form interactive design changes. Such conceptualization tools will not necessarily only have a role to play at the beginning of the design phase.

As mentioned previously, the product development process should morph seamlessly from conceptualization to embodiment and then onto detailed design and VR is a tool which can potentially support this shift. It is likely that VR/AR systems will be used in conjunction with conventional legacy CAD systems for some considerable time into the future; therefore, where there is still a need to support the full transfer of 100% correctly configured bi-directional data between CAD and VR systems along with the ability to bolt on VR/AR solutions to CAD systems. More rigorous comparative testing is required to identify the strengths and weaknesses of VR/AR solutions when compared to traditional CAD and other computer aided engineering (CAE) systems throughout the product development process so that engineers can be provided with the most effective computerized tools. The same applies to the generation of usable downstream engineering data. As with traditional computer integrated manufacturing (CIM) systems and approaches, we should be aware of the same bi-directional data needs identified as central to such systems when we are researching, developing and evolving VR/AR equivalent engineering systems.

Another key design area that is still lacking effective virtual solutions for their application is numerical modelling. Carrying out complex analysis, e.g. finite element analysis (FEA), computational fluid dynamics (CFD), etc. due to the processing needs of such technologies means that there is a significant lag between analyzing and displaying/interacting with the model in virtual reality. Reducing both the graphics and analytical computer processing times for complex 3D engineering products to facilitate real time analysis and interaction/modification will revolutionize the product development process. Potential lessons learnt may be available in the form of solutions derived in the games industry.

By using VR systems to engage with both external and internal customers at all stages of the product life cycle potential problems and issues can be identified which can, in turn, greatly enhance the design or planning process. There are many industrial applications of these technologies in this area. However, supporting the capture of new or modified design intent by logging users throughout a product's life cycle can considerably speed up and formalize design changes/modifications especially when integrated with some form of product data management (PDM) system or building information modeling (BIM) system. It should be borne in mind that engineers need to generate downstream data and feedback. With ever decreasing design lead times, the introduction of Industry4.0, global collaborative environments, digital twins, additive manufacturing for physical prototyping, etc. the effective utilization of such technologies will help substantially reduce time to market if applied in the right areas.

1.4 User Interface for Design

Traditional CAD system interfaces are difficult to learn and cumbersome to use. VR is creating new opportunities for designing much more natural interfaces. For example, gesture-based interfaces can be utilized to create complex designs by simple hand movements. Hand gestures can be used to sculpt a blob of material the same way a sculptor works on the clay. The designer can also hold and use virtual tools to carve the material and create the desired feature in a much more natural way. This allows people who have no experience in using CAD system to interact with the design and make changes to it. This holds the promise of democratizing the design process and expand the pool of people who can participate in the design process.

Virtual environments also allow multiple designers to collaborate on the design. This way people can discuss design and see what is being proposed and develop consensus around the desired features and shapes. This also enables bringing customers into the design process and allows them to interact with designers and communicate their requirements. Virtual environments also serve as a natural interface for capturing design discussions and design rationale.

1.5 Virtual Prototyping and Customer Input

Virtual Prototyping is a well-known and consolidated methodology for the evaluation of products "to-be", which do not exist in reality yet. Virtual Prototypes are simulation of products, enabled by Virtual/Augmented Reality technology. Typically, one can use Virtual Prototyping to test the appearance, the functioning, the performance, the ergonomics and usability of a new concept product, in a realistic and safe environment. Augmented Reality even allows us performing the tests in a specific context. Virtual Prototyping finds application in many industrial fields, allowing the simulation of any kind of products, systems or machines. An interesting use of Virtual Prototyping is in the development process of consumer products, where the methodology can be used for collecting customer input. Users can experience future products through a realistic interaction with their virtual representations. Thanks to current state-of-the-art technology, the user interaction can be now multi-sensory through a blend of visual, audio, haptic and olfactory modalities. Users can easily test various configurations of the same product, which can be set up quickly, and express opinions and preferences. Customer input can be collected and promptly used for improving the design or customizing the product.

1.6 Design for Assembly (DFA)

Virtual environments can be used to improve the design from assembly and manufacturing process point of view. By analyzing the assembly process for a product inside a virtual environment, the engineer can detect problems in the design early in the design process. After the individual components of an assembly have been modeled in a CAD system, the engineer must perform assembly planning to come up with the most efficient and reliable way for operators to assemble the device. In the absence of a virtual environment, the engineer must perform the assembly planning either using the CAD system, which can be difficult and error-prone, or using a physical prototype, which can be expensive. If the designed device is very large, then a scaled down version of the prototype may have to be created. The scaled down prototype may conceal assembly issues that affect its full-scale version. The CAD system often does not provide a convenient interface to experiment with different assembly possibilities. Engineers generally interact with CAD systems using keyboard and mouse. The virtual environment allows an engineer to create a shop floor environment and experiment with a full-scale virtual models into an environment where the engineer can quickly and ergonomically try out different assembly possibilities using an intuitive, realistic interface composed of data gloves, trackers, and stereo display. This allows the engineer to detect accessibility and part interference problems early in the process. It also allows the engineer to quickly explore many assembly possibilities in order to come up with a good assembly plan in an environment which mimics reality with physics-based modeling and collision detection. Such approaches can also provide opportunities for other engineers to participate in DFA reviews and input to the process. However, the proposed logging, capture, formalization and automated output of any proposed changes becomes crucial to the effective modification of the product once this process has taken place.

For manual assembly operations, virtual environments can be used to assess ergonomic difficulty of the assembly process. Several virtual human models are available to simulate the force and reach needed to perform operations. These simulations can be used to compute the degree of difficulty in performing the operations.

Interactive tools for DFA are now being researched such that as a design evolves it is possible to evaluate it with regard to specific DFA regimes, e.g. Boothroyd and Dewhurst. Such systems should have a sketching and editing capability which allow design modifications to be made interactively. In addition to this, they will require integration with some form of virtual assembly system which will allow the engineer to both modify the design and check assemblability at the same time. As all of this is taking place, this will facilitate the background DFA evaluation of the design enabling the system to provide real time feedback to the engineer in the form of suggested modifications until an optimal assembly solution is found. Integrating such analyses with the real time modification of the product should considerably reduce design and, especially, DFA, lead times.

Design for Manufacture and Assembly (DFMA) incorporates the evaluation of designs requiring other manufacturing processes such as machining, forming, casting, etc. Their evaluation will subsequently be integrated with virtual assembly; the latter currently being more suitable operationally for VR/AR simulation. This is one area where early research work into manufacturing process simulation could point to the way for extending the application of VR to the wider DFMA domain.

1.7 Manufacturing Process Simulation

As mentioned previously within DFA, assembly planning has been an activity which has been researched in detail since the advent of VR and AR in the manufacturing domain. The intuitive and ergonomic natures of these technologies support the simulation and evaluation of product assembly sequencing. Much of this research has focused again on logging engineers carrying out such virtual tasks simultaneously during product design. This has enabled full blown assembly planning instructions to be automatically inferred from an engineer's logged activities, outputting practical sequences for product build. Such systems also incorporate the mapping of real-world times onto the ergonomic equivalent movements of the engineer in the virtual environment to provide an estimate of assembly time for each operation and the overall assembly. The question usually asked is do such systems require realism with haptics and free form assembly or can non-haptic environments be used just as effectively by using snapping to the final 3D model part positon within the assembly? Both solutions are possible but the choice really depends on the purpose of the assembly task carried out at any particular stage of the planning or DFA process. For example, if accessibility and ease of assembly are evaluated then a free form haptic solution will be required whereas if an assembly plan is required then a non-haptic, snapping environment will be more efficient. However, in general, one of the great strengths of VR/AR in the product engineering process is their application in some form in assembly environments, even as a means of evaluating the practicality of building a product from early on in the design phase.

Virtual machining studies have been carried out in the past, particularly with regard to material removal through some form of machining process. Early work has focused on the modelling and operation of a "realistic" virtual machine tool where the engineer operates it as they would a real machine tool. Although an interesting approach such studies did not provide a useful interface for the rapid planning and evaluation of machining sequences. As an interactive means of interfacing in VR systems, it was found that traditional CAD/CAM packages were far more effective at supporting the generation of machine tool control data; indeed many modern packages of this type could potentially be modified to use VR/AR HMD technologies. However, with the advent of the digital twin approach, in the future such detailed process models will have a role to play in future manufacturing systems design and monitoring.

Much virtual machining work has focused on the modeling and simulation of very specific cutting processes using finite element analysis (FEA) or molecular dynamics simulations (MDS). However, these methods whilst giving interesting outputs relating to the behavior of cutting processes and materials usually did not include the use of VR/AR other than to visualize outputs rather than interactively 'machining' components in real-time due to processing power limitations.

Material removal or machining planning usually comes under the heading of process planning. A few applications of VR in this area have adopted the routing approach used in traditional CAM packages by using 3D displays and haptics as a means of "cutting" the virtual material. Such systems can be used for CNC product manufacture and more traditional turning and milling applications. Combining the routing material removal paradigm with virtual assembly (for the definition of set up and changeover) provides a capability to carry out the full range of material removal planning activities. The user logging approach mentioned under virtual assembly can also be applied to machining and facilitates the generation and output of set up and machining instructions and times for the stage by stage manufacture of products as well as CNC control data, if required. Although in its infancy, such an approach could be integrated with virtual DFA to provide a novel DFMA approach for future product development.

Other manufacturing techniques such as casting and forming also have the capability of being simulated in VR/AR. However, the real-time processing and graphics rendering required to calculate and simulate changes in material shape provide the same challenges as highlighted in the use of FEA and MDS in design.

Some applications of VR/AR in manufacturing process evaluation do not require real time process simulation but provide operators with previously generated instructions along with animations and associated support information. This allows them learn and/or evaluate a process sequence before actual manufacture. This approach can also be employed in multi-user environments where manufacturing methods or approaches can be discussed and assessed in a manner similar to that mentioned under virtual design reviews.

Another key area where VR is now being applied is in the area of optimizing factory layouts. A number of simulation packages are now available to design and plan factory layouts. These provide powerful scheduling capabilities enabling the evaluation of different layouts for different product mixes. Some packages, e.g. WITNESS, have a virtual simulation capability which when combined with 3D immersive VR can support one or more engineers in reviewing a production layout at any scale, identifying bottlenecks and associated performance statistics from a systems level down to individual processes. Such a capability being available to engineers early on in the product life cycle allows products to be designed to fit both manufacturing processes and manufacturing systems.

1.8 Programming of Robots

A traditional way to program robots often requires use of a physical touch pendants. The operator presses button on the pendant and enters the instructions. Once instructions have been entered on the pendant, these instructions can be executed on the robot. The user needs to be very careful in entering the instructions. A wrong instruction can cause the robot to collide with objects in the environment. This can lead to serious damage to the robot and/or objects in the environment. Most users are very cautious in entering instructions in cluttered environments. This requires a long time to program a robot on tasks that require complex motions.

Augmented reality is offering an alternative way to program robots. The user can stand next to the robot. The user can see both physical and virtual robots at the same time. The user can enter instructions either using the virtual pendant or gestures. As the user enters the instructions, the virtual model of the robot can start moving. Since only the virtual model is moving, the collision risk is eliminated. This allows the user to quickly try out many different types of robot movements without working about collision. Once the user is satisfied with the motions of the virtual robot, the same motions can be transferred to the physical robot. This approach can speed up the robot programming. The use of augmented reality ensures that the user does not need to create digital models of all of objects in the scenes. Only digital models of robots are needed. This makes it convenient to utilize the technology. Gesture-based robot motion can be much more intuitive than specifying robot motions through pendants. This can also be useful in training operators on how to program robots.

1.9 Maintenance and Service

Maintenance and service are typically strenuous, demanding and expensive activities for companies operating in many fields, as aeronautics industry, construction sector, site inspection, quality control, and many others. There are two main issues related to maintenance and service: the training of the operational staff and the logistics of interventions. As for the first issue, it happens that technicians need training even for long periods, performed in unsafe environments, in situations where any errors can cause damage to machines and people. There are also situations in which maintenance is required for machinery that is no longer in production, or which is customized and therefore not physically available for operators' training at the company. Concerning the second issue, it happens that maintenance interventions must be done at sites remotely located, not easily and quickly reachable. This involves costs and the use of considerable time for the company providing the service.

Virtual Reality (VR) can be effectively used to train technicians before going to customers' sites. They can visit work environments, get familiar with the location, and practice in the activities and with the machines. VR gives technicians the possibility to repeat the same tasks more times until feeling confident and make mistakes at no cost or danger. Additionally, VR allows technicians to immerse in a "real" environment, which is realistically simulated. In fact, it is possible to simulate scenarios and events, where technicians can experience various and different situations, and change and test "what if" conditions.

Also Augmented Reality (AR) is an enabling technology with huge potentials for maintenance and service. AR can be used for augmenting machines to repair with superimposed digital information, i.e. plans, data sheets, and instruction manuals. Digital information can be triggered by QR codes. AR applications can also read data from sensors, i.e. pressure, force, temperature, to determine the state of the equipment. Digital items of information can be superimposed on tablets, smartphones, or glasses, or rendered directly on the equipment by means of projectors. AR allows technicians to be free from using traditional work tools, i.e. paper manuals. Particularly interesting maintenance scenarios have been developed where technicians can locally use AR to get help from remote experts by sharing the 3D visualization of environment and equipment with them.

With the advent of intelligent asset management and the digital twin approach then VR/AR will have a central role in supporting the time-phased monitoring and management of physical assets in the future, whether they be products, processes, equipment, people or infrastructure. The intelligent supervision of "smart" assets of any kind - and being able to track their function and performance in real time (even remotely) when linked to a digital twin - will provide a powerful approach and paradigm shift from preventative to predictive maintenance. Using generally accessible digital twins for what-if scenarios, providing maintenance practice/training, displaying annotated real time performance data and information, capturing engineering knowledge and practice from expert interactions with assets, providing evolving statistics and predictive analytics on asset performance, will enable better planned maintenance, less downtime and the maximization of both asset and assembly/component lifetimes. The use of VR/AR in this domain will be crucial in the development of tools and methods for capturing and evaluating asset performance, associated solutions and expert knowledge.

Of course, ultimately, by managing such "smart", networked assets through the internet of things (IOT) they will be linked together enabling the detection of potential asset, sub-system or system performance issues, gradual deterioration or failures.

1.10 Operator Training

Traditionally, most manufacturing operators train for performing manufacturing operations by first studying the text-based manuals and then practicing the acquired skills under the supervision of an experienced trainer, engineer, or technician. After adequately learning the required skills, the trainees take certification tests. This training model has been effectively used in the past and has produced well-trained professionals. However, the costs associated with this training model are usually very high, due to the amount of resources it requires. As we move towards an industry with a richer variety of specialized equipment, a highly mobile workforce, demands for instant service, maintenance, and production, and mounting cost pressures, companies need to explore ways to significantly improve training for performing service, maintenance, and manufacturing operations. Furthermore, due to the rapid influx of new and changing technologies and their associated complexities, accelerated training is becoming a necessity in order to promote and maintain an advanced and educated workforce.

Augmented reality and virtual reality-bases training systems are emerging as useful tools that can be used to educate and train individuals in a safe environment that allows for users to make and learn from their mistakes without consequence.

Over the last few years many different training applications have emerged where the use of virtual environments is being explored. A significant amount of research in this field is devoted to teaching of motor skills. Representative areas where VR-based training research has received recent attention is in the medical field, where VR-based surgery training is growing. VR-based training is also finding use in preflight training operations to simulate certain aspects of microgravity and to be an effective countermeasure for space motion sickness and spatial disorientation. This section will describe representative applications from civilian and defense applications areas.

The following is a partial list of advantages to training in a virtual environment:

- It can occur at any time without the need for the physical components or other workers' assistance.
- It does not involve the real components, so cost savings can be realized if practicing the assembly is destructive or detrimental to the components. The need and the associated costs for physical mock-ups are also eliminated.
- It is safe and isolated from industrial and environmental hazards.
- It can be repeated multiple times.
- Individual steps can be repeated, giving the trainee an opportunity to analyze the process from different perspectives and views.
- Automated in-training evaluation and assessment can take place through trainee monitoring.

Manufacturing workforce in most industries requires continued training and update. Traditional training methods, for the most part, involve a combination of paper-based manuals, video-based instructions and/or hands on master-apprentice training. Due to the rapid influx of new and changing technologies and their associated complexities, accelerated training is a necessity in order to maintain an advanced and educated workforce. Virtual reality has emerged as a tool for improving existing training methods in terms of cost, effectiveness, time expenditure and quality through the use of virtual reality and augmented reality. New training approaches become possible particularly via these technologies, one such being the use of serious games for engineering training and evaluation. The advent of personal virtual environments offers many new possibilities for creating accelerated training technologies.

1.11 Conclusions

The use of VR/AR in manufacturing has many benefits. The most noteworthy benefits are listed below:

- It reduces the product development time by reducing the needs for physical prototyping.
- It reduces the waste produced during the physical prototyping associated with design iterations.
- It enables the consideration of a large number of design options and hence increases the probability of creating a product with superior quality.
- It can link design and manufacturing more closely, facilitating concurrent engineering.
- It reduces the chances of errors on manufacturing lines and reduces expensive repair and rework.
- It enables customers to participate during the design process and hence enables the design team to create a product that meets customer needs without a large number of design iterations.
- It reduces the cost associated with the product development process by accelerating the design process and reducing physical prototyping.
- It can support the time-phased capture and formalization of engineering data, information, and knowledge, including their provenance, for individual or team-based engineering reviews throughout the product life cycle.
- It speeds up the training process and increases the productivity of human operators on small production volume manufacturing applications.
- It is a technology that will be central to supporting the engineering function in the design, planning, application and management of Industry 4.0 manufacturing systems and intelligent asset management through the use of digital twins.
- It can provide new opportunities for researching human behavior in the engineering domain, e.g. human factors, psychology, behavioral studies, and serious games.

https://doi.org/10.1142/9789811222863_0002

Chapter 2

Collaborative VR-CAD for Industrial Product Design: CAD Parameter Modification with 3D Interaction on Heterogeneous Immersive Platforms

Yujiro Okuya, Nicolas Ladevèze, Olivier Gladin, Cédric Fleury, and Patrick Bourdot

2.1   Introduction

Immersive product reviews of digital mock-ups are increasingly becoming a vital factor during product development process in industrial companies.[1] These reviews let various specialists (e.g. stylists, engineers, ergonomists) assess the design of the product and conduct manufacturing simulations in a virtual environment with the use of digital mock-up that result in fewer physical mockups. More and more non-CAD experts are also involved in product development to consider the executives and end-user point of views as early as possible. Some research works and applications support collaborative Virtual Reality (VR) design reviews[2–4] that are now common for industrial companies to use in today's decentralized organizations.

The current industrial design process requires products to be modeled by parametric Computer-Aided Design (CAD) software to support the whole manufacturing process. These CAD data are difficult to interactively modify in an immersive virtual environment because of their complexities. While some collaborative applications allow remote participants to observe shared CAD data in a virtual environment, no modifications of the native CAD data are currently possible during collaborative meetings. The expected modifications are usually recorded by annotations and will be applied afterward by a CAD engineer on a workstation. Despite recent advancements in commercial CAD applications and VR-CAD studies, none of them fulfill requirements of a remote collaborative VR-CAD application.

Industrial CAD systems (e.g. 3D CAD® from SolidWorks or CATIA V6® from Dassault Systèmes) only support a collaborative design interface between remote

17

workstations. Even if users could see the CAD model with stereoscopic rendering, interaction with CAD parameters is still performed on the 2D interface that requires CAD expertise. Whereas some research works[5] proposed solutions for VR-CAD integration allowing direct modification of native CAD data in the immersive environment, none of them support both remote collaboration and interaction techniques suitable for non-CAD experts; parametric-based modifications often cause unpredictable shape deformation in 3D space which makes it difficult for them to reach the expected 3D shape.

Our goal is to develop a collaborative VR-CAD system allowing modifications of native CAD data in a shared virtual environment from remote locations. Such a system could improve the current design process by involving several experts in design activities and reducing the number of iterations between VR systems and traditional workstations.

In this chapter, we describe the key features required to achieve a collaborative VR-CAD system: direct modifications of native CAD data in an immersive environment, a distributed architecture for remote collaboration, and an interaction technique to modify such data in 3D space. Our proposed system architecture aims to deal with the heterogeneity of immersive platforms and the variability of interaction techniques to fit different users' needs. For example, stylists might prefer a high-resolution 2D visualization with touch interactions, while ergonomists might prefer an immersive rendering with 3D interaction.

This chapter first reviews previous works in Section 2.2, and then details the current industrial design process and presents a use case for our system in Section 2.3. Section 2.4 describes the methodology of native CAD data modification, and Section 2.5 illustrates a system architecture for our collaborative VR-CAD system with a proof of concept between a CAVE-like system and a large wall-sized display. Section 2.6 presents a 3D interaction technique for CAD data modification in a 3D environment with its evaluation. Finally, Section 2.7 concludes the chapter and presents future work.

2.2   Related Work

There is a vast amount of literature on VR applications in industrial design. We review the previous works based on the following keywords for a required VR-CAD system: native CAD data modification in VR, collaborative industrial design and 3D interaction techniques.

2.2.1 *Native CAD data Modifications in VR*

Current immersive product reviews performed in most industrial companies do not involve any modifications of CAD data and only CAD experts perform the data processing on workstations. Although much work on the integration of VR and CAD systems has been carried out, only a few research works enable modifications of CAD parameters from a virtual environment.

One of the preliminary works on VR-CAD integration was performed by Fakespace and Dassault Systèmes.[6] They embedded VR rendering in an industrial CAD system (CATIA V5®) to deliver fast and seamless VR reviews of a product to users. Schilling et al.[7] presented a middleware framework in which the users can also edit properties of the product (materials or textures) during immersive reviews. This system was extended to support remote collaboration and to deal with heterogeneous VR platforms with further studies.[8] Other studies allowed users to perform VR assembly tasks based on native CAD data imported from industrial CAD systems.[9,10]

In these VR-CAD systems, the parameter modifications of native CAD part was not supported. A critical issue on CAD part editions in a virtual environment is that it is difficult to load and manage a dataset of parametric CAD parts: Boundary Representation (B-Rep) and Constructive History Graph (CHG).[11] cReaVR[5] proposed a solution to parse and manage such data for real-time modification during a VR session (described in detail in Section 2.4). Users can edit the parameter values of a CAD part with a horizontal hand motion in a CAVE. The modifications were directly applied to the native CAD data by a commercial CAD engine (CATIA V5®).

This breakthrough on VR-CAD integration made it possible to perform a CAD part edit during VR reviews, yet the collaborative design and 3D interaction technique that we propose in the following chapter were not achieved.

2.2.2 *Collaborative Industrial Design*

While some VR applications for product reviews start supporting a Collaborative Virtual Environment (CVE), VR-CAD design activities in CVEs are still at the research stage.

2.2.2.1 *Product reviews*

CALVIN,[2] for example, focused on collaborative architectural design for multidisciplinary experts, such as architects and engineers. The experts could explore and manipulate objects in a shared virtual environment. They were supported with distinct viewpoints according to their expertise: an inside-out view for engineers, and an outside-in view for architects. Lehner et al.[12] developed a collaborative review system for vehicle design. This work focused on the awareness of other collaborators: the system provided video and audio streams for communication between users in the CVE to improve awareness.

2.2.2.2 *VR-CAD application*

A few previous works allowed multiple users to interact with CAD data in a CVE. MAS (Multi-Agent System)[13] addressed collaborative product design meetings across a VR platform and workstations. This system used commercial CAD software. Engineers and ergonomists could manipulate the global position/orientation of CAD objects from each platform but they could not modify the shapes of these objects (i.e. parameter modifications of CAD parts resulting in mesh updates in VR). DVDS[14] enabled users to create a 3D model with hand gestures in a virtual environment. It used a customized CAD system. Consequently, it could not load and modify existing native CAD data designed by commercial CAD software. Even if a collaborative architecture was also discussed in this paper, it was not implemented.

2.2.3 *3D Interaction for VR-CAD Applications*

Many VR-CAD research works have attempted to carry an interaction space from 2D to 3D space. Clark, who demonstrated the first VR-CAD application in the '70s, concluded:

> *"3-D computer-aided surface design is best done in real-time with 3-D tools. To expect a designer of 3-D surfaces to work with 2-D input and viewing devices unnecessarily removes a valuable degree of freedom."*[15]

These studies can be classified broadly into two kinds according to the targeted design activity: aesthetic design and solid modeling. In industrial design, aesthetic design is mostly considered at the conceptual design stage where stylists design the preliminary draft of the product, and the model has to be rebuilt as a solid-model at a later product design stage to consider its engineering and manufacturing feasibility.

2.2.3.1 *Aesthetic design*

Immersive drawing applications provide users a one-to-one design capability of 3D objects. Israel et al.[16] allowed users to draw 3D lines in the air within a CAVE system using a 6DoF pen device. Fleisch et al.[17] and Keefe et al.[18] presented 3D drawing techniques inspired by tape-drawing, which is often used in automotive styling to easily create a full-size drawing or to highlight the design lines on clay models. More recently, a 3D drawing application with HMD, Tilt Brush, has been developed for artistic design.[19] Regarding geometric modeling applications, 3-Draw[20] is the first application for free-form modeling using a 3D interaction technique. The users can draw 3D wireframes by handling a stylus in 3D space. 3DIVS[21] and SpaceDesign[22] presented surface modeling tools by co-located interactions with digital mockups between the users' real hands and its visualization. Paljic et al.[23] confirmed that manipulation of digital mockups at a closer distance is significantly more efficient for localization tasks in a 3D space. More recently, Mockup Builder[24] proposed a co-located bimanual finger interaction for rapid 3D prototyping.

2.2.3.2 *Solid modeling*

Many research works attempted to change the interaction for solid modeling, from an alphanumeric input with mouse-based interaction to direct shape-based interaction. JDCAD[25] is the first VR-CAD application in which users can create or edit primitives and perform boolean operations by 3D interaction. JDCAD proposed a *Region-based reshaping technique*: the users can manipulate specific parameters by dragging relevant control points mapped on the surfaces of the primitives. ARCADE[26,27] extended this approach by also considering the users' subsequent 3D gestures to determine the optimal object behavior according to the users' hand strokes. However, this approach was not well suited to address complex objects that include internal geometric constraints.

To support constraint-based CAD models, Gao et al.[28] and Ma et al.[29] presented VR-CAD systems that contain customized data models storing information relating to parameters, operators and constraints of CAD objects. These systems can recognize the related constraints from a selected element and enable consistent shape deformation via the users' hand motions. Nevertheless, those approaches did not allow the direct loading and editing of native CAD data by industrial CAD systems since the systems relied on customised data structures.

2.2.4 *Summary*

Despite many previous works addressing remote collaboration and 3D interaction techniques for industrial design, they have not focused on native CAD data modifications. We believe that direct CAD data modifications during VR sessions can optimize the current product design processes.

2.3   Collaborative Design in Industry

In this section, we present an example of an industrial product design process and demonstrate the need for modifications of native CAD data in an immersive CVE. Generally, industrial design encompasses two distinct processes: product design and process design. The latter addresses many issues of product manufacturing, such as the design of assembly procedures, including for instance, ergonomic studies to prevent workers' health disorders, through the full design of the industrial requirements. Our focus is only the product design process where an industrial product is conceptualized based on the considerations of aesthetics and end-user oriented ergonomic studies finishing with engineering analysis.

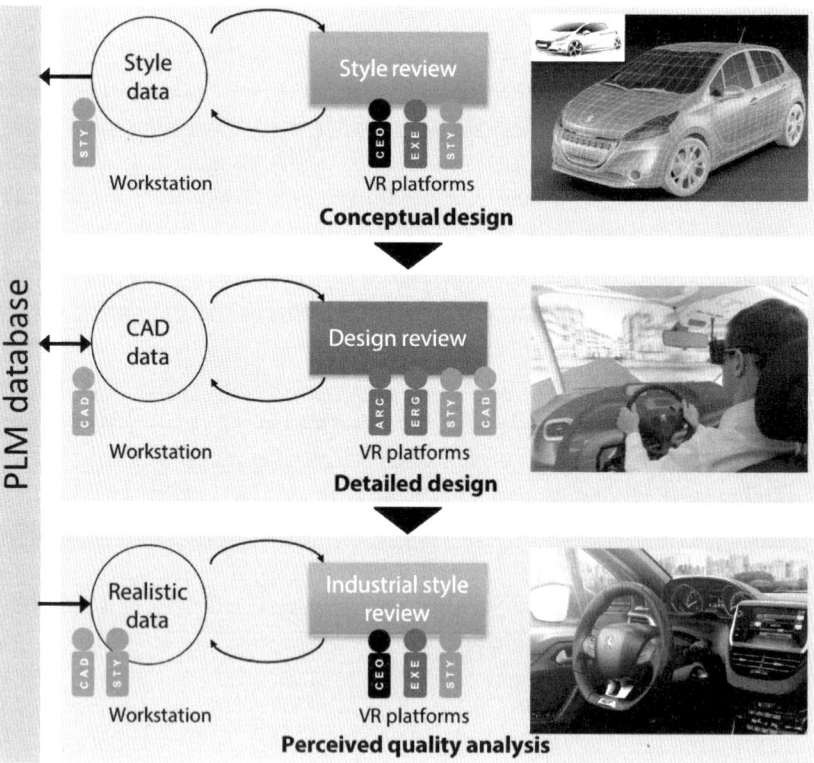

Fig. 2.1. Collaborative product design meetings across the industrial design process. CEO: Chief Executive Officer, EXE: Other executives, STY: Stylist, ARC: Architect, CAD: CAD engineer, ERG: Ergonomist.

2.3.1 *Industrial Product Design*

Industrial product design is a sequential process. For example, some automotive companies split this process into three main stages (see Fig. 2.1):

- Conceptual design: style designers sketch a preliminary draft of the product based on expectations and requirements of end users. They create a conceptual model using dedicated tools specialized in aesthetic design (e.g. Alias®).
- Detailed design: CAD engineers build a digital mock-up using parametric CAD software (e.g. CATIA®, SolidWorks®) from the conceptual model designed at the previous stage.
- Perceived quality analysis: stylists and CAD engineers tune rendering materials and textures on high-quality meshes exported from the CAD data to create a realism-oriented virtual scene using a high-resolution rendering system (e.g. Deltagen®). Stylists, CEO and other executives analyze the perceived quality of the product to validate the final digital mock-up. If modifications are required, it is mandatory to go back to the detailed design stage to apply these modifications on the CAD data.

At each design stage, review meetings are often conducted in immersive platforms to allow several experts to assess the virtual prototype at full scale and in a realistic environment. As the workplaces of each expert are not located in the same place in most cases they need to travel or use remote communication tools at each meeting.

The digital mock-ups are stored and exchanged through a PLM (Product Lifecycle Management) database in various formats according to the dedicated software used at each product design stage. Consequently, this data heterogeneity imposes conversions to pass it from one stage to another. Also, the use of VR environments usually imposes time-consuming conversions or transcriptions between the virtual environment and the PLM database.

2.3.2 *Detailed Design*

During review meetings at the detailed design stage, digital mock-ups based on CAD data are presented in the virtual environment to verify or compare possible design solutions. However, as highlighted in Section 2.2, current systems do not support direct modifications of CAD part parameters during these meetings because of the complexity of CAD data.

In particular, CAD objects are usually defined by a set of operations (e.g. Extrusion, Sweep, Boolean operations) applied from primitives and 2D sketches, based on many parameters and geometrical constraints. Figure 2.2 is an example of a real industrial CAD model designed by CAD engineers in an automotive company: i.e.

the *Rear-view mirror* of a car. This *Rear-view mirror* is generated from a Sweep operation following a guide curve (Fig. 2.2), which is defined by different parameters (radius, lengths) and geometric constraints (tangency and symmetry).

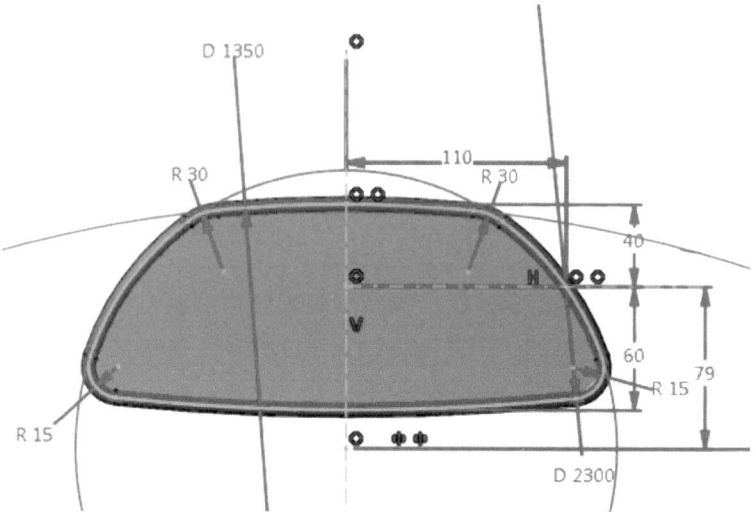

Fig. 2.2. Sketch of the *Rear-view mirror*, an example of industrial CAD part designed using CATIA V5®. The 3D shape is generated by a sweep operation based on the guide curve. Several constraints and parameters define the curvatures and distances of corners, width and height of the *Rear-view mirror*.

These CAD objects are generated by a commercial CAD engine outside the virtual environment and there is usually no direct link between the CAD engine and the VR system. Consequently, review meetings at the detailed design stage require data conversion before the VR session, creation of several versions of the 3D model, and post-modification of original CAD data afterward. This back-and-forth between the virtual environment and the workstation is time-consuming and a potential source of errors.

To avoid these issues, we want to provide a direct way to modify the CAD data parameters during collaborative review meetings at the detailed design stage. Consequently, we will focus on this stage as the main context of our collaborative system.

2.3.3 *Collaborative Modification Scenario*

Direct modifications on a CAD model during a design review could improve the current modification scenario, which relies on using both a workstation and an immersive setup. An ideal VR-CAD system should allow several experts to collaboratively modify the same CAD model from remote places along with the support of heterogeneous VR platforms which fit the requirements at each expertise.

Our proposed system aims to make the following example scenario possible. An industrial company is divided into several departments around the world. Stylists work at the parent company while CAD engineers and ergonomists work in different countries. With our VR-CAD system, stylists could check the design of a car through a large screen with a high-resolution visualization system while ergonomists evaluate the customer comfort (e.g. driver seat, cockpit space, a field of view) in an immersive VR system. Both of them can discuss with CAD engineers who also participate in the CVE and ask them to provide some modifications on the digital mock-ups. As CAD engineers or anyone else in the meeting can directly modify the CAD data from the immersive system, experts and non-CAD experts can perform collaborative modifications together. Communication between remote sites is enhanced by streaming video and audio in the CVE.

In the following section, we will detail key features of our VR-CAD system designed to fulfill above scenario.

2.4 VR-CAD Integration

As introduced in Section 2.2.1, various research works have attempted to allow users to interact with native CAD data in a virtual environment. However, VR-CAD data integration still suffers from data interoperability between the VR and CAD systems. For example, most immersive product review systems are using static meshes generated after tessellations of the CAD data, and do not contain semantic information such as Constructive History Graph (CHG). CHG stores the information relating to the design history of CAD objects, e.g. operators, parameters, transformation matrices. Some previous work has enabled users to access CAD data and modify it in the virtual environment,[30, 31] nevertheless, they could not apply their modifications to the original CAD file.

2.4.1 *VR-CAD Data Linkage*

Only a few researchers have focused on the VR-CAD data linkage for CAD part design in VR. One interesting approach is based on *labeling*[32] where a direct link is formed between VR rendering of the CAD objects B-Reps with the nodes of the CHG. This aimed to allow an implicit edit of the CHG when users interact with B-Rep of the objects in the virtual environment. Martin et al.[5] extended this model with an encapsulation technique to apply it on the CHG nodes and the B-Rep elements of most CAD systems used by industry. A proof of concept, named cReaVR, has been implemented into CATIA V5®, allowing users to implicitly access the parameter values of relevant CHG nodes from a surface selection in 3D space.

2.4.2   *VR-CAD Server*

To make this approach functional for multiple users remotely, we decomposed the system architecture of cReaVR and designed *VR-CAD server*, which deals with all communications between a CAD engine and the VR applications. The *VR-CAD server* is based on the core concept of cReaVR and implemented with C++ embedding CAA V5 (API for CATIA V5).

The *VR-CAD server* relies on the data flow illustrated in Fig. 2.3. First, the *VR-CAD server* loads a specified CAD data (.catpart) and generates related meshes and a linkage information file (.xml). As meshes output by the CAD software often have defects (e.g. non-manifold geometry), a *Mesh cleaner* handles these post-tessellation issues using a VCG library.[a] Then, meshes are converted to a Wavefront standard format (.obj) before deployment on the CVE. For the modification of a CAD part, the *VR-CAD server* receives the information of a selected part (B-Rep ID and constraint ID) and the new parameter value for the targeted constraint as input from VR process. Lastly, it sends back the computed meshes and a new link file as output.

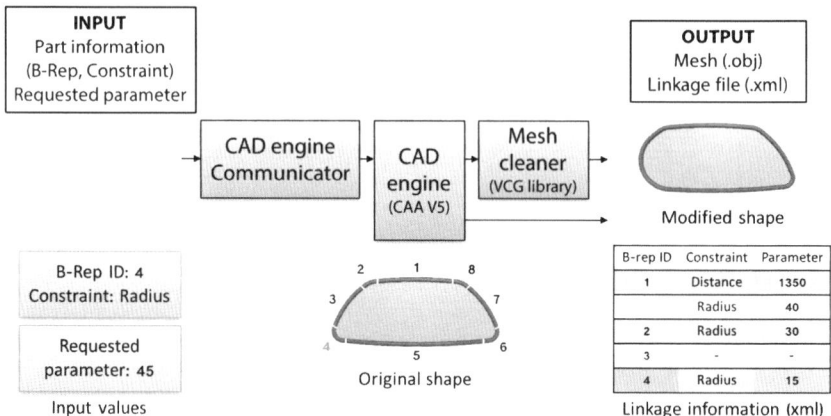

Fig. 2.3. Data flow of the VR-CAD server. Meshes (.obj) and linkage information (.xml) are generated based on modification requests.

For example, Fig. 2.3 details the behavior of the *VR-CAD server* when a user wants to change the curvature of the bottom left corner of the *Rear-view mirror* of a car (Fig. 2.2) from 15 mm to 45 mm. First, the information "$B - Rep\ ID = 4$", "$Constraint = Radius$" and the new "$parameter\ value = 45$" are transmitted from the user's VR platform to the *VR-CAD server*. Then, the CAD engine communicator asks the CAD engine to edit the parameter of the specified CHG node

---

[a]http://vcg.isti.cnr.it/vcglib/

with the new value. The CAD engine updates the whole CHG (e.g. relevant opera-tors) and generates new meshes from the computed B-Reps. This process takes 700 ms on average for the *Rear-view mirror*. After all this processing, the new meshes and the updated linkage file are delivered to each platform.

2.5 Collaborative VR-CAD System

A key requirement is that a VR-CAD system must support a collaborative design on several immersive platforms between remote locations. We designed a distributed architecture which allows multiple users on heterogeneous VR platforms to modify shared CAD data through the *VR-CAD server*. This architecture should meet the following requirements:

- Modification of native CAD data at runtime: the system should be able to load and modify existing CAD data without any data conversion before/after the VR session.
- Collaborative modification of CAD parts: multiple users should not only be able to modify different parameters of a part but also the same parameter of this part.
- Distribution of CAD data among remote locations: the system should dynami-cally update the CAD data on each remote platform.
- Interconnection between heterogeneous platforms: the system should deal with the various visualization systems and interaction devices of each platform.

To support these features, we use a hybrid network architecture which combines both a centralized architecture to connect remote platforms to the *VR-CAD server* and peer-to-peer connections to allow fast communication between platforms. This architecture is independent of the technical specifications of each platform and can connect heterogeneous platforms with different visualization systems and interac-tion devices.

In this section, we first detail the distributed architecture that connects the VR platforms and the *VR-CAD server*. Then we illustrate how multiple users can col-laboratively manage parameter modifications on the shared CAD part. Lastly, a proof of concept of this VR-CAD system is described as a use-case between a CAVE-like system and a large wall-sized display.

2.5.1 *Distributed Architecture*

We propose a hybrid network architecture to connect the remote platforms together and with the *VR-CAD server* (Fig. 2.4). All information about non-CAD objects (e.g. avatars, pointers) is transmitted with a peer-to-peer architecture between each platform; whereas, all the data relative to CAD objects (meshes and linkage files) are transmitted with a client/server architecture between the platforms and the *VR-CAD server*.

A *Workspace server* (*WS server* in Fig. 2.4) is used for authentication and for establishing the connection between each platform and the *VR-CAD server*. This notion of *Workspace* allows the storage of a particular configuration of a work session and to retrieve it later in order not to have to redo the network configuration for each similar work session. Each user just has to connect to a specific *Workspace* to be connected to the other user. The *WS client* is the communication layer which manages the network communication on each platform and the *VR-CAD server*. The communication between the *WS server* and the *WS client* is managed by the WebSocket protocol, which allows real-time full-duplex communication.

The communication between each *WS client* is handled by WebRTC[b] protocol allowing peer-to-peer connections. We choose this open protocol to be able to connect various remote locations with different network architecture and deal with network constraints such as firewall and security issues. The *WS client* running on each platform streams application data to all other platforms for synchronizing interaction events and non-CAD object positions in the CVE. The *VR-CAD server* also exchanges the CAD data or the modification requests with each platform through a *WS client*.

For the internal communication inside each platform, the *WS client* uses the Transmission Control Protocol (TCP) to interact either with the application running on VR platform or with the CAD engine. Each application sends information about the local elements (e.g. positions/orientations of user's head and hand, events) to the local *WS client* which transmits updates about the state of the CVE to the remote platforms. Conversely, information on the remote platforms is transmitted to the local application by the local *WS client*. If a VR platform is composed of computer clusters (such as for CAVE systems), the *WS client* only communicates with a master node of its local clustering system.

Each platform can also stream media data (audio and/or video) with the WebRTC protocol through a Media manager. The Media manager is connected via WebSocket to the local *WS client* which controls the media streams. The audio and video stream can thus be delivered to all the other remote platforms.

As the communication module is independent from the platform, this architecture can easily be adapted to several visualization systems and interaction devices. Figure 2.4 describes the architecture with two platforms, but additional platforms can be included with the same communication scheme.

---

[b]https://webrtc.org/

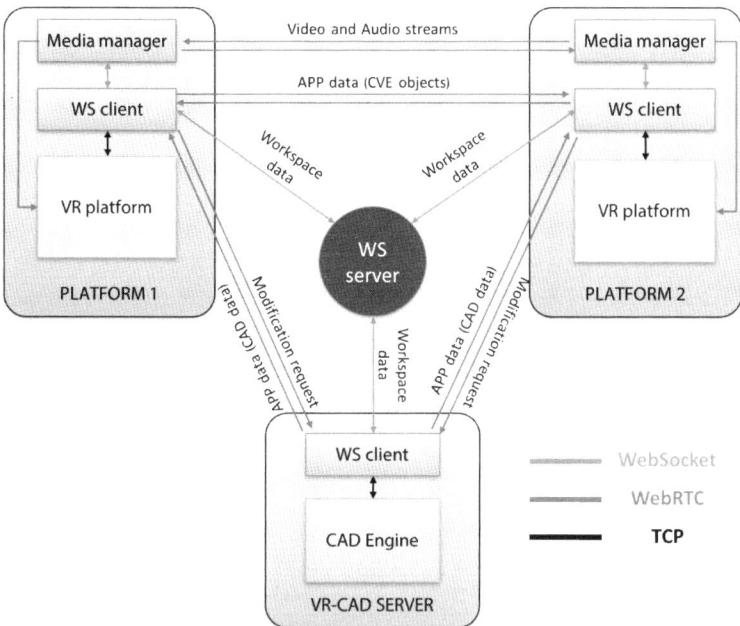

Fig. 2.4. Distributed architecture for collaborative CAD data modification between remote VR platforms.

2.5.2 *Collaborative Interaction*

Cooperative activities in the CVE can be classified into three levels.[33] The first level is defined as basic cooperation: each user can perceive each other in CVE through an avatar or with other communication tools. The second level, mostly used in collaborative product reviews,[2] allows users to act on an individual scene by changing the visual contexts of the scene (e.g. change the location and properties of objects). At the third level, multiple users can act on a same virtual object for manipulations or modifications. This last level can be further divided into two sub-levels: (i) the users can act on the independent properties of the same object (e.g. location and color) and (ii) the users can concurrently act on the same or linked properties of the same object. In many research works,[34,35] this sub-level (ii) is called cooperative manipulation.

Our distributed architecture was designed to support all levels of cooperative activities, with media streaming (first level), by allowing multiple users to act on individual visual context (second level) and to concurrently modify the same or linked parameter values of a specific CAD part (third level). Currently, we have not focused on the first level; usage of media data and avatars of other users in CVE.

Illustrated below are the common interaction flow for CAD parameter modification and an example of cooperative activities with two categories: independent and cooperative modifications.

2.5.2.1   *Interaction flow*

To achieve the parameter modification of a CAD part in the virtual environment users must perform the following actions:

- Selection: the users start by picking a specific part of the 3D model using a virtual tool. Once they have selected a part, they need to pick a specific constraint in a list of constraints (e.g. distance, radius) linked to the part.
- Parameter modification: the users can then modify the selected parameter value using a dedicated manipulation metaphor to increase/decrease the value, e.g. in cReaVR[5] used a horizontal scroll technique.
- Validation: when the users validate their modification, the resulting modification request is sent to the *VR-CAD server* which updates the CAD data and distributes the new version over the network. If the value is not acceptable for the CAD engine (i.e. exceeds the limit of the constraints), the users receive an error and have to continue the parameter manipulation.

Each remote user can independently act on different CAD parameters but we also want to allow multiple users to simultaneously modify the same parameter to support different cooperative activities. This cooperative manipulation could be adjusted by considering the expertise and roles of the collaborators. For example, a CAD engineer could assist the parameter manipulation conducted by a stylist to refine its modification by either providing possible discrete solutions or constraining its manipulation range in real time. The system can thus support two kinds of collaborative modifications:

- *Independent modifications* which occur when each user modifies a different parameter of the CAD data at the same time. Each user can see the visual proxy of the other users' hand and can thus check their actions. When one of the users validates its parameter value the CAD data will be updated regardless of the ongoing parameter manipulation on the other platforms.
- *Cooperative modifications* which happen when more than one user simultaneously select the same CAD data parameter. In our current implementation, we use a *Mean* technique by averaging the parameter values of each user after their validation. This is a simple way to combine users' action,[36] but some other techniques have been proposed[34,35] and we can envision the use of a more sophisticated technique in the future. However, we must pay attention to the fact

that some of them do not fit our scenario: for example, we cannot use *DoF separation*[36] since our targeted parameter manipulation is only in one-dimension.

2.5.3   *Interaction Between Heterogeneous VR Platforms*

As a proof of concept, we use our distributed architecture for enabling two remote users to achieve a collaborative CAD data modification from two different VR platforms: a wall-sized display and a CAVE-like system (Fig. 2.5). The wall-sized display and the CAVE-like system have distinct visualization and interaction capabilities: a 2D high-quality rendering system with touch interaction and a stereoscopic rendering system with a force feedback device. While both VR platforms are located on our campus, they are not on the same local network. We detail the implemented system architecture and propose the use-case for design review as follows.

2.5.3.1   *Wall-sized display*

The wall-sized display is composed of 75 thin-bezel screens for a total resolution of 14.400 x 4.800 pixels (5.90m x 1.96m). Applications run on a server that distributes the environment to 10 machines, each one driving 7 or 8 screens. Clustering rendering is managed by customized *Unity* environment. Simulated images are depicted with an adaptive user perspective rendering based on a user's head position and orientation tracked by *Vicon*[c] infrared tracking system. The user's touch input on each screen is detected by a*PQLabs*.[d] 4k IP streaming camera (AW-UE70,[e] Panasonic) is set up to record and transmit the video of the user to other platforms.

2.5.3.2   *CAVE-like system*

The CAVE-like system is composed of four back-projected stereoscopic screens: 4.8 x 2.7m (front & floor) and 2.7 x 2.7m (left & right). The resolution of each screen is 1920 x 1080 pixels. This CAVE-like system is controlled by a cluster of 5 PCs (4 PCs for graphics rendering and one PC for the master of synchronization). An *ART*[f] infrared tracking system is used to track the orientation and position of the users' head. *MiddleVR for Unity*[g] manages the clustering rendering and computes adaptive view based on the tracking data. A *Scale-One*[h] is composed of a *Virtuose* from *Haption* (6 degree of freedom force feedback device) and a 4 degree

---

[c]https://www.vicon.com
[d]http://www.pqlabs.com
[e]http://business.panasonic.com/AW-UE70.html
[f]https://ar-tracking.com
[g]http://www.middlevr.com/middlevr-for-unity/
[h]https://www.haption.com/fr/products-fr/scale-one-fr.html

of freedom carrier. The *Virtuose* is attached to the carrier with upside down. When the users move in the CAVE-like system while grabbing the handle of the *Virtuose*, the carrier automatically follows them and moves to the most convenient position to let them interact freely anywhere in the system. The *Scale-One* is controlled by our own program, namely *VH server* (Visuo-Haptic server), locally connected to the controller of a *Scale-One*. The user in the CAVE-like system is also surrounded by IP cameras.

2.5.3.3 *Network architecture*

Figure 2.5 shows an actual implementation of our distributed architecture between two platforms: platform 1, a wall-sized display (left in Fig. 2.5) and platform 2, a CAVE-like system (right in Fig. 2.5).

As the *VR-CAD server* belongs to same network group as the CAVE-like system, two *WS client* run on platform 2. Each VR system communicates with the *WS client* through a master node of clusters. All of the CVE data (e.g. tracking data, the object data, CAD data) pass through the master node. When the *WS client* receives the CAD data from the *VR-CAD Server*, the CAD data is saved on a local data server and the master node copies this data to deploy it to the slave nodes.

In the wall-sized display the information of the user's touch inputs and the tracking data are directly transmitted to the master node of the clusters. *Unity* scene gathers all information and distributes it to slave nodes.

In the CAVE-like system, the *VH server* receives haptic handle's position/orientation and user's head tracking data, then broadcasts them as VRPN format to the master node of clusters. *MiddleVR for Unity* handles the VRPN data over the cluster nodes. When the CAD data is distributed to each platform, this CAD data is loaded in *VH server* and used for the force feedback computation. The video of each user can be transmitted through the WebRTC protocol to each other. Each IP camera streams the video to the *Kurento media server*[i] which can distribute the received streaming data to clustering nodes.

2.5.3.4 *Use case for industrial design*

In the example in Fig. 2.5, remote users can collaboratively modify native CAD data of the *Rear-view mirror* within a simulated cockpit of a car, instead of using the desktop interface of industrial CAD systems.

As we illustrated in section 2.3, several experts in industrial companies could make use of these VR platforms for collaborative CAD data modification during product reviews. Presumably, some features of the wall-sized display would fit

---

[i]https://www.kurento.org

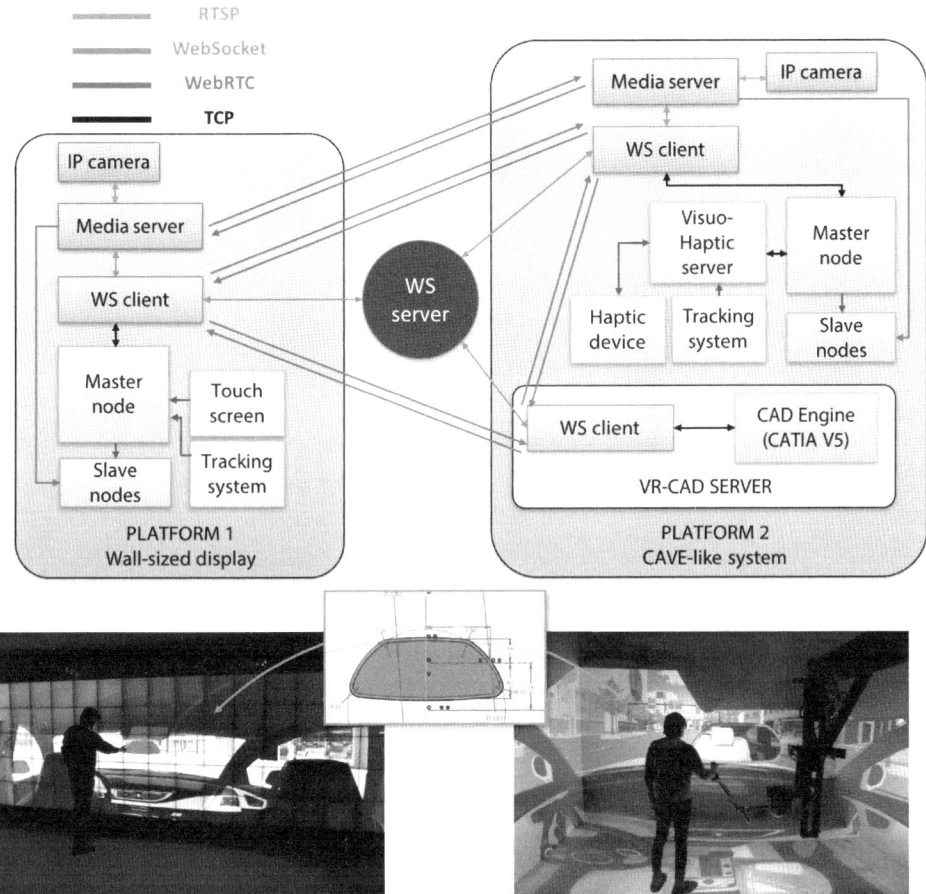

Fig. 2.5. Distributed architecture of a proof of concept: native CAD data modification between a Wall-sized display (left) and a CAVE-like system (right). Remote users can collaboratively modify the *Rear-view mirror* without using classical desktop interface.

needs from stylists and executives (e.g. CEO), such as a high-resolution rendering and multi-touch interaction system, which is conventionally used in mobile phones or tablets. The wide field of view is also of benefit to multiple users to review the product.

Whereas CAD engineers and ergonomists would prefer the CAVE-like system, a 3D visualization space provides them with a spatial feeling in a realistic environment and force feedback can enhance the precision of their 3D manipulation and let them feel collisions with other objects.

In this example, ergonomists can virtually sit at driver's sheet to check the reflection of the *Rear-view mirror* and ask CAD engineers to modify its parameters while stylists advise them with an aesthetic consideration from a wall-sized display.

2.5.3.5   *Summary*

We designed a collaborative VR-CAD system architecture and implemented it between two VR platforms. This system can facilitate communications across different disciplines and involve all of them in CAD data modification. However, suitable interaction techniques on CAD parameter modifications were investigated in the VR system and the method to increase the awareness of other users in CVE.

The following section describes this study of 3D interaction techniques on CAD parameter modifications including a user study carried out in a CAVE-like system.

2.6   3D Interaction Techniques for CAD Parameter Modification

Although industrial CAD systems are effective and necessary tools for product design in automobile companies, the mastery of such CAD skills is complex, time consuming and costly.[37] We believe that integrating the CAD process into VR could simplify the interaction with CAD systems but Stark[38] pointed out two major problems on merging desktop CAD and VR systems:

- The usability of current VR-based user interfaces for CAD systems is limited.
- 2D interaction techniques in current CAD systems cannot be transferred one-to-one into VR systems.

In our targeted scenario, we focus on only the product refinement process during product reviews, therefore the complex CAD operations meant for the creation of the CAD model can be ignored. In this section, we present a shape-based 3D interaction technique for CAD parameter modification, namely *ShapeGuide*,[39] that enable users to deform the CAD part with their hand motion instead of using parametric space interaction through alphanumerical input. The *ShapeGuide* approach could also provide force feedback guidance to users during part deformations.

2.6.1   *ShapeGuide Methodology*

To modify the parameter values of a CAD part with shape-based interaction we computed several possible shapes from a set of discrete parameter values at the user's selection step.

The computation process of *ShapeGuide* (Fig. 2.6) is described as follows:

(i) **Part selection**: When users select a sub-part, a part of a CAD model (e.g. a bottom part of *Rear-view mirror*, Fig. 2.6) in a virtual environment, the VR platform retrieves the selected "$B-RepID$" and "$Constraint$" using the linkage file (Fig. 2.3). After the constraint selection, it transmits this information

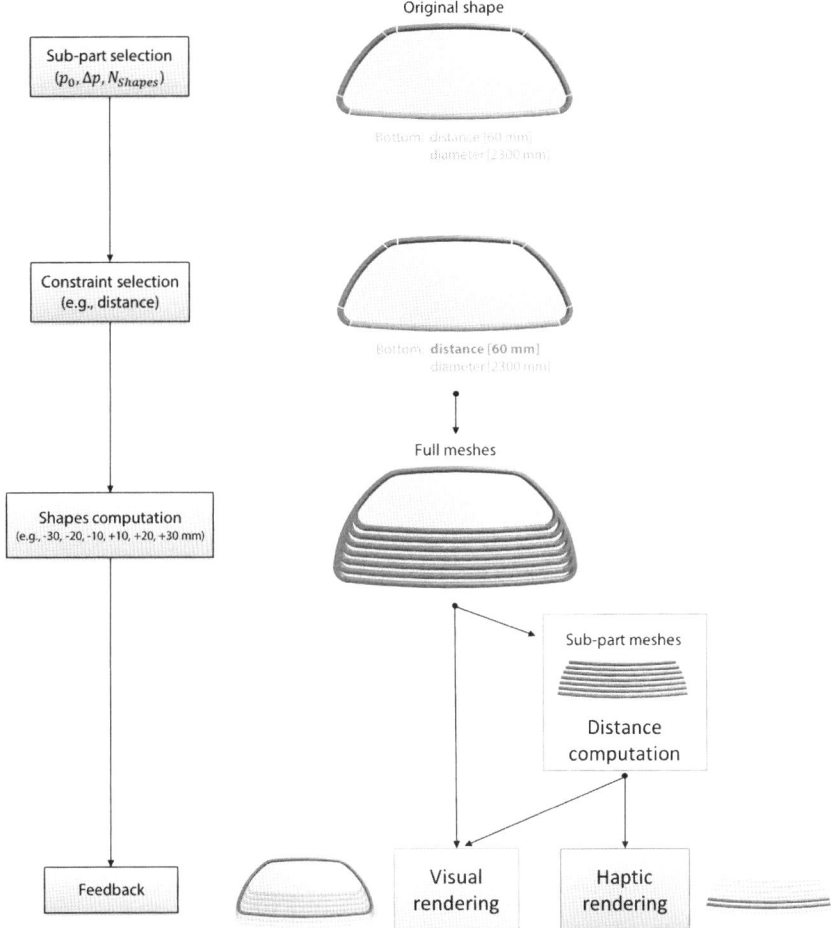

Fig. 2.6. An example of computation process of *ShapeGuide*.

with a list of N_{shapes}, parameter values computed from the current parameter value p_0 and a chosen parameter step size Δp to the **VR-CAD** server. Due to tessellations of B-Reps in the **VR-CAD** server, the VR representation of the CAD part is composed of several sub-part meshes (e.g. the *Rear-view mirror* comprises nine sub-part meshes.). The values N_{shapes} and Δp can be tuned by users at each selection to be able to set any parameter values with the required precision.

(ii) **Shape computation**: *VR-CAD* server computes and generates meshes of the selected part based on the given parameter settings. Computed meshes are used for both visual rendering and physics computation in later processes.

(iii) **Physics computation**: the *VH* server imports only sub-part meshes to compute in real time the nearest points on these meshes from the user's hand position. The shortest distances computed are used for haptic rendering (see section 2.6.3) and the closest mesh ID is transmitted back to the VR platform.

(iv) **Update visualization**: the VR platform loads full meshes after the *Shape computation* and displays only the nearest mesh from the user's hand in the virtual environment during modifications. In this way users feel that the CAD part is deformed as they push/pull its surface regardless of its hidden internal geometric definition.

(v) **Validation**: Once the modification is finished, the VR platform transmits the validated parameter value to *VR-CAD server*. Then the *VR-CAD server* exports an updated linkage file to the *VR platform*.

In the current system, we did not implement a user interface to allow the user to tune these values, N_{shapes} and Δp as well as the one to select the constraint within the list fetched by VR-CAD linkage. For the experiment purpose described in Section 2.6.4, we did not let users manipulate these values during the experiment. Instead, we imposed static values for N_{shapes} and Δp and specified a default modifiable constraint for each sub-part to control the loading time fitting our experimental hardware capabilities and time limitation for immersive experiments.

Tessellation time of B-Reps varies depending on complexity of the CAD model. For example, generating the six full meshes of the bottom part of *Rear-view mirror* presented in Fig. 2.6 takes between 0.9 to 1.2 seconds.

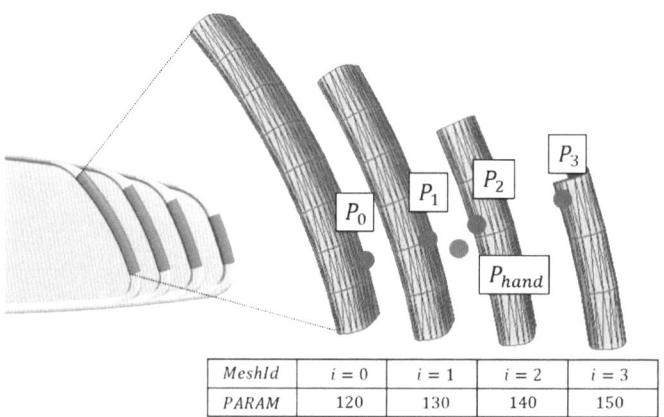

MeshId	$i = 0$	$i = 1$	$i = 2$	$i = 3$
PARAM	120	130	140	150

Fig. 2.7. Example of computed sub-part meshes of the right side part for 3D interaction. P_{hand} is the user's hand position. P_i is a nearest point on each surface from P_{hand}.

2.6.2   *3D Distance Computation*

Once the shapes are computed from a given parameter set, users can select one of them from their 3D hand position P_{hand} (Fig. 2.7).

Each nearest point and minimal distance on each mesh, within a set of generated sub-part meshes, are computed in the *VH server*. This computation function is based on the nearest point computation method on each triangle of a mesh [40, p. 141-142] from a given hand position P_{hand}. This function returns two closest points ($P_{closestA}$ and $P_{closestB}$) and nearest mesh IDs ($MeshId_A$ and $MeshId_B$). After this computation, the nearest mesh ID ($MeshId_A$) is sent to VR platform to display only the nearest shape in a virtual environment, and the two closest points ($P_{closestA}$ and $P_{closestB}$) are used for force feedback computation.

2.6.3   *Force Feedback Assistance*

One additional benefit of *ShapeGuide* is to be able to convey haptic feedback while modifying a CAD part. The force feedback model is based on a force feedback grid,[41] which stabilizes a user's hand onto attraction points distributed on a Cartesian axis. As a visual proxy comes close to the attraction point, the amount of force becomes higher, similar to a magnetic attraction force.

This magnet metaphor is extended from homogeneous Cartesian grids to arbitrary axes in 3D space. This force feedback attracts the user's hand onto the surface of the nearest sub-part mesh ($P_{closestA}$ or $P_{closestB}$) during the shape edition to hold the user's hand steady and to guide the hand toward neighbor meshes.

2.6.4   *Experiment*

In order to assess the efficiency of *ShapeGuide* on a CAD deformation task, we conducted a controlled experiment with 16 participants to compare it with a scroll technique, named *Scroll*. We also wanted to assess the effect of an additional magnetic force feedback on both interaction techniques. This magnetic force feedback enables participants to feel the different parameter values during modification.

The *Scroll* technique allowed participants to manipulate a parameter value of the CAD object by scrolling their arm onto a horizontal axis. The parameter value increases with the motion of the arm towards the right and vice versa. The direction of *Scroll* was static, which means that it did not rely on the direction of the shape deformation; therefore, the direction of *Scroll* may not be consistent with the shape in most cases.

In this experiment, we limited the number of computation shapes to $N_{shapes} = 10$ and a parameter step size of $\Delta p = 10$ mm to avoid participant-related variability regarding these settings and to focus on a fair comparison of the two interaction

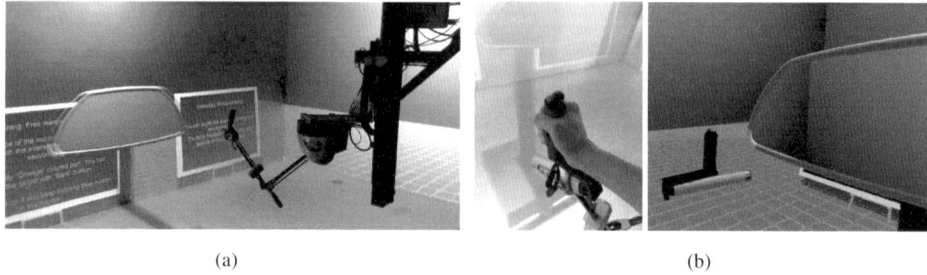

(a)   (b)

Fig. 2.8. (a) Experimental set-up. (b) Haptic arm handle of *Scale-One* and its visual proxy. 3D representation of the virtual handle is co-located with the actual one in a CAVE-like system.

techniques. As an example, generating the 10 full meshes of *Rear-view mirror* takes between 1.5 to 2.0 seconds, which was an acceptable loading time for participants according to our pilot test.

From our assumptions based on the related works and some initial pilot tests, we formulate four hypotheses: participants achieve the deformation task faster with *ShapeGuide* than with *Scroll* (**H1**), participants are more likely to start the deformation in the correct direction with *ShapeGuide* than with *Scroll* because of the consistency of the gesture with the deformation direction (**H2**), participants prefer *ShapeGuide* to *Scroll* (**H3**) and the magnetic force feedback helps participants to reach the desired parameter values with more precision, especially with *ShapeGuide* (**H4**).

2.6.4.1 *Experimental task*

The experiment was carried out in a CAVE-like system (see Section 2.5.3) with a *Scale-One* haptic device (Fig. 2.8 (a)). During the experiment, participants were asked to perform a deformation task on the *Rear-view mirror*. Four parts of the *Rear-view mirror* (Fig. 2.2) were used for the task: *LeftBottomCorner*, *RightBottomCorner*, *Bottom* and *RightSide* (Fig. 2.9). In the *Scroll* condition, the shape evolution was consistent with the user's hand motion in *RightSide* and *LeftBottomCorner*: right-hand motion led to shape deformation towards the right for both parts. On the contrary, it was inconsistent in *RightBottomCorner* and *Bottom*: right-hand motion led to shape deformation towards the left for the *RightBottomCorner* and towards the bottom for the *Bottom*. We chose these four parts (two consistent ones and two inconsistent ones) to analyze how the consistency between the interaction and the deformed shape affects the deformation task.

A virtual representation of a *Virtuose* handle was displayed in the virtual environment (Fig. 2.8 (b)). This virtual handle was co-localized with an actual handle of *Scale-One* in the CAVE-like system. This virtual handle was used as an interaction pointer allowing the users to interact with the *Rear-view mirror*.

The deformation scenario is composed of the following steps:

- *Selection* of a part: the participants could select the part by pressing a button on the handle while the virtual handle was colliding on the surface.
- *Modification*: after selection, the scenario automatically switched to modification mode. The participants could start switching between possible shapes by their hand motion after some waiting time for the shape computation. Once they reached the desired 3D shape, they could validate the deformation by pressing the same button once again.

For each trial, participants had to deform the *Rear-view mirror* to fit a target shape, i.e., from an initial parameter value to a targeted parameter value. Only this part of *Rear-view mirror* was modifiable at each trial (Fig. 2.8). The targeted shape was displayed (Fig. 2.9). If participants failed to deform the shape with the correct targeted parameter value, they had to select the same part and attempt to deform the shape again. We counted this as an error. Once participants achieved the task, the next targeted shape appears. The participants were instructed to accomplish the task as fast as possible.

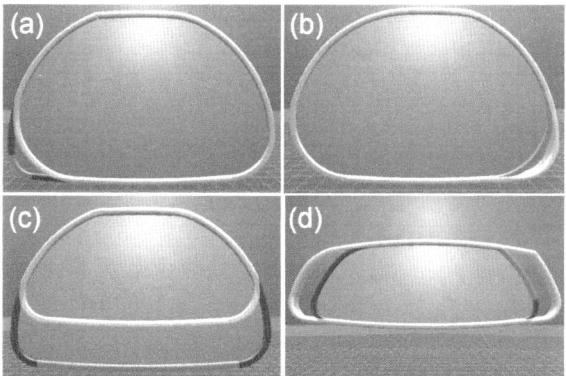

Fig. 2.9. 4 examples of the experimental task, (a) *LeftBottomCorner*, (b) *RightBottomCorner*, (c) *Bottom* and (d) *RightSide*.

2.6.4.2 *Method*

The experiment had a [2 x 2 x 4] within-subject design with the three following factors:

- TECHNIQUE with two levels: *ShapeGuide* and *Scroll*.

- FEEDBACK with two levels: *NoForce* for which the magnetic force feedback is not available and *Force* for which the magnetic force feedback is available.
- PART with four levels: the four deformable parts of *Rear-view mirror* (*LeftBottomCorner*, *RightBottomCorner*, *Bottom* and *RightSide*).

TECHNIQUE and FEEDBACK are the two main factors, and trials are grouped by TECHNIQUE×FEEDBACK. The order of TECHNIQUE×FEEDBACK was counterbalanced across participants using a balanced Latin Square; the order of PART was counterbalanced for each TECHNIQUE×FEEDBACK.

2.6.4.3 *Procedure*

For each condition, participants performed a training and 4 trials for each one of the 4 PARTs of the *Rear-view mirror*. The initial and targeted parameter values were different between each trial and the order was randomized.

For each trial, we logged the time, the evolution of the parameter value and the number of attempts to complete the task. From this data, we extracted four different measures: *Task Completion Time (TCT)*, *Wrong Direction Starts (WDS)*, *Overshoots* and *Errors*.

The *TCT* measured the total duration of the modification step during the deformation task. The measure started when the participants selected the part to deform, and stopped when participants validated the deformation with the correct parameter value. For *WDS*, we considered that the participants started their motion in the wrong direction if they started by deforming the part in the opposite direction to the targeted parameter/shape. An *Overshoots* was counted when the participants reached the targeted parameter/shape, but continued their gesture further away to a higher or smaller parameter value. Several overshoots can be accumulated during one attempt. The number of *Errors* was computed from the number of wrong parameter/shape selections in a trial.

Finally, a questionnaire based on the NASA Task Load Index (TLX)[42] assessed the participant preferences.

2.6.4.4 *Results*

We ran an analysis of variance on *TCT* with a Student's *t*-test.[j] For *WDS*, *Overshoots*, *Errors* and Likert scale data, we used a Wilcoxon Signed Rank test to analyze such count data.

For *TCT*, the results showed that *ShapeGuide* (avg. 2.41s) was significantly faster than *Scroll* (avg. 4.14s, $p < 0.0001$) (Fig. 2.10[k]). It provides evidence

---

[j]All analyses were performed with the *SAS JMP* statistical platform.
[k]In all barplots, error bars show the 95% confidence intervals (CI).

that *ShapeGuide* technique significantly increases user performance on parametric modification of CAD data in comparison to a one-dimensional scroll technique. More precisely, participants were able to achieve the deformation task 42% faster with *ShapeGuide* than with the *Scroll* technique, which supports **H1**.

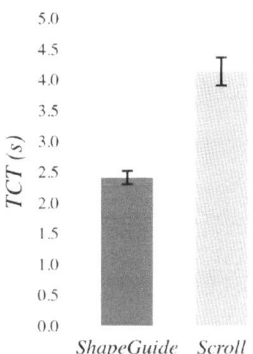

Fig. 2.10. Mean *TCT* by TECHNIQUE. Error bars show 95% the confidence intervals (CI).

This improvement can be explained by a better consistency between shape deformation and user hand motion with *ShapeGuide*. For WDS, *ShapeGuide* led to significantly fewer *WDS* (7% of *WDS*) than *Scroll* (35% of *WDS*, $p < 0.0001$) (Fig. 2.11, left). In other words, *ShapeGuide* reduced by 80% the chance that participants move their hands towards the wrong direction at the beginning of their gesture, in comparison to *Scroll*. This is especially true on parts which produce an inconsistent deformation motion according to the gesture direction (*RightBottomCorner* and *Bottom*). Particularly, *RightBottomCorner* induced significantly more *WDS* (45% of *WDS*) than the *RightSide* (8% of *WDS*, $p < 0.0001$), the *LeftBottomCorner* (13% of *WDS*, $p < 0.0001$) and the *Bottom* (19% of *WDS*, $p = 0.0266$)(Fig. 2.11, right). This is beneficial for users since they can expect the same behavior in every part. For these reasons, **H2** is validated.

For *Overshoots*, the results showed that *ShapeGuide* led to significantly more *Overshoots* (avg. 0.54) than *Scroll* (avg. 0.23, $p < 0.0001$) (Fig. 2.12, left). This is one of the limitation of *ShapeGuide*. A possible explanation is that it is harder to reach the desired shape with *ShapeGuide* when the distance between consecutive shapes is small.

However, in spite of this limitation, most participants reported in subjective questionnaire that they preferred *ShapeGuide* to the *Scroll* (avg. 4.28 vs. 3.06, $p = 0.0040$). Specifically, *ShapeGuide* was perceived less *mentally demanding* (avg. 4.28 vs. 3.16, $p = 0.0046$), less *frustrating* (avg. 4.56 vs. 3.44, $p = 0.0098$), less *difficult* to use (avg. 4.28 vs. 3.56, $p = 0.0093$) and more consistent (avg. 4.5 vs.

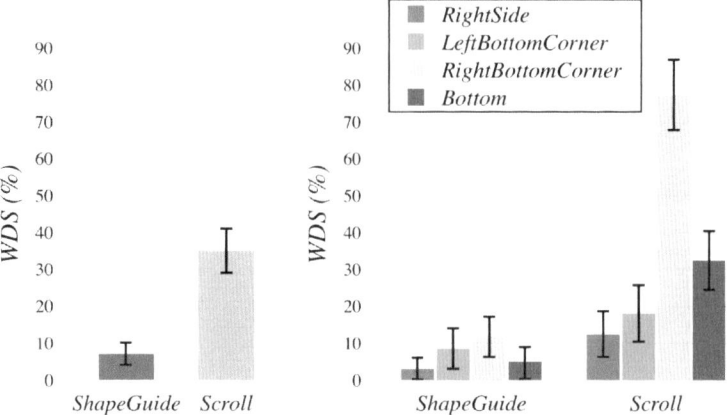

Fig. 2.11. *WDS* rates by TECHNIQUE (left) and TECHNIQUE×PART (right). Error bars show 95% the confidence intervals (CI).

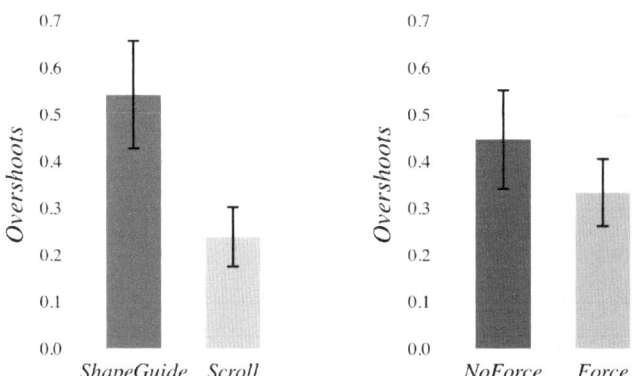

Fig. 2.12. Mean *Overshoots* by TECHNIQUE (left) and FEEDBACK (right). Error bars show 95% the confidence intervals (CI).

2.88, $p = 0.0005$) than *Scroll*. These results support **H3**.

With respect to the issue about *Overshoots*, magnetic force feedback can be an effective solution to reduce the number of *Overshoots*. The results showed that *Force* significantly reduced the number of *Overshoots* (avg. 0.33) in comparison to *NoForce* (avg. 0.45, $p = 0.0240$) (Fig. 2.12, right). That says, participants achieved the deformation task with 27% fewer *Overshoots* with the magnetic force feedback than without, which supports **H4**.

In terms of *Errors*, we did not observe any significant differences.

2.6.5 *Summary*

We confirmed that *ShapeGuide*[39] is a faster and more preferred interaction technique for users than one-dimensional interaction for parameter modifications in 3D space. Currently, we implemented the *ShapeGuide* technique in a 3D environment; however, we think that a precomputation method of *ShapeGuide* could also be applied in a 2D environment, such as a wall-sized display: e.g. users could compare and select a shape among a list of shape variations. From this assumption this technique could potentially be a generic interaction technique for different visualization systems.

2.7 Conclusion

This chapter describes three features to achieve a collaborative VR-CAD design system that could improve current industrial design processes by facilitating collaborative design during VR product reviews between several experts at remote locations. In comparison to the vast amount of previous VR-CAD research, our contribution focuses on native CAD data modification capability in the CVEs using direct shape-based interaction.

As a basis for our VR-CAD system, we first developed a *VR-CAD server* to interact with the native CAD data of an industrial CAD system, i.e. which cannot only load but also edit and save semantic information (e.g. CHG) in actual industrial CAD systems. The *VR-CAD server* outputs updated meshes of CAD data according to user input (e.g. selected part ID, a parameter value) which can allow users to directly deform the CAD data from remote environments.

The *VR-CAD server* is then integrated into our distribute architecture supporting remote collaborative modifications. This architecture enables remote users to collaboratively modify parameter values of CAD parts in a CVE. We designed it with a hybrid network architecture: the CAD data (meshes and CHG information) are distributed to each VR platform by the *VR-CAD server*, while information about non-CAD objects and media streams are directly transmitted between each platform. As an example, we implemented a proof of concept between two heterogeneous platforms: a haptic capable CAVE-like system and a large wall-sized display.

Regarding user interaction on CAD data editing, we designed and studied a 3D interaction technique, namely *ShapeGuide*, allowing users to modify parameter values of the CAD data by directly pushing/pulling surfaces. *ShapeGuide* proposes a set of shape variations by computing several meshes from different parameter values. Consequently, users can select the desired shape from a 3D hand motion with an optional force feedback guidance during shape deformation. Results of a controlled experiment demonstrated that *ShapeGuide* was faster on CAD part deformation tasks than the *Scroll* technique: a horizontal scroll interaction on parameter manipulations. This can be explained by the fact that the shape deformation was more consistent ergonomically with users' hand motions when using *ShapeGuide*. As a consequence, most participants preferred *ShapeGuide*.

These studies are still the first step towards enhancing the current industrial design process but we expect that these achievements will potentially lead to following contributions:

- Direct CAD data modifications that can decrease the number of iterations between workstations and VR platforms during industrial product reviews.
- Remote collaborations between several experts on distinct VR system/devices that can reduce travel costs and time associated with gathering at a specific VR facility.
- Shape-based interaction for CAD parameter modification could help non-CAD experts to access and deform shapes without a deep understanding of an internal organization of the CAD data or system.

We are aware that our VR-CAD system and *ShapeGuide* currently have some limitations. Even if the hybrid architecture ensures a high consistency of CAD data distribution in the CVE, the 3D-mesh generation on the *VR-CAD server* and their distribution to all platforms cause some delays. For *ShapeGuide*, results of the experiment showed that it could be less precise in selecting the desired shape during shape deformation than the *Scroll* technique.

We are currently in the process of studying a user interaction technique on a wall-sized display for parameter modifications using an adaptation of *ShapeGuide*. Future developments will target collaborative modifications of combined CAD parameters and the design of collaborative interactions using, at best, the expertise of remote CVE participants in real time. Also, future studies will compare remote collaborative design tools currently in use in our framework to measure added value for industry. Last, the impacts on CAD design work habits and company organizations will be examined.

Acknowledgments

This research was partially supported by RTA Digiteo and Labex DigiCosme (Idex Paris-Saclay ANR-11- IDEX-0003-02), and by EquipEx DIGISCOPE (ANR-10-EQPX-26-01) operated by the French Agence Nationale de la Recherche, as part of the program "Investissements d'Avenir".

References

1. G. Lawson, D. Salanitri and B. Waterfield, VR Processes in the Automotive Industry. In *Human-Computer Interaction: Users and Contexts*, M. Kurosu (ed.). Springer International Publishing, (2015).

2. J. Leigh, A. E. Johnson, C. A. Vasilakis and T. A. DeFanti, Multi-perspective collaborative design in persistent networked virtual environments. In *Proceedings of the IEEE 1996 Virtual Reality Annual International Symposium*, pp. 253–260 (1996), 10.1109/VRAIS.1996.490535.

3. A. Sivanathan, J. M. Ritchie and T. Lim, A novel design engineering review system with searchable content: knowledge engineering via real-time multimodal recording, *Journal of Engineering Design* **28**, (10-12), 681–708 (2017) http://arxiv.org/abs/https://doi.org/10.1080/09544828.2017.1393655.

4. S. Kuntz $improov^3$ The VR collaborative meeting room, MiddleVR Company, Paris, France. http://www.improovr.com/home/ (Accessed August 25, 2020).

5. P. Martin, S. Masfrand, Y. Okuya and P. Bourdot, A VR-CAD data model for immersive design. In *Augmented Reality, Virtual Reality and Computer Graphics*, L.T. de Paolis, P. Bourdot and A. Mongelli (eds.). Springer International Publishing (2017). https://doi.org/10.1007/978-3-319-60922-5_17.

6. J. Berta, Integrating VR and CAD, *IEEE Computer Graphics and Applications* **19**(5), 14–19 (1999).

7. A. Schilling, S. Kim, D. Weissmann, Z. Tang and S. Choi, CAD-VR geometry and meta data synchronization for design review applications, *Journal of Zhejiang University-SCIENCE A* **7**(9), 1482–1491 (2006).

8. S. Choi, H. Jo, S. Boehm and S. D. Noh, ONESVIEW: An integrated system for one-stop virtual design review, *Concurrent Engineering* **18**(1), 75–91 (2010).

9. S. Jayaram, U. Jayaram, Y. Wang, H. Tirumali, K. Lyons and P. Hart, VADE: A virtual assembly design environment, *IEEE Computer Graphics and Applications* **19**(6), 44–50 (1999).

10. Q.-H. Wang, J.-R. Li, B.-L. Wu and X.-M. Zhang, Live parametric design modifications in CAD-linked virtual environment, *The International Journal of Advanced Manufacturing Technology* **50**(9), 859–869 (2010).

11. P. Bourdot, T. Convard, F. Picon, M. Ammi, D. Touraine and J.-M. Vézien, VR–CAD integration: Multimodal immersive interaction and advanced haptic paradigms for implicit edition of CAD models, *Computer-Aided Design* **42**(5), 445–461 (2010).

12. V. D. Lehner and T. A. DeFanti, Distributed virtual reality: supporting remote collaboration in vehicle design, *IEEE Computer Graphics and Applications* **17**(2), 13–17 (1997).

13. M. Mahdjoub, D. Monticolo, S. Gomes and J.-C. Sagot, A collaborative design for usability approach supported by virtual reality and a multi-agent system embedded in a PLM environment, *Computer-Aided Design* **42**(5), 402–413 (2010).

14. R. Arangarasan and R. Gadh, Geometric modeling and collaborative design in a multi-modal multi-sensory virtual environment. In *Proc. of ASME Design Engineering Technical Conferences and Computers and Information in Engineering Conference*, pp. 10–13 (2000).

15. J. H. Clark, Designing Surfaces in 3-D, *Commun. ACM* **19**(8), 454–460 (1976).

16. J. H. Israel, E. Wiese, M. Mateescu, C. Zöllner and R. Stark, Investigating three-dimensional sketching for early conceptual design—Results from expert discussions and user studies, *Computers & Graphics* **33**(4), 462–473 (2009).

17. T. Fleisch, G. Brunetti, P. Santos and Stork, Stroke-input methods for immersive styling environments. In *Proceedings Shape Modeling Applications*, pp. 275–283 (2004).

18. D. F. Keefe, R. C. Zeleznik and D. H. Laidlaw, Drawing on air: Input techniques for controlled 3D line illustration, *IEEE Transactions on Visualization and Computer Graphics* **13**(5), 1067–1081 (2007).

19. D. Skillman and P. Hackett, Tilt Brush application, Google Inc., Available at https://www.tiltbrush.com/ (Accessed August 25, 2020).

20. E. Sachs, A. Roberts and D. Stoops, 3-Draw: A tool for designing 3D shapes, *IEEE Computer Graphics and Applications* **11**(6), 18–26 (1991).

21. F. Kuester, M. A. Duchaineau, B. Hamann, K. I. Joy and A. E. Uva, 3DIVS: 3-dimensional Immersive Virtual Sculpting. In *Proceedings of the 1999 Workshop on New Paradigms in Information Visualization and Manipulation in Conjunction with the Eighth ACM Internation Conference on Information and Knowledge Management (NPIVM'99)*, pp. 92-96, New York, USA, (1999).

22. M. Fiorentino, R. de Amicis, G. Monno and A. Stork, Spacedesign: A mixed reality workspace for aesthetic industrial design. In *Proceedings of the International Symposium on Mixed and Augmented Reality*, pp. 86–318 (2002).

23. A. Paljic, S. Coquillart, J.-M. Burkhardt and P. Richard, A study of distance of manipulation on the responsive workbench. In *Immersive Projection Technology Symposium*, Orlando, United States (2002).

24. B. R. D. Araújo, G. Casiez, J. A. Jorge and M. Hachet, Mockup Builder: 3D modeling on and above the surface, *Computers & Graphics* **37**(3), 165–178 (2013).

25. J. Liang and M. Green, JDCAD: A highly interactive 3D modeling system, *Computers & Graphics* **18**(4), 499–506 (1994).

26. A. Stork and M. Maidhof, Efficient and precise solid modelling using a 3D input device. In *Proceedings of the Fourth ACM Symposium on Solid Modeling and Applications (SMA '97)*, pp. 181-194, New York, USA (1997).

27. R. De Amicis, M. Fiorentino and A. Stork, Parametric interaction for CAD application in virtual reality environment. In *International Conference on Design Tools and Methods in Industrial Engineering, Pages D*, vol. 3, pp. 43–52 (2001).

28. S. Gao, H. Wan and Q. Peng, An approach to solid modeling in a semi-immersive virtual environment, *Computers & Graphics* **24**(2), 191–202 (2000).

29. W. Ma, Y. Zhong, S.-K. Tso and T. Zhou, A hierarchically structured and constraint-based data model for intuitive and precise solid modeling in a virtual reality environment, *Computer-Aided Design* **36**(10), 903–928 (2004).

30. V. Meyrueis, A. Paljic and P. Fuchs, D^3: An immersive aided design deformation method. In *Proceedings of the 16th ACM Symposium on Virtual Reality Software and Technology (VRST '09)*, pp. 179-182, New York, USA (2009).

31. M. I. Toma, F. Gîrbacia and C. Antonya, A comparative evaluation of human interaction for design and assembly of 3D CAD models in desktop and immersive environments, *International Journal on Interactive Design and Manufacturing (IJIDeM)* **6**(3), 179–193 (2012).

32. T. Convard and P. Bourdot, History based reactive objects for immersive CAD. In *Proceedings of the Ninth ACM Symposium on Solid Modeling and Applications (SM '04)* pp. 291-296, Aire la Ville, Switzerland, (2004).

33. D. Margery, B. Arnaldi and N. Plouzeau, A general framework for cooperative manipulation in virtual environments. In *Virtual Environments*, M. Gervautz, D. Schmastieg and A. Hildebrand (eds.). Springer (1999).

34. M. S. Pinho, D. A. Bowman and C. M. D. S. Freitas, Cooperative object manipulation in collaborative virtual environments, *Journal of the Brazilian Computer Society* **14**(2), 53–67 (2008).

35. L. Aguerreche, T. Duval and A. Lécuyer, Comparison of three interactive techniques for collaborative manipulation of objects in virtual reality. In *CGI 2010 (Computer Graphics International)*, Singapore (2010).

36. R. A. Ruddle, J. C. D. Savage and D. M. Jones, Symmetric and asymmetric action integration during cooperative object manipulation in virtual environments, *ACM Trans. Comput.-Hum. Interact.* **9**(4), 285–308 (2002).

37. Y. Bodein, B. Rose and E. Caillaud, A roadmap for parametric CAD efficiency in the automotive industry, *Computer-Aided Design* **45**(10), 1198–1214 (2013).

38. R. Stark, J. H. Israel and T. Wöhler, Towards hybrid modelling environments—Merging desktop-CAD and virtual reality-technologies, *CIRP Annals* **59**(1), 179–182 (2010).

39. Y. Okuya, N. Ladeveze, C. Fleury and P. Bourdot, ShapeGuide: Shape-based 3D interaction for parameter modification of native CAD data, *Frontiers in Robotics and AI* **5**, 118 (2018).

40. C. Ericson, Basic primitive tests. In *Real Time Collision Detection,* C. Ericson (ed.). Morgan Kaufmann (2005).

41. T. Yamada, D. Tsubouchi, T. Ogi and M. Hirose, Desk-sized immersive workplace using force feedback grid interface. In *Proceedings IEEE Virtual Reality 2002*, pp. 135–142 (2002).

42. S. G. Hart and L. E. Staveland, Development of NASA-TLX (Task Load Index): Results of empirical and theoretical research. In *Human Mental Workload*, P.A. Hancock and N. Meshkati (eds.). North-Holland (1988).

https://doi.org/10.1142/9789811222863_0003

Chapter 3

Improving Maintenance Services through Virtual Reality

Nicola Riboldi, Giulia Wally Scurati, Francesco Ferrise,
Monica Bordegoni, and Simone Pedrini

3.1 Introduction

In recent years, the interest of industries in Virtual Reality (VR) technologies has grown due to a rapid decrease of hardware and software costs, and an increase of the performances and achievement of high maturity level. In this context, VR emerged as a versatile means potentially exploitable to improve companies' competitiveness. Many successful VR applications have been developed in different contexts. Choi et al. published an extended review of VR applications for the manufacturing industry, with the main focus on the product development phases.[1] In both conceptual and advanced design stages, VR offers effective functionalities for design reviews, allowing the reduction of the overall product development time and costs, and the improvement of the quality of the new designed products.[2,3] Then, in the final phases of the product development process, VR can be used for supporting the manufacturing process, including activities to set up, evaluate and optimize complex production systems.[4,5] or to design and simulate assembly production lines.

Virtual Reality can be also effectively used to implement applications for training, supporting operators in learning how to perform assembly and maintenance tasks.[6,7] The main advantage offered by VR in this context is the possibility of recreating real environments and situations where operators can practice and train, as if they were in a real similar context, but without the risk of harming themselves or damaging the machines. Particularly interesting is the use of VR for training operators in maintenance activities. In fact, VR provides the possibility to understand and learn procedures, explore and practice in the use of machines, in protected virtual environments, thus avoiding stopping the production, and with no risk of injuries and damages.

The issue related to maintenance of industrial systems is particularly complex. In fact, it includes economic, managerial and technical aspects. A major issue is the production of instructions and documentation materials for machine maintenance and operators' training. Another regards the identification and management of information about spare parts that need to be retrieved, purchased and replaced. The production of these items of information and materials is particularly critical, due to the continuous modification and upgrade of the machines, which require a related update of the documentation. Another major issue concerns the organization and performance of training sessions, which can also be delivered in remote customers' premises. These activities may require the participation of many experts, including engineers, production technicians, administrative staff members, and in some situations also interpreters, who has to travel to reach the place where the operators to instruct are. All this makes the training activities expensive and time demanding.

Finally, an additional issue to consider is that maintenance operations require a considerable cognitive effort from the operators for the identification of parts of the system to be fixed or replaced, the use of the various tools and the necessity to follow the right sequence of actions, which may also be complex. Therefore, memorizing and performing maintenance procedures is also critical from a psycho-physical point of view.

Virtual Reality can be an effective solution to support all the activities mentioned so far, as it can improve and speed up gaining know-how and skills about the tasks to perform, with respect to traditional methods.[8]

Similar considerations can be done regarding serious games, which make use of training and learning tools exploiting typical elements and structures of entertainment applications.[9]

Nevertheless, the development of VR applications is not trivial. In fact, they should be designed taking into account the complexity of the maintenance issue, considering the multiple aspects listed above. Furthermore, a VR application should be always designed for the specific context, requiring a deep knowledge of the subject.[10] In fact, it implies a series of choices concerning the kind of users' experience to provide, and a consequent selection of hardware and software technology to use for the implementation.

In this chapter, we explore the use of non-immersive VR technology to support maintenance training, and describe an application developed for an industrial case study. The application was finally tested with both professional and non-professional operators.

3.2 Related Works

Virtual Reality (VR) technologies have been largely explored as educational and training tools in various fields, with several case studies focusing on the military[11] and medical training.[12] These two different fields share similar issues related to the performance of the training sessions in the real world, due to a high risk for the trainees of harming themselves and other people. In virtual environments the user can learn and practice through simulated real situations and events, while he is placed within a physical protected environment. This is particularly convenient when the operations take place in complex and risky contexts. For instance, VR training has been tested to make the general public as well as firefighters, both novices and commanders, experience different fire situations, evacuate places, communicate and take decisions.[13]

The effectiveness of VR tools for skill transfer has been proven for various applications. Several studies demonstrate it for VR surgical training platforms, showing a general improvement of performances as described in the review presented by Seymour.[8] Their use has been then extended to other contexts, as education and industry. Abulrub et al.[14] highlight that in engineering education VR allows to reduce costs related to the purchase of expensive equipment as well as the risks due to the use of hazardous material, while it would be able to motivate students and improve their learning attitude. Also, in the industrial context, VR trainees were reported as learning faster, committing fewer errors and being generally more efficient than the ones exposed to conventional training methods.[15]

The interest of the industry in using VR is due to many reasons. As for the medical and military contexts, maintenance can be performed in particularly complex and unsafe environments such as the case of high-voltage overhead power lines.[16] Moreover, risks do not only regard safety, but also economical aspects: in the industrial context, maintenance procedures and training sessions can affect the production, as they require it to interrupt. Furthermore, in case of low skilled workers the costs are also increased by possible damages of components due to errors, which results in further maintenance costs and spare parts costs.

Using VR for these purposes enables novices to investigate tasks in a detailed way compared to traditional media, furthermore, it allows training when the product is in the design phase, before a physical prototype has been developed.[17] This also permits us to evaluate the assembly design, including several aspects related to the workspace, tools and people involved, predicting assembly time.[18] In fact, VR tools have been proposed to verify human performances, evaluating related qualitative factors (e.g. the perception of the workspace and handling of tools) and estimating quantitative ones (e.g. capability to lift weight, task cycle time).[19] Also, ergonomic and accessibility aspects during maintenance tasks or assembly evaluation can be addressed through VR platforms.[20]

All the described activities can be performed using games, for instance setting them as timed challenges: they can be used by manufacturers and customers to configure products, explore and assemble parts.[21] Furthermore, these serious games can address not only hard skills (e.g. product development, manufacturing and management), but also soft skills (e.g. team building, collaboration and communication), which is a desirable feature for the complexity of the industrial context.[10]

VR applications can be divided into two main categories depending on the kind of experience and environment they provide, which can be immersive or non-immersive. Considering industrial applications, both approaches have been reported in literature.

Jayaram et al.[18] present VADE (Virtual Assembly Design Environment), an application for assembly planning, which delivers an immersive virtual environment where the user can perform a series of operations, as assembly and inspecting components, during maintenance phase. The authors also highlight the importance of haptic feedbacks in VR applications, especially for immersive environments. In this regard, De Sa and Zachmann[3] point out that the absence of force feedback makes difficult performing assembly tasks in VR. Therefore, in order to overcome this problem, they propose an immersive environment simulating assembly, disassembly and maintenance procedures at BMW, developing a constraint-based application using a device – a Cyber-Touch- which provides tactile feedback.

Brough et al. developed Virtual Training Studio (VTS), which is a tool for performing assembly and disassembly tasks within an immersive environment without any haptic device, but just using a virtual laser.[22] According to their studies, the system accelerates the learning process, and the workers' errors probability is reduced.

Immersive VR can be used to support remote collaboration, as discussed by Pouliquen-Lardy et al.[23] a participant (manipulator) is instructed by a passive one (guide). They claim the need of perspective-taking tools for the former and manipulation tools (e.g. collision detection) for the latter.

Collaborative applications can also be developed for non-immersive environments, as the one presented by Ferrise et al.[24] for maintenance training. A virtual environment is in fact used by the guide operator to provide instructions to a remote manipulator in Augmented Reality (AR).

Li et al. proposed VR (V-REALISM), a desktop-based tool to practice disassembly for maintenance assisting users by suggesting the optimal disassembly sequence, based on the minimal changes of disassembly orientation and tools.[7] Another example of non-immersive VE based on desktop displays for maintenance training of high-voltage overhead power lines is described by Garcia et al.,[16] allowing trainees to explore equipment that would be too dangerous or not accessible.

Immersive and non-immersive experiences require the use of different technologies. The latter consist of computer desktops and projectors, while the former are essentially based on Head Mounted Displays (HMDs). Using HDMs, users are located in the VE isolating them from the surrounding space and the presence of other people and objects. When using non-immersive technologies instead, the user still perceives the real environment and is able to interact with persons and items around him. An overview of VR technologies and devices is provided by Anthes et al.[25] As they illustrate, HMDs can be stationary or mobile. Mobile ones are cheaper and more versatile, as they are not wired but on the other hand, they present limited interaction. Mobile devices include both smartphone cases as the Google Cardboard and standalone systems as the Samsung Gear VR. Examples of stationary devices are the HTC Vive and the Oculus Rift.

Immersive environments can provide a more realistic experience, compared to non-immersive platforms. Indeed, this feature makes them the optimal option for certain fields. For example, for military and emergency training the level of fidelity and the sense of presence are determinant aspects for the applications to be successful.[11,13] However, the implementation of immersive environments requires the use of hardware and software technologies that have major usability, practical and economic issues. Those issues have been extensively proved and reported in literature. Cobb et al.[26] describe a series of effects related to sickness, but also postural instability and ergonomics. A considerable percentage of the participants reported those symptoms as irritating.

Anthes et al.[25] investigated the current devices available on the market and evaluated them considering their correlation with the problem of "cyber-sickness". Cyber-sickness is a feeling of sickness that users may experience when they are moved, or move their hands, in the virtual environment, and is generally related to latency.

Sharples et al. compared the use of HMDs with desktop and projector displays.[27] During some experimental tests, the participants reported an increased sense of nausea, oculomotor and disorientation symptoms when wearing HMDs with respect to other conditions. Moreover, wearing HDMs may entail ergonomic discomfort due to its weight, fit and adjustability.[28]

Furthermore, there are economic issues to consider related to the cost of equipment, and practical issues due to the fact that the technology chosen for the implementation of VR applications affects the organization of their context of use. With this respect, non-immersive VR applications – as desktop-based platforms – do not require the use of advanced software and hardware nor the presence of a specific training room. Therefore, they can be considered as a more versatile, economical and also portable solution.[7,16] An example of non-immersive application for maintenance and assembly procedures using a screen combined with a haptic device is provided by Gavish et al.[6]

An open issue in literature is the one of defining a learning method and guidelines to develop effective training tools. Bellotti et al.[9] distinguish two kinds of approaches: a "formative" assessment, where the system continuously provides feedback signals to the user during the experience, or a "summative" one, presenting a final evaluation of the user's learning level at the end of the game. They suggest that the former is more effective than the latter.

Another point is that training applications are context dependent, as stated by Riedel and Hauge.[10] Therefore, the knowledge of the subject is a key factor for their development, which should follow the analysis of the specific case study.

3.3 VR Maintenance Training: A Case Study

The aim of the research work hereafter presented is demonstrating the effectiveness and benefits of using non-immersive VR for maintenance training. In this regard, a case study has been proposed by OCRIM, a company producing wheat mill machines. The case study consists of the following scenario, mainly addressing industrial machines maintenance instructions and manuals.

For any commercial machinery, the manufacturer (the OCRIM company in this case) has to guarantee the customer a set of services. Those include manuals for its maintenance and safe use, according to the European standards [DM 2006/42/CE] a training for maintainers, and an assistance service, along with the supply of spare parts, in case of failure of components.[29]

However, manuals are not always consulted in a proper way before executing the maintenance operations. The reasons for that can be many. First, technical documentation can be inaccurate, due to upgrades of the machinery, which may affect some procedures. Moreover, instruction manuals may refer to a series of machineries rather than to a specific model. Consequently, there would be a lack of correspondence between the items of information included in the manual and the machinery, which may mislead the operators, who often proceed by trials, thus slowing the maintenance process and risking damages of the machinery.

Furthermore, the company providing the case study supplies plants and machineries in several countries, as it is the case for many companies today operating in international contexts. Consequently, instructions and items of information included in the manuals should be provided in many languages. This would require a team of people working on the implementation and update of the manual, including engineers, translators and customers. In addition, the communication between the company technicians and the remote customer operators represents a very critical aspect, due to translation and time zone issues, which make the exchange and understanding of information extremely time consuming.

Instruction manuals for complex machineries typically include a section dedicated to the identification of spare parts, in order to allow the operators to select and buy the required pieces. This section contains several exploded drawings of the machine, where a number is assigned to each component according to the Bill of Material (BOM). The comprehension of the drawings is often difficult, due to the high complexity of the machine. In addition, it may be hard recognizing small components.

Considering the described scenario, requirements for the application have been set, concerning both the software and hardware components, and the technology to use to implement the solution has been selected. The study proposed in this chapter is based on the hypothesis that a VR application could help in overcoming the issues related to manuals including out of date and inconsistent instructions, availability of version in different languages and the retrieval of spare parts. The VR application proposed allows the exploration of milling machines and the performance of critical maintenance tasks.

The complexity of both the machines and maintenance operations is challenging for the operators. Therefore, a major requirement is that the interaction with the virtual environment has to be natural and intuitive so as to allow operators to quickly learn how to use the VR application and focus only on maintenance tasks. Natural interaction is also fundamental for what concerns the learning method. In fact, in this way the operator would be able to easily memorize the various procedures and associate them with natural movements.

Furthermore, the VR application should be easy to update and should adapt to different types of machines. It should also support different languages by using a minimum amount of text, in order to simplify and speed up the translation process. The VR application should also serve as a platform to rapidly identify and purchase spare parts when customers need to perform replacement.

The complexity of simulating maintenance operations also affects the adoption of an immersive or a non-immersive approach, and the related hardware and software components for the VR application implementation. With this respect, it is necessary to make some considerations.

Indeed, the fact that maintenance training requires prolonged use of the virtual environment makes usability and ergonomic issues related to the use of VR particularly relevant. Moreover, in case it is decided to use an immersive setup, it is necessary to dedicate a specific space to the VR application, and also involve additional personnel to assist the VR application users and avoid the risk of injuries, as they cannot see the real world.

Therefore, it is possible to conclude that projection and desktop displays are more convenient than immersive technologies, as HMD, and they do not force the user to be connected through cables with a PC or a screen.

Comparing the use of desktop displays and projectors, the most flexible solution is certainly the former one, as they do not require any specific environment and lighting condition.

3.4 Implementation of the VR Application

The VR maintenance training application consists of a non-immersive virtual environment where users can see the virtual scene displayed on a common full HD screen, offering a wide view, and can move and interact with virtual objects through a body tracking system and a hand controller. This section describes the specifications of the VR application and the hardware and software setup.

3.4.1 *VR Application Specifications*

The scenario selected by the OCRIM company is a maintenance procedure that is considered particularly critical. It consists of tasks necessary to remove a roll bearing of a machine. The company detected that some damages on the machine occur when low skilled maintainers perform this operation. For example, it happens that the operator performs maintenance operations in wrong sequence when tightening the screws of the bearing extractor. Therefore, the VR application should correctly simulate each step of the sequence to allow the operator to learn the right sequence.

Fig. 3.1. Simulated maintenance sequence. The components to move are indicated by the arrows.

In order to simplify the comprehension and memorization of the correct procedure, the whole task has been split into five sub-operations, including basic tasks, such as removal and insertion actions: the removal of the cover (Fig. 3.1-a), back cover fixing (Fig. 3.1-b), ring nut removal (Fig. 3.1-c), extractor insertion (Fig. 3.1-d), bearing removal (Fig. 3.1-e).

3.4.2 *Hardware Setup*

The VR application is used by a user standing up in front of a full HD screen where the virtual environment is displayed. The screen acts as a sort of window on the virtual world.

The interaction is handled through the acquisition of the user's body motion. The user's body is tracked by means of a Kinect One sensor positioned below the screen. The sensor is able to detect the user inside a tracking area whose dimensions are highlighted in Fig. 3.2. Once the user is tracked, the application automatically associates with his head a camera that looks at the virtual scene. The point of view on the virtual world is changed according to the user's movements. The interaction with virtual objects is performed through the movement of the user's hand. A menu including a list of options can be handled through a remote controller (Nintendo Wii remote controller).

The positioning of these hardware components is quite flexible. However, there are some constraints that need to be respected. The sensor must be placed on a support whose height is between 60cm and 70cm, and the height of the screen should be between 60cm and 100cm. The VR application is calibrated so as to place the virtual machine at a height that is similar to the real one. The controller can be managed by both left- and right-handed users, since the system is able to trace both hands. This should improve the flexibility of the application with respect to the user 's needs and capabilities.

The area within which the user can move due to the sensor constraints, and to the field of view and distance from screen is shown in Fig. 3.2.

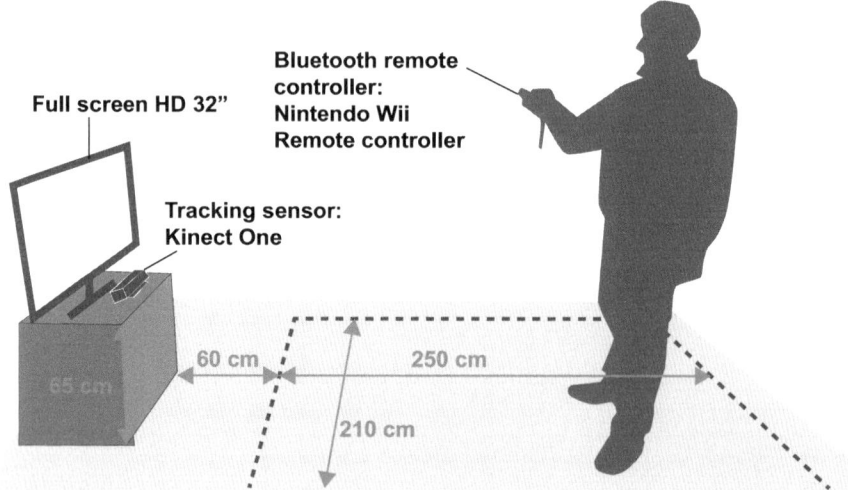

Fig. 3.2. Configuration of the system showing the positioning of the equipment. The sensor can detect the user in the area highlighted by the dashed line.

3.4.3 *Software Setup*

The application is developed using Unity 5 (unity3d.com), an authoring cross-platform tool typically used to develop video games and simulations for computers, consoles and mobile devices.

In order to make the use of the application simple, three scenes have been created, where a different specific function has been assigned to each of them.

In detail, the application provides three main functions: exploration of the machine, maintenance training, and support for components purchasing, which includes the creation of a .PDF file to order spare parts for the selected sub-assembly.

Therefore, the VR application consists of four scenarios, which implement the three main functions and an additional initial scenario where the user can first observe the whole machine, which is placed on a rotating platform. By using the remote control, the user can select one of the sub-assemblies. Next to it the application displays three options, which allow the user to select one of the main functions: order, explore and training (Fig. 3.3).

In the second scenario (Fig. 3.4) the user can order spare parts. It is possible to choose the desired quantity of each component in order to create the spare parts order, which is then automatically saved into a .PDF file. This procedure allows a simple recognition of components and avoids mistakes in matching the parts listed in the BOM with the ones represented in the exploded technical drawings.

Fig. 3.3. Home scene. The user can access all the other scenes: order, explore, and training.

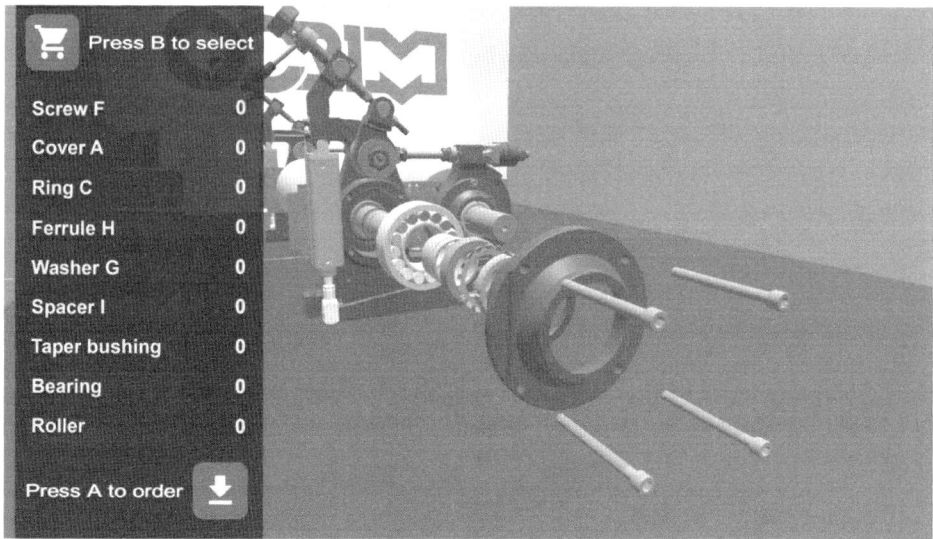

Fig. 3.4. Spare parts and BOM scene. The user can select the parts to purchase in the assembly and in the menu on the left. Then, it is possible to set the required quantity and order.

In the third scenario (Fig. 3.5), the user can explore and interact with the selected sub-assembly and its exploded view, obtain information about its components, and the tools necessary or removing or inserting the components during the training phase.

Fig. 3.5. Exploration scene showing the components and assembly order.

The last scenario (Fig. 3.6) consists of the maintenance training phase, where the user can learn the correct maintenance procedure. Here, the user is provided with instructions concerning the maintenance tasks and performs trials. He receives feedbacks about his performance immediately after each action, using a formative approach, as described in Section 3.2. He can interact with components and tools respectively through his tracked hand and through the remote control.

3.5 Experimental Setup and Testing

The application has been tested by a group of experts, who knew the machinery, and a group of unskilled people, who did not have any knowledge of the machine and did not have specific maintenance skills. A testing protocol has been designed for this specific application, and includes the following steps:

- Pre-test questionnaire collecting personal information about participants has been submitted, including: age, gender, height, vision problems, experience level with computer graphic software, video games and VR or AR technologies;
- Pre-test explanation of the aims of VR application and test;

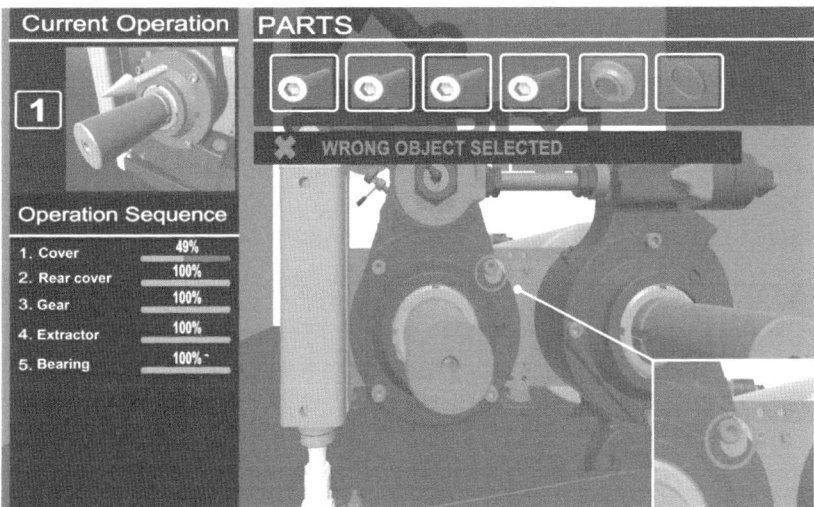

Fig. 3.6. Training scene: on the left, the list of operations to accomplish. On the top, the list of parts to remove. The selected object is wrong, as indicated.

- Pre-test tutorial, showing how the VR application works and what are its main functions, and explaining what kind of devices the user must use during the test, and how he can interact with the virtual environment. This phase is fundamental to allow the user to improve its familiarity with the application and technology before starting the training experience;
- During the testing sections, an expert observes the participants in order to check if there are errors, to provide help in case of necessity, to register possible discomfort symptoms;
- Post-test questionnaire collecting opinions about the experience is finally submitted to the participants;
- Post-test analysis is made by experts accessing the file generated by the application including the final scores for each sub-operation for each participant.

In the following, more details are provided concerning the participants and the questionnaire.

3.5.1 *Participants*

Twenty participants performed the test. Ten of them were expert in using the machinery. They were OCRIM company employees as maintainers, technicians and engineers. The opinion of these people is particularly important, as they are supposed to be the future users of the VR application.

The participants were all male and right-handed. Four of them were engineers, four operators and two technicians. The mean age was 40.9 years, with a range of 20-58. Two operators have never used any kind of computer graphics or VR application, and only two engineers have used VR applications. Therefore, 80% of participants have never used VR applications and have never tried to interact with a virtual environment. The familiarity with VR technology is negligible for the three oldest participants. All ten users know the maintenance sequence proposed by the case study, but only four operators have performed this procedure on the real machine.

The other ten participants are unskilled people, who had never seen the machine and in some cases had no experience in using mechanical tools. The participation of this kind of users to the tests is useful to evaluate the learning method, since the first group of participants already had some knowledge about the procedures to carry out. Seven participants were male and three female, while all of them were right-handed. They belong to different occupational contexts: in particular there are four students, two engineers, one expert of computer systems, one mechanic, one teacher, one manager. The mean age was 32.7 years, with a range of 18-58. Only two participants have never used any kind of computer graphics or VR application. Seven youngest participants have already used VR applications. In particular five users have tried an immersive experience on a roller coaster. All of them have negative opinion about this immersive experience due to the low quality of images provided by the visualization system. The familiarity with VR technology is negligible for the three oldest participants. All unskilled users do not know the maintenance sequence proposed by the case study. Only two participants have never used mechanical tools before. All participants speak Italian, so the test has been provided in this language.

3.5.2 *Pre-test Tutorial*

Each participant has been provided with instructions before starting the test. First, they are explained the task to carry out during the test. Then, they go through a training phase, to get familiar with the application. During the training phase, they are shown a tutorial of the application based on paper instructions, to enable a quick learning. When participants feel ready, the test starts. The tutorial is the most expensive phase in terms of time, due to the presentation of the VR application and learning functions performed within the virtual environment. It lasted 16-20 minutes for the company's users (M = 18.2 minutes, SD = 1.2) as

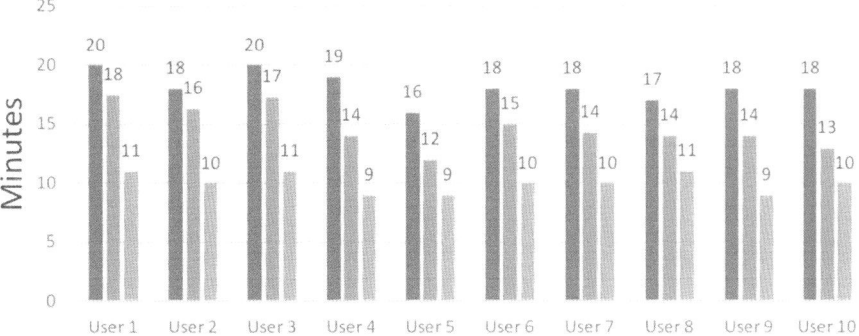

Fig. 3.7.   Measured time for experts of the machine.

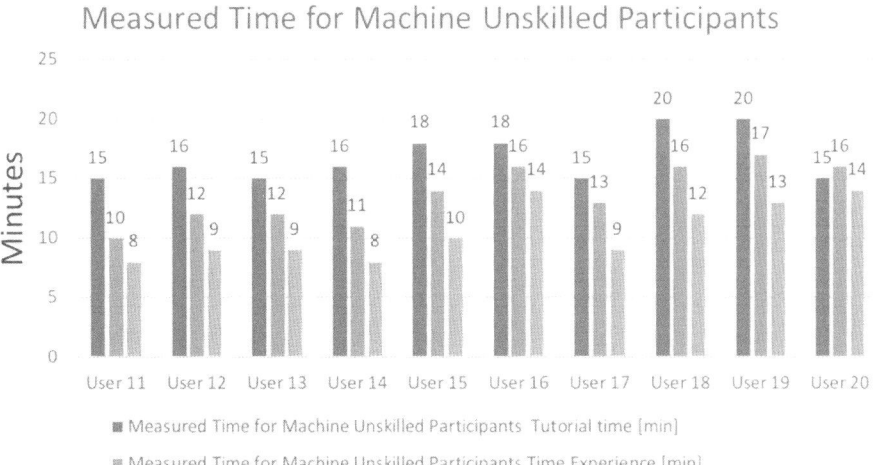

Fig. 3.8.   Measured time for unskilled users.

shown in Fig. 3.7, and 15-20 minutes for unskilled users (M = 16.8 minutes, SD = 2.0) as shown in Fig. 3.8. The duration depends on the level of confidence of the user with the application. By considering both the groups of participants the younger ones were in general faster in this phase due to the higher knowledge of digital systems compared to older users, which make them faster learners.

3.5.3 *Questionnaire*

The questionnaire provided to each user consists of two main parts. The first part is submitted during the pre-test phase and is aimed at collecting personal information about the user characteristics and attitudes in using digital devices. A probing of the familiarity level of each user with computers, video games, VR or AR tools is useful to understand if the system can be used also by people who are inexperienced with this kind of devices. The second part is provided at the end of the experience and it is aimed at getting opinions of the user concerning the usability of the system and the effectiveness of training.

The second part of the questionnaire is based on a five-point Likert scale. Some of the questions are worded so a response of "agree" would indicate a negative opinion about that expression: in this way the user is involved to think about his experience in VE and avoid answering in a casual or automatic way. This solution is in contrast with Brown [30], who concluded that negative questions should be avoided to reduce the ambiguity both for the answers and for the post-test analysis. In order to reduce these issues, two solutions are found: double negative questions are avoided, and each negative worded question is reverse scored in order to obtain homogeneous scores between negative and positive worded expressions. In particular for all questions a high score indicates a positive feeling about the system. All negative questions are indicated in the questionnaire in the column headed. A score of 3 is equivalent to a response of "neutral" for all questions. The questionnaire is divided in seven main parts to allow the user to easily associate each expression with what he has experienced in each scene:

- Ten items regard general opinions on the application: quality of the visualization, movements, feelings, symptoms.
- Five items regard the initial scene which is the first approach with VE;
- Seven items concern the usability in exploration scene, in particular about the movements needed to explore the sub-assembly and effort required;

- Four items concern the training aspects in exploration scene, specifically about the usefulness of exploration for memorizing information about training phase;
- Three items regard the order scene usability, for correctly creating the order file;
- Five items are investigating the usability during training phase;
- Six items regard the training and learning methods;
- One final question is used to evaluate the learning level of users.

3.6 Analysis of Test Results

This section reports the results of the testing sessions, by analyzing the observations made during the test, the maintenance training test, and the answers provided in the questionnaire.

3.6.1 *During Test Observations*

The observations made during the tests highlighted some critical points of the application. The training scene usability is affected by some difficulties in selecting the objects with the spherical cursor associated with the user hand. It has been noticed that even if the users feel ready to start the experience after the tutorial phase, this problem seems to be constant. In particular, the first group of users had more problems than the second. This could depend on the different levels of familiarity with digital devices. It could also depend on the difficulty to see a connection between the hand and spherical cursor. In an immersive environment the user can see the controller in his hand increasing the perception of having control. In a non-immersive environment, the cursor can be thought as a laser beam point on a wall, but this requires tracking also the rotations of the hand that cannot be detected by Kinect in a stable way. However, only 30% of both groups of testers partially agree that the cursor is difficult to be detected in the scene, while 70% have no problem in finding it. Another issue is represented by the controller during tools selection inside the toolbox. For the testers who have used only PC games some buttons are too sensitive to pressure or in some cases the cross shape of control pad induces to press more than one button at the same time.

3.6.2 *Training Test*

The mean time for the training phase is M = 10 minutes, SD = 0.8 for the first group of participants, while it is M = 10.6 minutes, SD = 2.4 for the second group, however there is no relevant difference between the two groups of participants. It has to be noticed that in the skilled users group two workers over four and the younger user can perform the complete procedure in 9 minutes, while the other users, even if expert in the machinery, performed it in 10 or 11 minutes. In the other group the younger users have performed the training phase in no more than 9 minutes and in two cases 8 minutes. In the former group this fact is assumed to be caused by the higher skills of workers in maintenance tasks: they are more expert in performing manual activities and in choosing the correct tool with respect to engineers and technicians.

In the latter, the attitude in using digital devices overcomes the limitation given by low knowledge of the machine and maintenance procedures. Even if the tutorial phase was longer for older participants, there was always a gap concerning the confidence with digital devices. Indeed, the older participants in the second group are the slowest in performing the complete procedure, since they do not have any knowledge of the maintenance procedures, nor a high confidence with the technologies used. Two users are completely unskilled in using mechanical tools, so they have some difficulties in completing the procedure alone and they proceed by trials, requiring more time to complete the task. However, while the knowledge of elementary tools and notions of mechanical tasks appear to be fundamental also in time analysis, the missing knowledge of machinery can be overcome by the user familiarity with the system improved during the tutorial phase.

Similar considerations can be made regarding error rates. For each task, error rates were generally higher for the second group. Operation 2 (back cover fixing) was the one with the lower error rate: M = 0%, SD = 0.0 for the first group and M = 0.4%, SD = 0.8 for the second one. The task with a higher error rate is operation 3 (removal of the ring nut): M = 8.4%, SD = 4.4 for the first group and M = 10.1%, SD = 4.7 for the second one. However, the two users which have no skills in using mechanical tools have the higher error rates compared to the other participants of the same group. Instead, the only mechanic in this group performed similarly to the participants of the first group. Regarding the first group, maintainers performed better than the other participants. Therefore, having maintenance skills lead to better performances, while the knowledge of the machine is less relevant.

3.6.3 *Post-test Questionnaire*

The quality of the environment was evaluated as good by both the groups of participants: within the expert group 80% agree and 20% completely agree, while in the second group 70% agree and 30% completely agree. None of the users reported to have any kind of discomfort or nausea. Only one user in the first group disagrees that the movements to perform to visualize objects are intuitive. The participants who had no experience with immersive environments felt immersed in the VE, conversely, if they had previous experience with immersive system they partially agree. Nine users partially agree and seven agree on the fact the system was not prompt enough in reacting to their movements, which may be the reason why eight of them found they did not have a complete control of the events in the VE. However, only two users partially agree on the fact that the first use of the application was complicated, while the others disagree, or completely disagree.

Also, 40% of the users agree and 35% completely agree that using the system for a long time does not require a high effort. 95% the users agree or completely agree that it is easy to understand how the machine is made and the rotation is useful for this purpose. All the participants agree or completely agree that the user movements were useful to completely explore the machine, only 30% of the first group partially agrees. 90% of the users agree or completely agree that icons clearly represent the tools and are useful to carry out the training. 40% of the users partially agree and 25% agree that the cursor to select the objects is not always stable and 30% partially agree that it is not easy to detect the cursor in the scene. However, observations performed during the test let us associate these problems only with the detection of small objects. A critical point is the one of the remote control: 40% of the users agree, and 50% partially agree there are issues in responding when pressing the buttons. This problem is highlighted by participants that had no experience with video games, or only had experience with computer games: they find the cross-shape pad too sensitive and find it difficult to press only the intended button. Regardless these issues, all the users agree or completely agree they felt more confident with the application after the first use. 85% of the users agree or completely agree on the usefulness of visualizing the list of operations to understand the correct sequence, which was one of the main problems highlighted by the company. 70% of the users agree that the system was effective to memorize the procedure, while six users partially agree that the system was distracting.

3.6.4 *Post-test Application Adjustments*

The testing phase provides insights about an average time within which the task should be completed using the application. The first attempt takes about 10 minutes, however, an expert user of both the application and the machine can perform the training task in 3 minutes. Therefore, the training scene has been provided with a timer (Fig. 3.9) that allows the user to take track of the time he is using to carry out that procedure, at the end of which the time is stopped and it is compared to an ideal time, which is the target. If the current time is greater than the target one, the timer becomes red colored and the user is suggested to try the procedure again through a specific information panel. Otherwise, the user receives a message of successful training, in this case the timer becomes green.

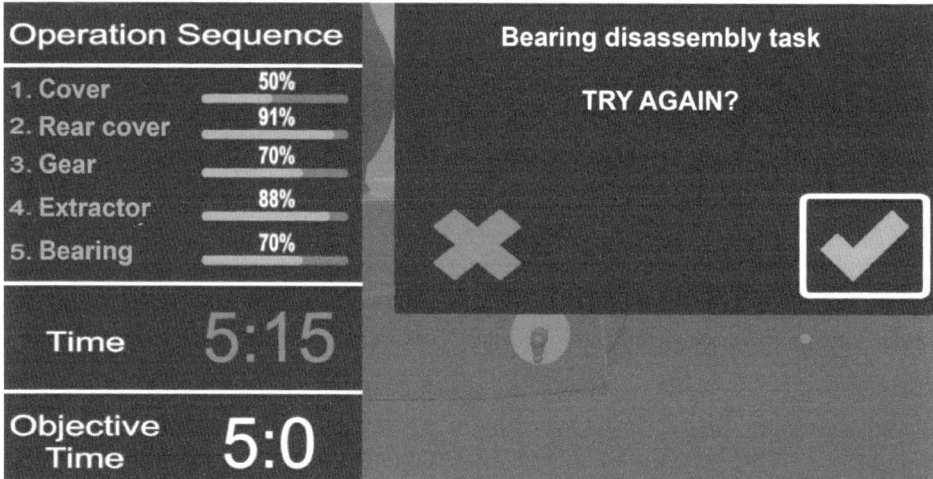

Fig. 3.9. Failed training: the time the user needed to complete the task is greater than the target time set for the specific task. The user can then perform a new trial.

3.7 Discussion and Conclusion

The aim of the research presented in this chapter was developing a low-cost training VR application to improve operators' skills during maintenance session and also to reduce time to develop instruction manuals. After implementation, the VR application proposed by a company operating in the wheat mill machine sector has been tested with a group of selected users.

As a general comment, it is possible to state that the test participants were able to use the system quite rapidly since the first time. Indeed, each user required up to twenty minutes of tutorial, but the experience of using the application demanded no more than fifteen minutes on average. For this reason, the application can be used also by operators who are not familiar with VR technology, since the non-immersive environment and control devices are simple to handle. The VR application does not require any previous calibration and no sickness symptoms were reported by the testers during the experience.

The advantage of this simulation is that the user can learn the sequence of maintenance operations to perform in few minutes (about 10 minutes for the first attempt), while in reality the case study training procedure requires at least 60 minutes. Furthermore, typically there is the need to perform previous operations to access the bearing area, which require 30 minutes more. It means that, for the case study, a low skilled operator who has never used the VR application can repeat several times the training session in the same time that is needed to perform a single real training procedure. In addition, by repeating the procedure the user would learn, reducing the number of attempts and enhancing confidence with tasks and tools choices. A very expert user of the application and of the maintenance sequence would be able to perform the simulation in about 3 minutes, even though this is supposed to occur only after several attempts.

In conclusion, it is possible to state that the simulation of tasks in VR allows us to reduce the time needed for training sessions without using the real machine.

The results of tests highlight that workers, are faster in performing training session compared to unskilled participants as expected, and also compared to other experts of the machinery: the high skilled workers have no doubts in performing the correct maintenance sequence.

This is surely related to the experience acquired during their life. On the other hand, the familiarity with digital devices by younger users facilitates them to learn how to use the application. Indeed, it is noted that younger people are able to learn the system functioning more rapidly than older users during tutorial phase. In this way they are as fast as expert of machinery workers during training phase, but they spend more time in exploration phase in order to better memorize the required tools.

The advantage of the younger users is that they can cover the low knowledge level of machinery and maintenance sequence with the higher confidence in using digital devices.

It has also been highlighted that, for the company, this application has a great potential in managing orders of spare parts. The solution adopted allows us to simplify instruction manuals of 29% on average. The compatibility of virtual application and 3D models allows reducing the time spent to optimize exploded drawings on paper manuals.

The resources spent for developing the VR application are very low due to the use of common technology that can be easily substituted with other similar devices available on market. The only requirements are that the remote controller could be connected via blue-tooth and that the screen is sufficiently large to clearly show all the elements inside the virtual scene.

The training method developed has the potential of reducing production costs because it is not required to stop the machine for training sessions; in addition, it could reduce time losses due to wrong order handling. For what concerns the costs related to damages for low skills of staff, a test with unskilled users, who are asked to repeat the same operations on a real machine, is necessary in the future.

The VR application has been improved after tests and the most critical aspects as controller and cursor stability have been reduced. The timer introduced in the training phase is fundamental to give an immediate feedback about the user performances. Time is an important index of performances also at the end of the training session, because it is compared with an objective time set.

Future developments include a deeper investigation of the effectiveness of the application by performing sessions both in the virtual and real environment. Moreover, the application will be compared to other kinds of training tools and media (e.g. video and paper manuals).

References

1. S. Choi, K. Jung and S.D. Noh, Virtual reality applications in manufacturing industries: Past research, present findings, and future directions, *Concurrent Engineering* **23**(1), 40–63 (2015).
2. A. Attridge, M. A. Williams, and C. Tennant, The role of physical modelling in the design verification stage of the automotive NPI process in the premium sector, *International Journal of Automotive Technology and Management* **7**(1), 32–54 (2007).
3. A.G. De Sa and G. Zachmann, Virtual reality as a tool for verification of assembly and maintenance processes, *Computers & Graphics* **23**(3), 389–403 (1999).
4. N. Menck, X. Yang, C. Weidig, P. Winkes, C. Lauer, H. Hagen, B. Hamann and J. Aurich, Collaborative factory planning in virtual reality, *Procedia CIRP* **3**, 317–322 (2012).
5. Kibira and C. McLean, Virtual reality simulation of a mechanical assembly production line, In *Proceedings of the Winter Simulation Conference*, vol. 2, pp. 1130–1137 (2002).
6. N. Gavish, T. Gutiérrez, S. Webel, J. Rodríguez, M. Peveri, U. Bockholt and F. Tecchia, Evaluating virtual reality and augmented reality training for industrial maintenance and assembly tasks, *Interactive Learning Environments* **23**(6), 778–798 (2015).

7. J. R. Li, L. P. Khoo, L. P. and S. B. Tor, Desktop virtual reality for maintenance training: An object oriented prototype system (v-realism), *Computers in Industry* **52**(2), 109–125 (2003).

8. N. E. Seymour, VR to OR: a review of the evidence that virtual reality simulation improves operating room performance, *World Journal of Surgery* **32**(2), 182–188 (2008).

9. F. Bellotti, B. Kapralos, K. Lee, P. Moreno-Ger and R. Berta, Assessment in and of serious games: an overview, *Advances in Human-Computer Interaction*, 1 (2013).

10. J. C. Riedel and J. B. Hauge, State of the art of serious games for business and industry, *in* 17th International Conference on Con-current Enterprising (ICE), IEEE, 1–8 (2011).

11. M. Zyda, From visual simulation to virtual reality to games, *Computer* **38**(9), 25–32 (2005).

12. G. Gallagher and C. U. Cates, Virtual reality training for the operating room and cardiac catheterisation laboratory, *The Lancet* **364**(9444), 1538–1540 (2004).

13. M. Cha, S. Han, J. Lee and B. Choi, A virtual reality based fire training simulator integrated with fire dynamics data, *Fire Safety Journal* **50**, 12–24 (2012).

14. H. G. Abulrub, A. N. Attridge, and M. A. Williams, Virtual reality in engineering education: The future of creative learning. In *Global Engineering Education Conference (EDUCON)*, pp. 751–757 (2011).

15. R. Stone, Virtual reality for interactive training: an industrial practitioner's viewpoint, *International Journal of Human-Computer Studies* **55**(4), 699–711 (2001).

16. A. García, I. G. Bobadilla, G. A. Figueroa, M. P. Ramírez, and J. M. Román, Virtual reality training system for maintenance and operation of high-voltage overhead power lines, *Virtual Reality* **20**(1), 27–40 (2016).

17. A. Boud, D. J. Haniff, C. Baber and S. Steiner, Virtual reality and augmented reality as a training tool for assembly tasks. In *Proceedings of International Conference on Information Visualization*, pp. 32–36 (1999).

18. S. Jayaram, H. I. Connacher and K. W. Lyons, Virtual reality assembly using virtual reality techniques', Computer-aided design **29**(8), 575–584 (1997).

19. G. Chryssolouris, D. Mavrikios, D. Fragos and V. Karabatsou, A virtual reality-based experi-mentation environment for the verification of human-related factors in assembly processes', *Robotics and Computer-Integrated Manufacturing* **16**(4), 267–276 (2000).

20. C. Louison, F. Ferlay, D. Keller and D. R. Mestre, Operators' accessibility studies for assembly and maintenance scenarios using virtual reality, *Fusion Engineering and Design,* **124**, 610–614 (2017).

21. S. Blackman, Serious games...and less!, *SIGGRAPH Comput. Graph.* **39**(1), 12–16 (2005).

22. J. E. Brough, M. Schwartz, S. K. Gupta, D. K. Anand, R. Kavetsky and R. Pettersen, Towards the development of a virtual environment-based training system for mechanical assembly operations, *Virtual reality* **11**(4), 189–206 (2007).

23. L. Pouliquen-Lardy, I. Milleville-Pennel, F. Guillaume and F. Mars, Remote collaboration in virtual reality: asymmetrical effects of task distribution on spatial processing and mental workload, *Virtual Reality* **20**(4), 213–220 (2016).

24. F. Ferrise, G. Caruso and M. Bordegoni, Multimodal training and tele-assistance systems for the maintenance of industrial, *Virtual and Physical Prototyping* **8**(2), 113–126 (2013).

25. C. Anthes, R. J. García-Hernández, M. Wiedemann, and D. Kranzlmüller, State of the art of virtual reality technology. In *2016 IEEE Aerospace Conference*, pp. 1–19 (2016).
26. S. V. Cobb, S. Nichols, A Ramsey and J. R. Wilson, Virtual reality-induced symptoms and effects (vrise), *Presence: Teleoperators & Virtual Environments* **8**(2), 169–186 (1999).
27. S. Sharples, S. Cobb, A. Moody and J. R. Wilson, Virtual reality induced symptoms and effects (vrise): Comparison of head mounted display (HMD), desktop and projection display systems, *Displays* **29**(2), 58–69 (2008).
28. S. Nichols, Physical ergonomics of virtual environment use, *Applied Ergonomics* **30**(1), 79–90 (1999).
29. European Parliament, C. o. t. E. U. (2006-05-17), Directive 2006/42/EC of the European Parliament and of the Council of 17 May 2006 on machinery, and amending directive 95/16/EC, *Official Journal of the European Union* **L 157**, 24–86 (2006).
30. J. D. Brown, *Using Surveys in Language Programs*. Cambridge University Press (2001).

Chapter 4

An Augmented Reality System Model for Integration with Maintenance Information Systems

Iñigo Fernández del Amo, John Erkoyuncu, and Rajkumar Roy

4.1 Introduction

Since the initial[1] definition of Augmented Reality (AR): "any system that has the following three characteristics: (i) Combines real and virtual, (ii) is interactive in real time and (iii) is registered in three dimensions", this technology has evolved including more capabilities due to the advancements in computer-science. As a Human-Computer Interaction technology, the relevant capabilities of each application can differ, and so do the definitions of AR:

- "Creates an environment where computer-generated information is superimposed onto the user's view of a real- world scene".[2]
- "Human–computer interaction tool that overlays computer-generated information on the real world environment".[3]
- "Enriches the way that users experience the real world by embedding virtual objects to coexist and interact with real objects".[4]
- "Technology that enriches the sensorial perception of a person showing information about the surrounding environment."[5]

From these definitions, it can be said that Augmented Reality is a technology that enhances human perception by adding contextualized virtual information in co-existence with the real world. So, four main AR features can be identified:

(1) Human-computer interaction.
(2) Enrichment of user's real-world experience and/or perception.
(3) Embedment of interactive, contextualized virtual information.

(4) Spatial and temporal co-existence between virtual content and real-world objects.

Therefore, Augmented Reality can be defined as follows:

"Augmented Reality is a set of human-computer interaction techniques[4] that enriches user's real-world perception[5,6] by embedding interactive, contextualised, virtual information[3] in spatial and temporal co-existence with real-world objects,[1] creating an augmented space[7] that can increase the knowledge of the user".

4.1.1 Augmented Reality for Maintenance

Maintenance is one of the most researched fields of AR application[8]. The increasing demand to "complex-products" manufacturers from customers to improve availability and safety, reduce costs and provide worldwide support at any time[9] has focused the attention on maintenance activities. The key features of these activities have already been described in literature:[3,6]

- There are a great number and variety of maintenance activities.
- They require extensive information from supporting systems and experts.
- They are often subjected to standard procedures to be carried "in the field".

Most AR applications in maintenance activities focus on similar objectives: efficiency and safety increase.[3,4,6,10] For example, reducing repair time by better maintainer guidance (AR to display interactive instructions) or increasing repair quality by training maintainer's (AR to display potential errors on procedural tasks). Table 4.1 presents a comprehensive list of AR applications in maintenance with contrasted sources of research to consult.

Table 4.1. Consultation sources of Augmented Reality applications in maintenance.

Maintenance Processes	Source
Design, simulation and planning	3,4,11
Machine setup	3,6,11
Diagnostics, fault detection, inspection and testing	6,11
Repair guidance	3,4,6,11,12
Collaborative: tele-assisted and robotics	3,4,6,11,12
Training	4,6
Safety	6
Reporting	12

Augmented Reality can help to increase maintenance efficiency as it can provide real-time support to maintainers by embedding information into their interaction with the assets to be maintained. Zhu et al.[13] points out that AR maintenance solutions should be more than just an advanced data presentation tool as compared to the electronic manuals, hence the rendering of the virtual information should be adapted to the specific context of the technician. For instance, the guidance level of a maintenance AR system can be adapted to the technicians' pre-existing knowledge, resulting in different guidance levels.[14]

4.1.2   *Design of Augmented Reality for Maintenance Applications*

Augmented Reality research for maintenance applications is still one of the most attractive research areas. Different reviews in the field[3,6,10,15] have analyzed AR-maintenance applications from different perspectives. They all propose a common trend for most AR-maintenance applications: although these applications aim to improve similar objectives (efficiency and safety increase), they are designed case-specific and do not follow any generic design principles.

Besides, design-related topics in AR-maintenance research are not attracting sufficient attention for achieving common design principles. Topics like human-factors, ergonomics or information requirements are often not considered from an AR-maintenance design perspective. For example, a recent review in AR publications[16] indicated that only 10% of papers published considered user evaluation of AR applications. Dünser et al.[16] also pointed out that the number of formal qualitative analysis and general techniques for usability evaluation is small compared to informal techniques.

Design principles can be found in some AR application fields (e.g. learning[17]) or certain AR aspects (e.g. usability[18]). In AR-maintenance literature, there is evidence of design methods for AR systems' components specifically (e.g. hardware,[19] software[20]) as well as evaluation methods for existing designs.[21,22] These methods aim either to select existing technologies for a given AR-maintenance application or to determine performance levels of already designed AR systems. Nevertheless, there is almost no evidence of methods to determine which components are required to build an AR system for a given maintenance application or which are needed to implement in existing maintenance systems.

4.1.3   *Augmented Reality Conceptual System Model: Motivation*

Design of AR systems for maintenance applications requires to identify which AR technologies suit better users' requirements[4] and so, which components form the AR system.[20] Hence, a broader view of an AR system including all components that may be part of it is an important factor for effective design. For example, the use of AR for repair in explosive environments may require hands-free movement and ruggedized devices, limiting options for display and camera devices (no head-mounted devices but tablets with chest support). Then, these can further restrict options for other components such as software (only user-tracking is viable due to camera being placed in user's chest). Hence, a common structure for AR systems in maintenance applications may be useful. It can help identifying correlations between AR system's components and their associated requirements. It can also provide support to identify common design principles for maintenance scenarios. Besides, a common structure for AR systems can enable to further compare existing research, helping to identify research gaps.

After a review of existing literature, the authors have been able to identify little evidence on common structures for AR systems.[4,23] These provide descriptions of AR architectures but for specific maintenance applications: assembly[4] and simulation.[23] Other review papers in the area[3,11,20] describe in detail existing AR system's components researched for maintenance, but they do not provide comprehensive views on which may be the components of an AR system. Thus, it is the authors' belief that a common AR system structure for maintenance applications might contribute to the literature.

This chapter proposes a conceptual model of an AR system for maintenance applications based on the results of literature review. This model describes the structure of a common AR system in maintenance and the modules it may include. The chapter also describes the current state-of-the-art research linked to these systems' modules. The state-of-the-art description can help identifying future research needs towards AR system integration with maintenance systems, which is also presented in this chapter.

The rest of the chapter is structured as follows. Section 4.2 describes the conceptual model of the AR system as well as the literature review research method used to create the model itself. Section 4.3 uses the modules of the conceptual model to classify current state-of-the-art in AR-maintenance research and identify related research gaps. Finally, Section 4.4 discusses those gaps to determine future research for AR integration in maintenance systems and presents an experimental method to validate the system model proposed.

4.2 A Conceptual Model for Design of AR Systems for Maintenance

A conceptual model is the representation of a system, consisting of the set of concepts that the model represents.[24] In AR-maintenance research, most publications present their own conceptual models for the AR system into consideration.[25] Even though these models can share components (e.g. input device, camera, etc.), their correlation is not clear as their representation depends on each specific application.[10] Nevertheless, it may be possible to extrapolate from published models a list of components that an AR system for maintenance may have. These components could be used to develop a conceptual model for representing any AR system for maintenance (existing or to-be-designed). Then, representing each AR system would consist of defining the requirements for each maintenance application and determining the components that would fulfil them. Besides, analyzing AR systems through this common structure could identify the needs to integrate them into existing maintenance systems, which is an existing AR-research challenge.[3,10]

In order to generalize a common AR system model from published literature, a scoping review research method has been used. This research method aimed at:

(1) Identifying relevant AR-maintenance literature
(2) Collecting relevant information on AR-system components and definitions
(3) Comparing definitions and identifying common components.

The use of standard research protocols is crucial to enable the validity of research results.[10] Therefore, the SALSA framework[26] was selected due to its maturity and utilization in similar researches.[10,15,27] The key components of this research's protocol based on the SALSA framework are described in Table 4.2 for reproducibility purposes. The results of this scoping review are classified according to the themes utilized for synthesizing relevant studies: "terminology", "technological components", "models and frameworks", "applications descriptions", "research trends", and "challenges". The synthesis of "terminology", "technological components", and "models and frameworks" gave as result of the conceptual model proposed by this chapter, which is presented below. Instead, "application descriptions", "research trends" and "challenges" resulted on the state-of-the-art description are presented in the following section.

Table 4.2. Description of research's protocol key component according to the SALSA framework and research objectives.

Phase	Method	Description	Results	
Search	Database search	Search string	[Augmented Reality] AND [(Practices) OR (Applications) OR (Trends) OR (Gaps) OR (Advances) OR (Model) OR (Framework) OR (Terminology) OR (Literature)] AND [(Review) OR (Survey) OR (State-of-the-art)]	
		Sources	ACM	318
			IEEE Xplore	85
			Science Direct	104
			Scopus	99
			Web of Science	106
			Total	712
	Hand search		Total	6
Study selection	Iterative selection based on PICOC criteria	Inclusion criteria	Include non-primary research in journals from last 17 years Include evidence of surveys, current/future trends, literature reviews, state-of-the-art reviews in AR for maintenance	
		Exclusion criteria	Exclude primary research and non-journal articles Exclude papers not related to AR for maintenance	
	Selection results per iteration		Selected	Excluded
		Title	306	412
		Abstract	79	227
		Introduction and conclusions	39	40
		Full text	35	4
Study synthesis	Theme-related data extraction	Themes declared based on review objectives	Terminology definitions	Referring to any term defined in the paper
			Technological components descriptions	According to the technologies described in the paper
			Applications descriptions	Considering the applications for which AR has been utilised
			Models and frameworks	Adding any non-textual method to classify/describe any AR or technology or application model
			Research trends	Considering the trends proposed/validated in the paper
			Challenges	According to the challenges identified in the paper
Study analysis	Theme-based narrative comparison	Compare each study by theme and use a synthesis method to derive conclusions	Terminology definitions	Reciprocal translation
			Technological components	Framework synthesis
			Models and frameworks	
			Applications descriptions	
			Research trends	Narrative synthesis with tabular approach
			Challenges	

The AR system conceptual model for maintenance applications is shown in Fig. 4.1. It describes the components that an AR system may have, their relationships and links with real-world objects, users and virtual information. A brief explanation of how an AR system would work according to this model is presented in the paragraph below (starting at "Interface" and going clockwise).

AR blends virtual information in the user's real-world space. That occurs in the "Augmented Space", which is created in an "Interface" where virtual information is "Rendered" as "Augmented Content" (e.g. a 3D animation on top of an object explaining how it is disassembled). The "Augmented Space" is a blend of the virtual and the real environments that can be seen and interacted by the user. This is done by means of the "Display Device" and the "Interaction Device", respectively. Before "Rendering" can happen, "Augmented Content" has to be created from virtual information, which is stored in a different format within the "Information System"; this process is called "Authoring". In a different timeline, when the "Augmented Content" is consumed by the user, the 'Interaction Analysis' module tracks how the content is utilized (e.g. time to view and complete and instruction, what content has been checked and what doesn't, etc.). All the information used by the "Authoring" module or generated by the "Interaction Analysis" module is then treated by the "Information Manager", which retrieves or provides virtual data to the "Information System". Separately,

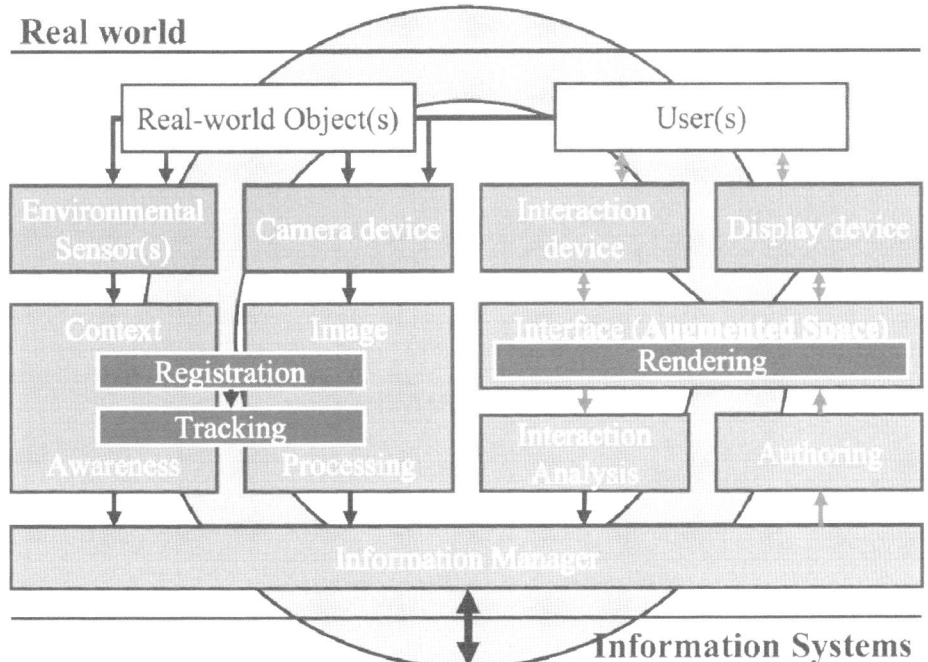

Fig. 4.1. Conceptual model for Augmented Reality systems in maintenance applications.

it is a requirement for the "Augmented Content" to be registered (blended) in the 3-dimensional real-world. This is done by "Registration" and "Tracking". Either a "Camera Device" and/or "Environmental Sensors" identify the position of an object, and/or a user in the real-world space; this is called "Registration". Once recognized, the object and/or user are followed through the real-world space for a seamless blending of the "Augmented Content"; this process is called "Tracking". However, the position and rotation of objects and/or users is not the only data that can be captured from the environment (e.g. status of the equipment to be repaired so instructions can be adapted). In more generic terms, capturing data from the environment to adapt or modify the "Augmented Content" are processes called "Context-Awareness" and "Image Processing". "Image Processing" is a subset of "Context-Awareness" algorithms used when the raw data comes from visual "Camera devices". "Context-Awareness" is the term used when other sensors (e.g., vibration, temperature, etc.) are used; it also refers to the algorithms for analyzing such sensor data.

As seen in the previous explanation, *"Augmented Reality utilizes several approaches to integrate the virtual and the real world. It is a concept instead of a sole technology[2]"*. The methods or techniques utilized for building each module presented in Fig. 4.1 can vary as well. Therefore, the conceptual system model needs accurate definitions for describing each module. A reciprocal translation was done within the scoping review to provide the most generic definitions for each module. These are presented in Table 4.3.

Table 4.3. AR system conceptual model modules' definitions based on reciprocal translational study's synthesis of the scoping review.

Level	Module	Definition
Hardware	Environmental Sensors	It refers to the sensors utilized to capture data about the scene, either regarding the user, the real-object or the environment. Apart from Augmented Reality applications in which real-world measurements are the core information to be embedded into the user's scene,[28] these sensors are used to localise and track the pose of either real objects and/or users (according to AR application's centre).[2,3]
	Camera Device	Due to its singularity in Augmented Reality, cameras (considered as sensors) are classified apart. They capture the video footage further utilised by image processing tools for determining geometric properties from captured images or point clouds, essential in displaying an AR.[2]
	Interaction Device	Apart from the information to be captured from the real world, there is also need to acquire data from the user to determine his/her interaction with the augmented content. Either for capturing visual gestures[4] or haptic feedback[3] it is still a fundamental AR enabling technology.[4]

Table 4.3. (*Continued*)

	Display Device	On the other hand, hardware devices have to be used also for delivering information to the user. That means, not only considering the interaction from the user to the system but vice versa. The same interaction modes should be equivalently applicable but using different technologies. Thus, mobile and spatial devices are still the most common.[6,28,29]
Software	Context-Awareness	Involves the software techniques utilised to determine the context of the augmented scene and modify accordingly the augmented content. While different techniques have been reported for different applications,[4,7,30] there are none identified standardised methods.
	Image Processing	Wang, Ong and Nee[4] describe it as the use of computer algorithms to support AR functions. These functionalities, mainly registration and tracking, involve the detection and the determination of the pose of the different real-world actors as users and objects.
	Registration	**Registration** is the process of placing of virtual objects with the correct pose in an augmented space.[3] Thus, AR systems can properly align real world objects and superimposed virtual objects with respect to each other.[31] It consists in determining every degree of freedom (DoF) that parameterizes one model to match another one.[29]
	Tracking	**Tracking** is the process of measuring the relative position and orientation of the camera in real time[28] to obtain and record the user position and orientation in space, in order to properly align the virtual image to the real one.[6] All the types of AR systems are based on the measurements of objects positions in the user-surrounding environment and of the user position and orientation. The tracking module can be considered the most important part of an AR system.[28]
	Interface (Rendering)	Interfaces are the algorithms in charge of controlling the inputs and outputs between the AR system and the user. As determined by Chi, Kang and Wang[2]: *"Designing and controlling intuitive AR user interfaces is currently a popular research topic"*. Thus, intuitive, easy to learn interfaces are the key to increase the usability of AR systems.
	Authoring	This comprises the creation and maintenance overtime of 'Augmented Content'. Although it has been reported as a challenge by different authors,[3,6,7,12] there is not a well-established definition in the literature. Wang, Ong and Nee[4] give a clear explanation of this, describing it as an: *"emerging topic in research that is attracting greater attention recently, but under-rated because of fewer past publications"*.
	Interaction Analysis	Defined as the analysis of user's task status to provide feedback automatically.[4] This topic has only been reported under specific training applications for maintenance.[4] Nevertheless, it can be of great importance if the need for self-learning systems[6] is considered.
	Information Manager	In the same line of thinking with the previous two, there is also an emerging topic in Augmented Reality research related to the need of data access in different applications. Information Management concerns the information collection from different sources.[4] Thus, giving the possibility to change and update more meaningful and variable information to enrich AR user's experience.[2]

All these concepts, which may be part of an AR system for a maintenance application, are nowadays subject of AR-maintenance research. According to this classification, it is possible to identify current state-of-the-art for each of them. The state-of-the-art is reviewed in the following section.

4.3 State-of-the-art Review in Augmented Reality for Maintenance

Augmented Reality is a technology that has been researched for almost half a century.[1] Since then, different techniques and methods have been developed for the technological components identified in Fig. 4.1. While some of these are generic for any AR application (e.g. camera device), others are application-specific (e.g. information manager or feedback analysis). In this section, a state-of-the-art review of the techniques used in AR-maintenance applications is presented. Section 4.3.1 focuses on hardware devices and methods, while Section 4.3.2 goes into software techniques.

4.3.1 *Hardware in Augmented Reality for Maintenance Research*

Hardware in AR are the set of physical parts, devices and methods aiming to execute the instructions given by the software. These four (Environmental Sensors, Camera, Interaction and Display) are four categories in which hardware devices and methods can be classified for AR systems. The different types utilized in Maintenance applications are presented in Fig. 4.2. The following subsections describe each category independently.

4.3.1.1 *Environmental sensors and Cameras*

Environmental sensors refer to any type of sensor capable of measuring any real-world data required for AR applications. Fig. 4.2 shows there are two main types, tracking (explained in Section 4.3.2.2) and measurement sensors. This classification is based on their purpose of use. Therefore, both types are not mutually exclusive but those mentioned as tracking sensors are mainly used by sensor-based tracking technologies. Nevertheless, measurement sensors are normally application specific and integrated ad-hoc in AR systems to provide data capturing special capabilities. Some examples can be found in Ref. 28.

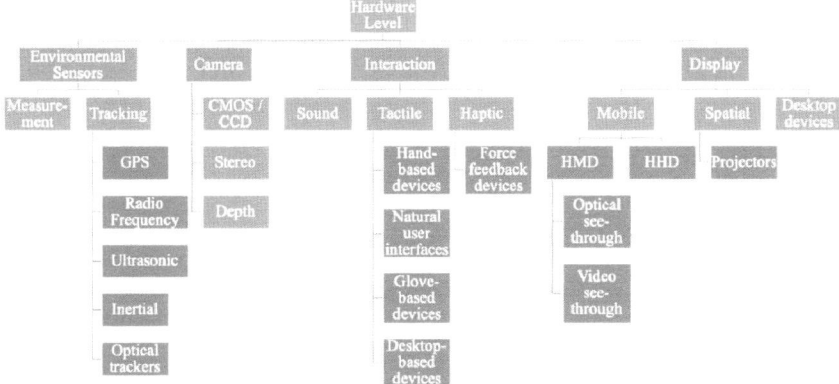

Fig. 4.2. Hardware methods used in Augmented Reality for maintenance applications.

Instead, cameras can be defined as a special type of image sensors capable of capturing light and other environmental features (e.g. depth). The three types shown in Fig. 4.2 are those which are mostly used in AR applications.[32,33] New advancements in cameras (e.g. depth cameras) allow to capture more data for improved image processing techniques. Nevertheless, the ergonomics of cameras is an important topic for AR integration. The ability to embed cameras into other devices is critical for designing ergonomic AR devices for maintenance environments (e.g. HoloLens in warship maintenance).

4.3.1.2 *Interaction*

Other senses rather than sight, which is the main human sense for virtual information display in AR, have been used to enhance interactions between the user and the augmented content (AR system). These senses are:[34]

- **Sound (hearing):** there are two main techniques in Augmented Aural Reality (AAR):[35] acoustic-hear-through and microphone-hear-through. The first uses bone conduction headphones, while the second uses headsets with microphones located on each ear. The main difference between them is the perception of the acoustic surrounding environment. In the first case the environmental noise is not reduced, while the second captures sound signals by microphones and mixes them with computer-generated ones. The result is a blend of real and virtual sounds which humans are not able to distinguish. Differently from visual displays, they do not narrow the user's attention.

- **Tactile:** refers to the sense of touch as described by Krevelen and Poelman.[36] It is complementary to the sense of vision and is often used in combination with sound or visual information in order to enrich the user's perception of a scene. Tactile devices are able to perceive and communicate parameters such as temperature, roughness, hardness, objects weight, size and shape. Compared to visual or aural, haptic is a very intuitive sense and does not require any kind of interpretation. Most of them are hand-based, such as glove-based technology,[37] with a continuous interaction between the user and the device[38] and a limited workspace. Another solution is the vibro-tactile bracelet. Compared to data-gloves, is smaller and enables user's free movements, within a higher working space. It detects the user's movements and gives a tactile feedback.

- **Haptic:** haptic devices are described as those aiming to enhance the "kinesthetic sense" (force and motion).[36] They are generally used for simulation of real-world tasks, planning or even training. Their main difference with tactile devices is the type of interaction between the user and the system. With a force feedback device, the type of interaction is direct, and the user has total control of the system. It means that the interaction starts after the user input, which is a physical interaction between the user and the device. Other kinds of devices include data-gloves, bracelets, handlers, joysticks, etc.[37]

Some examples of interaction devices can be seen in Fig. 4.3.

4.3.1.3 *Display*

Displays refer to all those hardware devices and methods aiming to overlay virtual information in the user's field of view. They focus on the sight sense and can be classified under three main categories considering where the information is overlaid: spatial (on the real-world object), mobile (in front of user's eyes), desktop (on a screen). Figure 4.4 presents some examples. The devices' categories used in maintenance applications are described below:

(a) Haptic gloves   (b) Force feedback controller

Fig. 4.3. Examples of interaction devices.

- **Mobile:** these refer to the devices that can be moved around an augmented scene by the user. Apart from the techniques used, there are two main types **Head-Mounted** and **Hand-Held. Head-Mounted Display (HMD)**, also called "Head Worn Display", is a device mounted on the head of the user, comparable to a normal pair of eyeglasses. The image is displayed in front of the user's eye, at the same level of the user's view, enabling different users to see different images in the same space. Most of the AR applications involve HMD devices, also if they have several ergonomic problems, like weight, eye strain after prolonged use, resolution, field of view and focal depth. **Hand-**

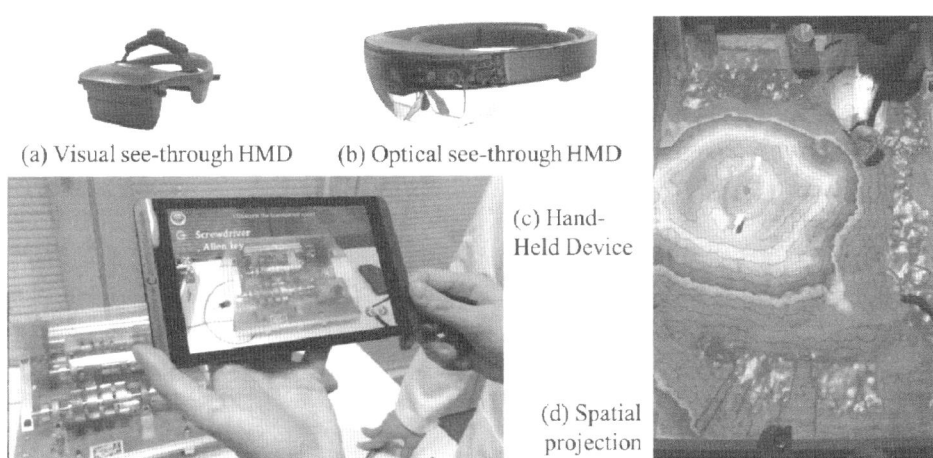

(a) Visual see-through HMD   (b) Optical see-through HMD

(c) Hand-Held Device

(d) Spatial projection

Fig. 4.4. Examples of display devices.

Held Devices (HHD) are those that use displays for rendering and a camera for tracking. They are video see-through but, Krevelen and Poelman[36] also described some examples of optical see-through and projective (HMPD) hand held devices. The new generation of devices has powerful processors, large screen and built in location sensors and cameras.[39] At the same time, the memory storage is low, and they need a server for image analysis and object recognition. Their usability in maintenance is limited as their biggest limitation is the operability for the technicians. Most of the applications are optical see-through, but, Krevelen and Poelman[36] also described some video see-through examples. These are the two techniques used in such devices:

- **Optical See-Through:** the virtual content is projected on translucent screens (optical combiners), e.g. glasses, which are placed in front of the user's eye. The user can look directly through the optical combiners to see the real environment, as they are partially transmissive. They are also partially reflective, so that the user can see the virtual content on the real scene.

- **Video See-Through:** the real scene is captured by a camera and transferred to a computer. The virtual content, created by a scene generator, is superimposed on the real scene and displayed on a monitor screen, which is placed in front of the user's eye.

- **Spatial:** a spatial display refers to the spatial augmented reality technique where screens are statically placed in the environment. Most of the applications are based on projective screens but there are also some applications using video see-through or optical see-through.[36] As they are fixed, they do not need any kind of tracking and the movements of the user, e.g. head movement, do not influence them. The virtual image is directly projected onto the surface of the real object and is particularly used for large presentations with small interactions.[36] Image projection, where the virtual content is projected over the surface of the real environment, is the most common technique used by these devices.

- **Desktop:** a desktop device refers to the use of screens to augment content using video-see-through techniques statically. These devices are used whenever the usage of mobile and/or spatial devices is not recommended. For example, when the accuracy of the overlay is critically important as in CNC simulation[40] or cranes teleoperation.[41]

4.3.2 *Software in Augmented Reality for Maintenance Research*

Software in Augmented Reality refer to all the computing methods and techniques for utilizing and processing all real or virtual data received by the AR system. Figure 4.5 presents all the techniques utilized in maintenance application within each category. These are described in the following subsections.

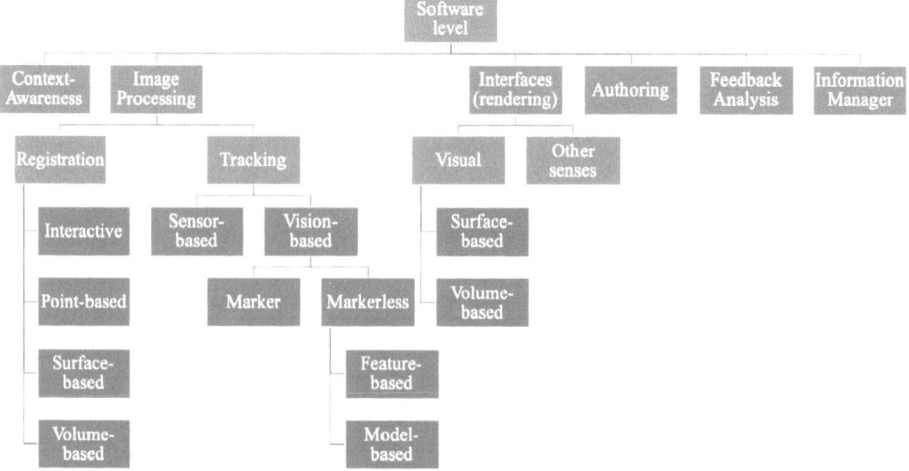

Fig. 4.5. Software techniques used in Augmented Reality for maintenance.

4.3.2.1 *Context-awareness*

A commonly well-accepted definition of context-awareness is stated by Flatt et. al.:[42] *"A system is context-aware if it uses the context to provide relevant information and/or services to the user, where relevancy depends on the user's task".* One example is shown in Fig. 4.6 where equipment status (contextual data) is used to overlay components' 3D models with different colors.

Koch[43] classifies eight categories of context factors, namely, user or person, activity or task, social environment, place, time, information or information sources, IT-environment or devices and physical environment, where the parameter values of each context factors would be captured by "context sensors".[44] The types and number of sensors will depend on the information needed in different maintenance scenarios.

According to Zhu et al.,[45] ontology has been widely used in context modelling, as it is independent of programming languages, enabling context reasoning (e.g. using first-order logic). The central element of the approach proposed by Götze et al.[44] is also an ontology-based context aware framework, aggregating and processing data from different sources. A Context Management (CM) module is included in the system architecture of some AR-based applications proposed in different works, for example ARAMS[46] and ACARS.[13] Zhu et al.[45] also presented a context database to store the authored context ontology and logical rules in the CM module.

Nevertheless, a context-aware system is that which provides relevant services for the user's tasks based on the context. So, for maintenance applications, that definition could involve giving decision support. For example, it could suggest the maintenance tasks to do using AR. Connecting an AR system to condition-based maintenance systems (Fig. 4.6), it could provide relevant information about the health of the equipment, proposing preventive maintenance tasks or enhancing diagnosis by the use of sensors data with decision-making algorithms.

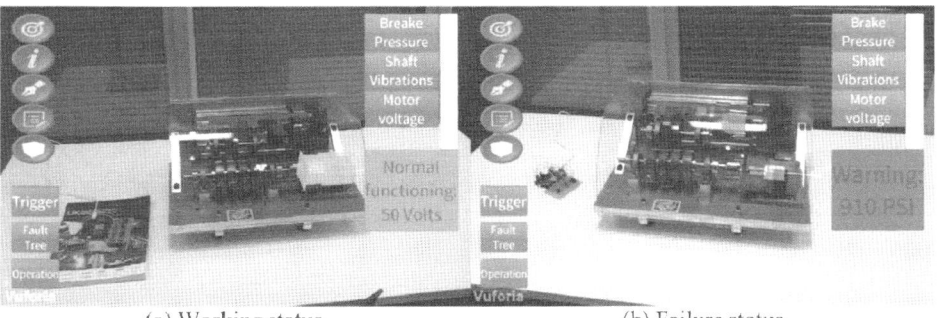

(a) Working status   (b) Failure status

Fig. 4.6. An example of context-awareness for equipment status validation.[75]

Owing to the potential of AR to transform maintenance operations, the way in which AR (operational level) can be linked with e-Maintenance systems (strategic level) must be analyzed. Its use for condition-based maintenance as a visualisation tool could have an effect in both directions, from strategic to operational and vice versa. AR could be used to enhance maintenance decision making, bringing maintenance strategy closer to maintenance technicians. However, it also could be used in the opposite direction. Because AR can register maintenance operations, it can be an acquisition tool for maintenance performance measurement (collecting information on time and errors).

4.3.2.2   *Image processing*

Image processing refers to all the image-related techniques used to manage the data coming from image-cameras in AR systems. Apart from those methods used in specific applications, the two most important are registration and tracking. The description of their state-of-the-art in maintenance applications is given below:

- **Registration:** aims to compute the camera pose accurately to make objects in the real and the virtual worlds properly align with respect to each other.[47] Thus, registration can be considered part of AR tracking systems. Once an object is detected in a scene, its relative position according to the user's point of view has to be registered. While tracking determines the scene view according to user's position and rotation relatively to the object to be tracked, registration defines the object's view, that is its perspective in the scene. Research in registration has tried to evaluate and minimize or eradicate errors that cause visualization problems in AR applications. Sato et al.[48] proposed an evaluation framework for uniform benchmarking and understanding of registration error's effect in AR. Yamato et al.[49] identified three major types of error sources for pose estimation and analyzed them regarding registration accuracy. Its findings can be generally applied to other AR applications. Yamaguchi et al.[50] and Roberts et al.,[51] proposed customized evaluation methods using key metrics. Finally, Livingston and Ai[52] tried to evaluate the effect of registration errors in user's performance when using different AR applications. Not only physical errors as orientation are considered, but also aspects like noise or latency of software systems taken into account. Besides, several articles have been reviewed regarding different approaches to tackle varied challenges for registration. For example, Hirose and Saito[53] validated a new algorithm for vision-based registration. Alternatively, Wei et al.[47] identified wide-area registration as a matter-subject for mobile AR. Apart from that, Garg et al.[54] propose new solutions for solving problems regarding motion registration. Generally speaking, registration errors can be measured and controlled at a certain degree under different conditions by different algorithms. But there is not one specific approach that could cope with all the requirements for accurate registration at the same time.

- **Tracking:** is a core feature in AR, as it obtains and records the user's position and orientation in space over time, in order to properly superpose the virtual image to the real one.[32] The movements of the user are tracked to display the virtual image at the right position. According to Hirose and Saito,[53] there are three main types of tracking:
  - **Sensor based:** magnetic and inertial sensors or GPS are some of the technologies used for tracking the position and orientation of the user regarding the object to be tracked in a map of the real scene.[55]
  - **Vision based:** uses cameras and vision computing to identify the user's point of view. These technique tracks the object and/or the user to create a virtual scene according to its view.[56] There are several methods: **Marker-based** are those where image patterns are used to detect the object; **Markerless feature-based** are those where key points, edges or vertices of the object are used to detect it; and **Markerless model-based** are those that detect an object by comparing it against its own 3D model.
  - **Hybrid:** when two or more of the previous techniques are mixed.

Advantages and disadvantages of each method can be seen in Ref. 53. Generally, sensor-based solutions are more expensive and robust, but also limited in range. Vision-based solutions are more accurate, but also more dependent on environmental conditions (e.g. movement or light), and more expensive computationally. Hybrid approaches can reduce weaknesses and develop the advantages of each method increasing accuracy and robustness, but at the expense of more computational resources and costs. Nevertheless, no specific approach or algorithm has demonstrated to meet the whole complete set of AR industrial implementation requirements under different environments nor display devices. Tracking accuracy and robustness are really dependent on other features (e.g. scale of applications, number of simultaneous tracking objects, indoor and outdoor environments, etc.). Latest trends in academia are attempting to fusion methods using hybrid algorithms. For example, Gedik and Alatan[57] using depth and vision to develop a markerless tracking solution. It is the same for Li et al.,[58] they merge inertial sensors with fiducial markers for developing an HHD specific approach. Wei et al.[47] propose to increase reliability in wide-area environments with the use of multi-sensors tracking platforms. Ha et al.[59] propose a parallel tracking and a matching framework for using different sensors allowing smooth transitions in outdoor/indoor environments. Multiple-object tracking is investigated by Ha et al.,[60] who compared different visual-based algorithms. Finally, Kopecky and Winer[61] presented a generic approach for sensor fusion.

4.3.2.3 *Interfaces*

Interfaces refer to the software in control of inputs and outputs between user and AR system. Within these, rendering modules are one of the most important. The 'Augmented Content' 'Rendering' refers to bringing virtual information to the AR 'Interface'. The virtual information must be defined in terms of content, format and registration, respectively representing what to render, how to render (e.g. color, transparency) and where to render.[6]

According to Wang et al.,[62] there are several types of human-machine interactions in AR: multimodal interaction, gesture interaction, 2D and 3D visualisation and text. Figure 4.7 presents some examples. These interactions use combinations of simulation and capturing methods: 3D-reconstruction, user-behavior tracking, multimodal interaction, 3D-interactive graphics, etc.[14]. Regarding the multimodal interactions and remote assistance, a previous work of Bottecchia et al.[63] presented a collaborative tele-assistance tool based in audio-

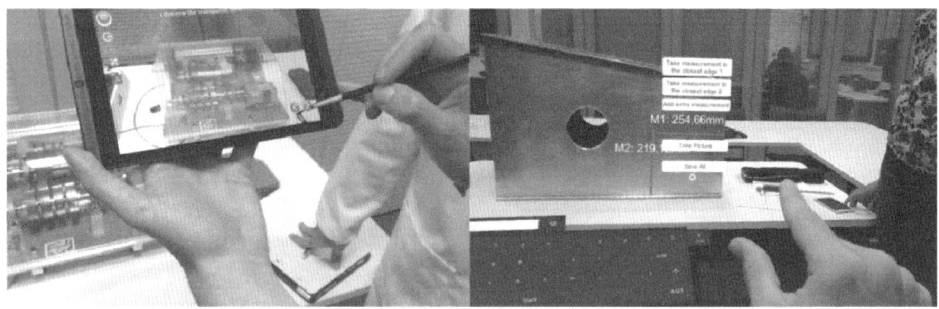

(a) Button interface   (b) Gesture interface

Fig. 4.7. Examples of interfaces.

video communication. This application highlights that to support implicit knowledge transfer between an expert and an operator, it is more efficient to add a "speech to text" type man-machine interaction mode. Wang et al.[62] also pointed out that there are two main types of data transferred between two sites: i) the on-site video from technician site to expert site; and ii) the remote authoring information from expert site to technician site, which is delivered in text in order to decrease the data quantity and improve the transmission speed.

4.3.2.4 *Authoring*

The development of AR applications is a process that requires a great amount of resources and expertise,[64] which is something that companies interested in using them do not ordinarily have.

In the AR context, authoring is a system component that allows the AR programmers and maintenance technicians to create, edit and update AR contents.[65] The authoring process in AR maintenance applications has been highlighted by various studies and some authors seem to agree that there should be more practical authoring solutions.[66] Thus, the creation of AR authoring tools to allow maintenance experts to generate virtual content without any programming skills is a topic currently being investigated.[67] Various authors have made an attempt to fill this gap in search of the industrial implementation of AR in different contexts.

Regarding the information needed to create content, there is extensive investigation in the area of maintenance. It goes from developing frameworks to ensure the consistency of technical documentation[68] to defining different ways of adapting the content to specific situations, as proposed in Refs. 64, 65. The structure given to the authoring tool is dependent on the maintenance situation; that is the specific type of tasks to be considered.

Most of the AR applications developed to support maintenance tasks discuss three types of authoring modules: i) On-site authoring, that allows the technicians to create and update the AR maintenance knowledge base actively, instead of just receiving the instructions passively;[13] ii) Offline authoring, for maintenance experts to develop context-aware contents into the system; and iii) Online authoring, that allows expert engineers to create maintenance instructions remotely in real-time to assist technicians in the field.[65]

4.3.2.5 *Interaction analysis*

Interaction Analysis techniques are defined as the software tool that analyzes the status of the interaction between the user and the augmented content to provide relevant feedback and/or improve the interaction itself.[69]

Regarding the effect of AR implementation on maintenance, most research has focused on analyzing technological challenges of application areas and demonstrating the benefits of AR for them. For example, Henderson and Feiner[70] demonstrate increased performance, but not in real life conditions. Roberts et al.[51] conduct field experimentation, but not in real operations. Previous works regarding the effects of AR on maintenance have mainly taken two different approaches.

One is more generic, regarding the technology itself and its features that directly affect to areas of implementation. In essence, they try to measure AR visualisation capabilities and how those relate to specific applications. That is the case of Puig et al.,[71] which analyzed quality assessment methodologies for AR visualisation.

The other is more specific to maintenance applications. This approach directly uses maintenance measures to assess the increase in performance of maintainers when using AR.[72] and the previous works analyzed in those papers follow that direction. For Khuong et al.,[73] the approach is slightly more general. They tried to systematize experiments for operations (mainly assembly tasks), defining metrics independently of the tasks used to measure them.

4.3.2.6 *Information manager*

Information Managers enable to detect how the knowledge is managed in the context of maintenance-support AR applications. Despite the existence of extensive bibliography regarding Knowledge Life Cycle — a process with conceptual framework to organize the knowledge throughout its useful lifespan[74] — there are no studies or frameworks that describe in detail how the knowledge is identified and captured from manuals, drawings, guidelines and other internal documentations, neither how the knowledge is transferred from maintenance experts into the AR application. As a result, there is a lack of knowledge regarding the process to collect data related to the maintenance tasks from the conventional sources; and how to translate this data in order to be used by AR technologies.[72]

4.4 Discussion, Conclusions, and Future Works

The need towards AR integration in existing maintenance systems have led the described research. Moreover, in this chapter the authors have:

- Identified research gaps in AR for maintenance: (1) categorization methods of AR systems requirements, (2) comparison methods for AR maintenance systems, (3) detection of research challenges in AR-maintenance integration, and (4) connection to design methodologies and other AR application.
- Proposed a conceptual model to describe the technological components that any AR system for maintenance may have.
- Surveyed AR-maintenance literature to present the state-of-the-art regarding the components of the model proposed.

It can be said the conceptual model contributes to research gaps (i) and (ii) and the literature survey does it for gaps (iii) and (iv). Nevertheless, it is still required to discuss: (1) conceptual model's validity, (2) extent to what these outcomes contribute, and (3) research conclusions and future works towards AR integration in maintenance systems. These ideas are discussed separately below.

4.4.1 *AR Conceptual System Model's Validity: Existing Research and Experiments*

The use of literature review research methods for designing the conceptual model aimed at ensuring its validity. Nevertheless, a theoretical conceptual model can have some limitations: (1) studies' sample utilized to generalize model's modules may have missed some important definitions that may vary the existing modules defined, and (2) it needs testing in real-life design scenarios.

This conceptual model has already been utilized for designing AR systems in various published AR-maintenance researches[75,76] and on-going works for assembly training and diagnosis reporting. It was used as a template to identify the AR system components to be built according to the research requirements and the expected contributions. Although, results may be classified as promising (all model's modules were included in the designs), research was not focused on validating the model and so there was no traceable evidence. Therefore, further experimentation is required to demonstrate conceptual model's validity for AR system's design in maintenance applications. The authors would like to propose two different validation methods applicable for all kinds of maintenance tasks:

(1) **Validation in design of AR-systems for maintenance research:** AR-maintenance research is a good opportunity for testing model's validity. The use of literature-based, objective criteria may be of help for quantitatively evaluating model's usefulness according to the number of modules utilized in the final design, the variations with current definitions as well as the number of more specific or additional modules that do not appear in the current model.

(2) **Validation through AR-maintenance design expert interviews and workshops:** the opinion of experts in AR-maintenance design may also be of help for validating this conceptual model. Proposing interviews or workshops where experts can evaluate the model against the same criteria used for real-life design testing can provide useful insights for comparison. Also, more detailed expert feedback could be obtained regarding potential improvements the conceptual system model may be subject of.

4.4.2 *AR Conceptual System Model and Maintenance State-of-the-Art Research*

Apart from identifying technological components for AR systems, the conceptual model also helps to compare existing systems from a research perspective. That is the reason why it could be used to analyze academic literature to find the research challenges towards AR integration in maintenance. Nevertheless, it is necessary to discuss whether the AR conceptual model meets its requirements and achieves what it claims for.

First, it can be said that the AR conceptual model proposed is an interrelated list of concepts which refer to the technological components any AR system could have. Besides, the model considers all the concepts found in literature, but does not determine what are the minimum requirements for an AR-maintenance system to work. At this point, its usage is limited to determine whether an AR system is complete. But it would require defining the necessary components for each maintenance application to be fully applicable.

Second, it can be said that the AR conceptual model links how hardware and software components of AR systems relate to each other. This is important from an AR design perspective; as it helps existing design methodologies to determine what other components would be needed to design complete AR systems. Nevertheless, it would require studying which design methodologies have been proposed, where do they focus and how they could be linked through the conceptual model.

Third, the AR conceptual model can be used to describe any AR system for maintenance applications and to compare between them. Therefore, differences between existing systems and needs towards specific objectives can be identified. From a research perspective this is really interesting, as it will help to detect the needs for AR integration in maintenance and link them to gaps in literature. Thus, enhancing AR technologies towards higher maturity levels. Nevertheless, the model is only applicable for maintenance applications. From a broader AR research perspective, it could be interesting to analyze its validity in other fields of application. Further research would be needed to study the differences in AR systems depending in the field of application and update the conceptual model accordingly.

Fourth, it also can be said the conceptual model is a representation of an AR system, and so it is also supposed to comply with the definition of AR. If we consider the knowledge transfer capabilities implicit in the AR definition, it would be good to understand which components enable such capabilities. Further research is required to determine these connections. Moreover, it has already been demonstrated that AR in maintenance enables knowledge transfer from the system to the user[4], but not from the user to the system. Therefore, further research is needed to demonstrate that AR is capable of provide knowledge capture capabilities.

Based on the opportunities and drawbacks described above, it can be concluded that the AR conceptual model is a valid method to describe AR systems for maintenance applications. Nevertheless, to achieve AR integration in maintenance services there is still research to conduct to improve the maturity of AR technologies.

The conceptual model helped to identify these research challenges, using it as a basis to survey the AR-maintenance literature. The challenges discussed in Section 4.3 provide a vision of AR systems and the requirements for their integration in maintenance systems. Based on that, it is possible to identify consequent steps towards the achievement of such integration. These steps in the field of AR-maintenance research are described in the following Section 4.4.3.

4.4.3   *Future Works Towards AR Integration in Maintenance Systems*

Future works can be suggested in two directions. One is towards the improvement of the AR conceptual model. The other is towards the research to be conducted towards AR integration in maintenance services. These are detailed below.

According to the improvements needed to extend the validity of the AR conceptual model in maintenance and other fields of application, the following research could be conducted:

- Study of the minimum requirements of AR systems, which components are critical, and which are not always necessary but for specific applications.
- Study of the relationships between the AR conceptual model and existing AR design methodologies to provide comprehensive design and evaluation principles. It would need to identify which design methodologies have been proposed, where do they focus and how they could be linked through the conceptual model.
- Study of the link between the components of the AR conceptual model (such as authoring, context-awareness and interaction-analysis) and AR knowledge transfer and capture capabilities.
- Study of the applicability of the conceptual model to other fields of AR application and the potential differences in the model accordingly.

According to the improvements in AR technologies towards their integration in maintenance services, the following research could be conducted:

- **Environmental sensors:** adaptation of sensors to different maintenance-environmental factors.
- **Camera devices:** study of the ergonomics and integration issues with other AR devices.
- **Interaction and display devices:** study of the ergonomics of maintenance operations, feasibility of gestures and movements and development of new data capture methods.
- **Image processing:** test of existing methods in real-life maintenance scenarios and requirements evaluation for their integration and applicability.
- **Interface:** evaluation of interaction methods depending on augmented content formats (e.g. 3D animations, audio) and maintenance-environmental factors (e.g. light, etc.)
- **Context-Awareness:** study of general ontologies to describe maintenance context as well as systematic methods to identify and describe these contexts.
- **Authoring:** study of new authoring methods to capture experience and knowledge from maintainers to enhance the value of AR in maintenance.
- **Interaction-Analysis:** joint research on authoring, context-awareness and interaction-analysis is required to analyze AR knowledge capture capabilities in maintenance.
- **Information manager:** study of automatic methods to detect formats and convert data to achieve AR integration.

Based on those, a vision of AR systems integrated within maintenance services can be provided, where these systems are used as tools for knowledge transfer between users and systems and vice versa.

Acknowledgements

This research was supported by the Through-life Engineering Services Centre in the Manufacturing theme at Cranfield University.

References

1. R. Azuma, A survey of augmented reality, *Presence* **6**(4), 355–385 (1997).
2. H.L. Chi, S.C. Kang and X. Wang, Research trends and opportunities of augmented reality applications in architecture, engineering and construction, *Autom Constr* **33**, 116–122 (2013).

3. A.Y.C. Nee, S.K. Ong, G. Chryssolouris and D. Mourtzis, Augmented reality applications in design and manufacturing, *CIRP Ann - Manuf Technol* **61**(2), 657–679 (2012).

4. X. Wang, S.K. Ong, and A.Y.C. Nee, A comprehensive survey of augmented reality assembly research, *Adv Manuf* **4**(1), 1–22 (2016).

5. P. Daponte, L. De Vito, F. Picariello and M. Riccio, State of the art and future developments of the augmented reality for measurement applications, Measurement **57**, 53–70 (2014).

6. G. Dini and M. Dalle Mura, Application of augmented reality techniques in through-life engineering services, *Procedia CIRP* **38**, 14–23 (2015).

7. F. Manuri and A. Sanna, A survey on applications of augmented reality, *Adv Comput Sci* **5**(1), 18–27 (2016).

8. S. Henderson and S. Feiner, Exploring the benefits of augmented reality documentation for maintenance and repair, *IEEE Trans Vis Comput Graph* **17**(10), 1355–1368 (2011).

9. O. Candell, R. Karim and P. Soderholm, eMaintenance-Information logistics for maintenance support, *Robot Comput Integr Manuf* **25**(6), 937–944 (2009).

10. R. Palmarini, J.A. Erkoyuneu, R. Roy and H.A. Torabmostaedi, A systematic review of augmented reality applications in maintenance, *Robot Comput Integr Manuf* **49**, 215–228 (2018).

11. S.K. Ong, M.L. Yuan and A.Y.C. Nee, Augmented reality applications in manufacturing: A survey, *Int J Prod Res* **46**(10), 2707–2742 (2008).

12. A.C.M. Oliveira, R.B. Araujo and A.K.S. Jardine, A human centered view on e-maintenance, *Chem Eng Trans* **33**, 385–390 (2013).

13. J. Zhu, S.K. Ong and A.Y.C. Nee, An authorable context-aware augmented reality system to assist the maintenance technicians, *Int J Adv Manuf Technol.* **66**(9), 1699–1714 (2013).

14. S. Webel, U. Bockholt, T. Engellke, N. Gavish, M. Olbrich and C. Preusche, An augmented reality training platform for assembly and maintenance skills, *Rob Auton Syst* **61**(4) 398–403 (2013).

15. I. Fernandez Del Amo, J.A. Erkoyuncu, R. Roy, R. Palmarini and D. Onoufriou, A systematic review of augmented reality content-related techniques for knowledge transfer in maintenance applications, *Comput Ind* **103**, 47–71 (2018).

16. A. Duenser, R. Grasset and M. Billinghurst, A survey of evaluation techniques used in augmented reality studies, SIGGRAPH (2008).

17. M. Dunleavy, Design principles for augmented reality learning, *TechTrends* **58**(1), 28–34 (2014).

18. S.M. Ko, W.S. Chang and Y.G. Ji, Usability principles for augmented reality applications in a smartphone environment, *Int J Hum Comput Interact* **29**(8), 501–515 (2013).

19. V. Elia, M.G. Gnoni and A. Lanzilotto, Evaluating the application of augmented reality devices in manufacturing from a process point of view: An AHP based model, *Expert Syst Appl.* **63**, 187–197 (2016).

20. R. Palmarini, J.A. Erkoyuneu and R. Roy, An innovative process to select augmented reality (AR) technology for maintenance, *Procedia CIRP* **59**, 23–28 (2017).

21. A.E. Uva, M. Gattullo, V.M. Manghisi, D. Spagnulo, G.L. Cascella and M. Fiorentino, Evaluating the effectiveness of spatial augmented reality in smart manufacturing: A solution for manual working stations, *Int J Adv Manuf Technol* **94**, 509–521 (2018).

22. P. Caricato, L. Colizzi, M.G. Gnoni, A. Gricco, A. Guerrieri and A. Lanzilotto, Augmented reality applications in manufacturing: A multi-criteria decision model for performance analysis. *In IFAC Proeedings Volumes*, pp 754–759, Cape Town, South Africa (2014).

23. W. Li, A. Nee and S.K. Ong, A state-of-the-art review of augmented reality in engineering analysis and simulation, *Multimodal Technol Interact* **1**(3), 17 (2017).

24. J.A. Sokolowski and C.M. Banks, *Modeling and Simulation Fundamentals: Theoretical Underpinnings and Practical Domains.* Wiley (2010).

25. A.Y.C. Nee, S.K. Ong, G. Chryssolouris and D. Mourtzis, Augmented reality applications in design and manufacturing, CIRP Ann - Manuf Technol. **61**(2), 657–679 (2012).

26. A. Booth, D. Papaioannou and A. Sutton, *Systematic Approaches to a Successful Literature Review.* Sage (2012).

27. A.C. Correa dos Santos, M.E. Delamaro and F.L.S. Nunes, The relationship between requirements engineering and virtual reality systems: A systematic literature review. In *Virtual and Augmented Reality (SVR) 2013 XV Symposium,* pp. 53–52 (2013).

28. P. Daponte, L. De Vito, F. Picariello and M. Riccio, State of the art and future developments of measurement applications on smartphones, *Meas J Int Meas Confed* **46**(9), 3291–3307 (2013).

29. S. Bernhardt, S.A. Nicolau, L. Soler and C. Doignon, The status of augmented reality in laparoscopic surgery as of 2016, *Med Image Anal* **37**, 66–90 (2017).

30. M. Akcayir and G. Akcayir, Advantages and challenges associated with augmented reality for education: A systematic review of the literature, *Educ Res Rev* **20**, 1–11 (2017).

31. A.H. Behzadan, S. Dong and V.R. Kamat, Augmented reality visualization: A review of civil infrastructure system applications, *Adv Eng Informaties* **29**(2), 252–267 (2015).

32. G. Dini and M. Mura, Application of augmented reality techniques in through-life engineering services, *Procedia CIRP* **38**, 14–23 (2015).

33. P. Daponte, L. De Vito, F. Picariello and M. Riccio, State of the art and future developments of the Augmented Reality for measurement applications, *Measurement* **57**, 53–70 (2014).

34. E. Galeotti, A methodology for the design of new augmented reality solutions: A user-centred approach (Online). Available at https://etd.adm.unipi.it/t/etd-06292017-144952/ (Accessed January 20, 2019).

35. R. Albrecht, T. Lokki and L. Savioja, A mobile augmented reality audio system with binaural microphones. In *Proc Interact with Sound Work Explor Context Local Soc Audio App.* pp. 7–11 (August 2011).

36. D.W.F. van Krevelen and R. Poelman, A survey of augmented reality technologies, applications and limitations, *Int J Virtual Real.* **9**(2), 1–20 (2010).

37. T.N. Hoang, R.T. Smith and B.H. Thomas, Passive deformable haptic glove to support 3D interactions in mobile augmented reality environments. In *2013 IEEE International Symposium on Mixed and Augmenter Reality (ISMAR),* pp. 257–258 (2013).

38. G.Y.G. Ye, J.J. Corso, G.D. Hager, A.M. Okamura, VisHap: Augmented reality combining haptics and vision. In *2003 IEEE International Conference on Systems Man and Cybernetics Conference Theme System Security and Assurance,* vol. 4, pp. 3425–3431 (2003).

39. M.E.C. Santos, J. Polvi, T. Taketomi, G. Yamamoto, C. Sandor and. H. Kato, Toward standard usability questionnaires for handheld augmented reality, *IEEE Comput Graph Appl* **35**(5), 66–75 (2015).

40. C. Liu, S. Cao, W. Tse and X. Xu, Augmented reality-assisted intelligent window for cyber-physical machine tools, *J Manuf Syst* **44**(2), 280–286 (2017).

41. Y.C. Chen, H.L. Chi, S.C. Kang and S.H. Hsieh, A smart crane operations assistance system using augmented reality technology. In *Proc 28th Int Symp Autom Robot Constr (ISARC),* pp. 643–649 (2011).

42. H. Flatt, N. Koch, C. Rocker, A. Gunter and J.A. Jasperneite, A context-aware assistance system for maintenance applications in smart factories based on augmented reality and indoor localization. In *International Conference on Emerging Technologies and Factory Automation*, pp. 8–11, Luxembourg (September 2015).

43. O. Koch, Informationsbedarf und Informationslogistik. In *Kontextorientierte Informationsversorgung in medizinischen Behandlungsprozessen.* Springer (2010).

44. J. Gotze, C-A. Schumann and E. Muller, Context awareness and augmented reality in facility management, *Int Conf Eng Technol Innov* **3**, 1–5 (2014).

45. J. Zhu, S.K. Ong and A.Y.C. Nee, A context-aware augmented reality assisted maintenance system, *Int J Comput Integr Manuf* **28**(2), 213–225 (2015).

46. S.K. Ong and J.A. Zhu, A novel maintenance system for equipment serviceability improvement, *CIRP Ann-Manuf Technol.* **62**(1), 39–42 (2013).

47. B. Wei, T. Guan, L. Duan, J. Yu and T. Mao, Wide area localization and tracking on camera phones for mobile augmented reality systems, *Multimed Syst.* **21**(4), 381–399 (2015).

48. K. Satoh, K. Takemoto, S. Uchiyama and H. Yamamoto, A registration evaluation system using an industrial robot. In *2006 ICCC/ACM International Symposium on Mixed and Augmented Reality*, pp. 182–190 (2006).

49. A. Belhaoua, A. Kornmann and J-P. Radoux, Accuracy analysis of an augmented reality system. In *12th International Conference on Signal Processing (ICSP)*, pp. 1169–1174 (2014).

50. Y. Yamaguchi, T. Nakagawa,, H. Kato and S. Nishida, Evaluation for adjustment method of vehicle's location by recognizing crosswalks. In *Lecture Notes in Computer Science (including subseries Lecture Notes in Artificial Intelligence and Lecture Notes in Bioinformatics)*, pp. 648–656 (2009).

51. D. Roberts, A. Menozzi, J. Cook, T. Sherrill, S. Snarski, P. Russler, B. Clipp, R. Karl, E. Wenger, M. Bennett, J. Mauger, W. Church, H. Towles, S. MacCabe, J. Webb, J. Lupo, J-M. Frahm, E. Dunn, C. Leslie and G. Welch, Testing and evaluation of a wearable augmented reality system for natural outdoor environments, *SPIE Digit Libr.* **8735**, 8735–A-1 (2013).

52. M.A. Livingston and Z. Ai, The effect of registration error on tracking distant augmented objects. In *Proceedings of the 7th IEEE International Symposium on Mixed and Augmented Reality (ISMAR)*, pp. 77–86 (2008).

53. R. Hirose and H.A. Saito, A vision-based AR registration method utilizing edges and vertices of 3D model. In *ICAT'05*, pp. 187–194 (2005).

54. A. Roussos, C. Russel, R. Garg and L. Agapito, Desnse multibody motion estimation and reconstruction from a handheld camera. In *11th IEEE International Symposium on Mixed and Augmented Reality (ISMAR)*, pp. 31–40 (2012).

55. M. Billinghurst, A. Clark and G. Lee, A survey of augmented reality, *Foundations and Trends® in Human–Computer Interaction* **8**(2–3), 73–272 (2015).

56. F. Manuri, A. Sanna, F. Lamberti, G. Paravati and P.A. Pezzolla, A workflow analysis for implementing AR-based maintenance procedures. In *Lecture Notes in Computer Science (including subseries Lecture Notes in Artificial Intelligence and Lecture Notes in Bioinformatics)*, pp. 185–200 (2014).

57. O.S. Gedik and A.A. Alatan, 3-D rigid body tracking using vision and depth sensors, *IEEE Trans Cybern* **43**(5), 1395–1405 (2013).

58. J. Li, M. Slembrouck, F. Deboeverie, A.M. Bernardos, J.A. Besada, P. Veelaert, H. Aghajan, W. Philips and J.R. Casar, A hybrid pose tracking approach for handheld augmented reality.

In *Proceedings of the 9th International Conference on Distributed Smart Camera (ICDSC)*, pp. 7–12 (2015).

59. P.P. Wang, T. Wang, D. Ding, Y. Zhang, K. Miao, C.K. Pickering, P. Tian and J. Zhang, Multi-sensor fusion for interactive visual computing in mixed environment. In *Proceedings of the International Conference on Multimedia (MM'10)*, pp. 1509–1510 (2010).

60. J. Ha, J. Jung, B. Han, K. Cho and H.S. Yang, Mobile augmented reality using scalable recognition and tracking. In *IEEE Virtual Real Conf.*, pp. 211–212 (2011).

61. K.E. Kopecky and E.H. Winer, MetaTracker: Unifying and abstracting 3-D motion tracking data from multiple heterogenous hardware systems, *IEEE Access* **4**, 189–203 (2016).

62. J. Wang, Y. Feng, C. Zeng and S. Li, An augmented reality based system for remote collaborative maintenance instruction of complex products. In *IEEE Int Conf Autom Sci Eng.*, pp. 309–314 (2014).

63. S. Bottecchia, J-M. Cieutat and J-P. Jessel, TAC: Augmented reality system for collaborative teleassistance in the field of maintenance through internet. In *Proc 1st Augment Hum Int Conf ACM*, pp. 1–7 (2010).

64. H. Ramirez, E.G. Mendivil, P.R. Flores and M.C. Gonzalez, Authoring software for augmented reality applications for the use of maintenance and training process, *Procedia Comput Sci.* **25**, 189–193 (2013).

65. S.K. Ong and J.A. Zhu, A novel maintenance system for equipment serviceability improvement, *CIRP Ann- Manuf Technol.* **62**(1), 39–42 (2013).

66. T. Engelke, J. Keil, P. Rojtberg, F. Wientapper, S. Webel and U. Bockholt, Content first-A concept for industrial augmented reality maintenance applications using mobile devices. In *International Symposium on Mixed and Augmented Reality*, pp. 251–252, Adelaide, Australia (October 2013).

67. J. Gimeno, P. Morillo, J.M. Orduna and M. Fernandez, A new AR authoring tool using depth maps for industrial procedures, *Comput Ind.* **64**(9), 1263–1271 (2013).

68. I. Stock and M. Weber, Authoring technical documentation using a generic document model. In *Proc 24th Annu Conf Des Commun.*, pp. 172–179 (2006).

69. S. Webel, U. Bockholt, T. Engelke, N. Gavish, M. Olbrich and C. Preusche, An augmented reality training platform for assembly and maintenance skills, *Rob Auton Syst* **61**(4), 398–403 (2013).

70. S.J. Henderson and S. Feiner, Evaluating the benefits of augmented reality for task localization in maintenance of an armored personnel carrier turret. In *Science and Technology Proceedings - IEEE 2009 International Symposium on Mixed and Augmented Reality (ISMAR)*, pp. 135–144 (2009).

71. J. Puig, A. Perkis, F. Lindseth and T. Ebrahimi, Towards an efficient methodology for evaluation of quality of experience in augmented reality. In *2012 4th Int Work Qual Multimed Exp,* pp. 188–193 (2012).

72. I. Porcelli, M. Rapaccini, D.B. Espindola and C.E. Pereira, Technical and organizational issues about the introduction of augmented reality in maintenance and technical assistance services. In *IFAC Proc Vol.*, pp. 257–262 (2013).

73. B.M. Khuong, K. Kiyokawa, A. Miller, J.J. La Viola, T. Mashita and H. Takemura, The effectiveness of an AR-based context-aware assembly support system in object assembly. In *Proceedings - IEEE Virtual Reality,* pp. 57–62 (2014).

74. M. Evans, K. Dalkir and C. Bidian, A holistic view of the knowledge life cycle: The Knowledge Management Cycle (KMC) model, *Electron J Knowl Manag.* **12**(2), 85–97 (2014).

75. J.A. Erkoyuncu, I. F. del Amo, M. Dalle Mura, R. Roy and G. Dini, Improving efficiency of industrial maintenance with context aware adaptive authoring in augmented reality, *CIRP Ann - Manuf Technol* **66**, 465–468 (2017).

76. I.F. del Amo, J. Erkoyuncu, R. Vrabie, R. Frayssinet, C. Vazquez Reynel and R. Roy, Structured authoring for AR-based communication to enhance efficiency in remote diagnosis for complex equipment, *Adv Eng Informatics* **45**(March), 15 (2019).

Chapter 5

Manufacturing Assembly Simulations in Virtual and Augmented Reality

Wenjin Tao, Ze-Hao Lai, and Ming C. Leu

5.1 Introduction

Virtual Reality (VR) and Augmented Reality (AR) technologies have been studied and prototyped in labs for decades without much public attention. However, in recent years, they have been introduced to the consumer market and are being applied to a wide range of fields due to the cost reduction of VR/AR hardware and the algorithm improvement of software. In the manufacturing assembly area, VR/AR technologies have been used to simulate the costly processes beforehand and help train the workforce using a more interactive way. This section introduces some basic terminologies and concepts to provide a brief introduction to this topic.

5.1.1 *Virtual Reality (VR)*

Although Virtual Reality (VR) is one of the current technology buzzwords, it is not a brand-new concept and actually has a history over 60 years. The Sensorama simulator[34] invented in the 1950s is believed to be the first functional VR machine that could provide users a realistic experience. From then on, many researchers have worked on this area, and various prototypes have been developed.

The term VR refers to a series of techniques for humans to visualize, manipulate and interact with computers in a realistic virtual environment, which provides an interactive graphics interface enhanced by non-visual modalities such as auditory, haptic, and smell feedback to enable the user feeling the presence of a real physical environment.[9,15,38] As shown in Fig. 5.1, an ideal VR system can generate a virtual environment for the user by providing the five senses, including sight, hearing, touch, smell, and taste. There are different VR systems such as CAVE VR systems,[21,80] desktop VR systems, and head-mounted VR systems.

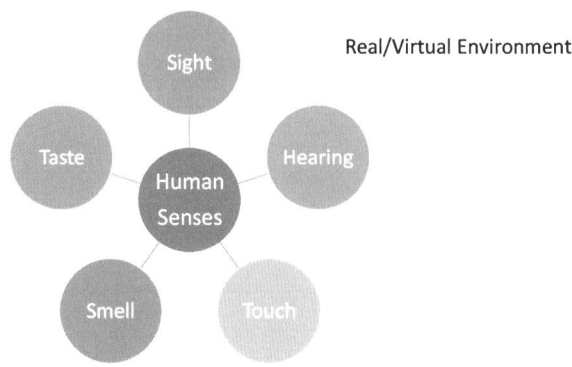

Fig. 5.1. Five human senses to perceive the real/virtual environment.

The cost reduction of hardware and the algorithm improvement of software over the years have been gradually pushing the VR technology from labs to the consumer market. In 2012, the company Oculus VR was founded and announced an affordable VR headset, which makes VR experiences easily accessible to consumers. Two years later, Facebook acquired Oculus VR for more than 2 billion dollars,[19] which further boosted the VR market and attracted lots of companies, researchers, and entrepreneurs to enter this field. Meanwhile, the VR technology has been employed to provide various solutions to all kinds of industries.

5.1.2 *Augmented Reality (AR)*

For VR, a virtual environment is generated to provide users with fully immersive experiences. For Augmented Reality (AR), instead of generating a virtual environment, the real-world environment is "augmented" by computer-generated perceptual information, ideally across multiple sensory modalities, including visual, auditory, haptic, etc., which is how the term AR is originally coined. The augmented information is appropriately overlaid onto the physical environment and presented in the user's view through an AR device, such as a hand-held display or a see-through Head Mounted Display (HMD). To have the optimal correlation between the virtual information and the physical world, it is required to keep sensing the physical world and tracking the AR device in the spatial context.

In addition to AR, the term Mixed Reality (MR) has also been used in the literature to represent the VR related technologies that involve the merging of real and virtual worlds. Milgram et al.[53] defined a "virtuality continuum" (see Fig. 5.2) and divided MR into AR and Augmented Virtuality (AV). For simplicity and following the common terminology, this chapter emphasizes AR and it has the same scope as MR shown in Fig. 5.2.

Fig. 5.2. Milgram's "virtuality continuum".[53]

There are some commercial AR devices currently available in the market. Google Glasses was first released in 2013, which is an AR product that needs to be paired with a smartphone. Microsoft released its AR glasses HoloLens in 2016. It is a standalone AR device that does not need to connect to a computer or smartphone. Recently, more smartphone-based AR technologies have been developed and are increasingly popular in a wide range of fields.

5.1.3 *Manufacturing Assembly Simulation (MAS)*

To keep pace with the vibrant technology revolution planned in the Industry 4.0 era, more and more manufacturers have been reconsidering their assembly systems. More flexible and efficient assembly methods and strategies have to be developed to meet the dynamic needs of customers and the shortened product lifecycle. In such a context, the current assembly systems must be upgraded in order for products to gain success and maintain competitiveness in the market. These goals could be achieved through assembly simulation in a virtual environment before launching a real factory to identify potential problems without the use of physical mockups, thus shortening the design cycle and improving product quality.

With the help of VR/AR technologies, which puts humans in the loop and takes the human's experience at the first place, the assembly process can be simulated in a more immersive, interactive manner, especially for worker-involved assembly tasks. Also, assembly training can be conducted in VR/AR environments to train workers and improve their skills. The main building blocks needed for assembly simulation in VR/AR are briefly described below.

Modeling. One of the primary tasks for developing a MAS application is to create the digital models. The 3D model of a physical part can be generated using CAD software or a 3D reconstruction process with the acquisition of part geometric data in digital form from an existing physical part. Unlike gaming VR/AR, the digital 3D models in the aspect of MAS should be accurate in dimensions, realistic in physics, and functional as real parts in the virtual environment.

Environment Sensing & Pose Estimation. In VR, we need to track the user's pose to change the digital contents in the user's view accordingly to make the user feel that he/she is in the real world performing a real task. In AR, sensing the environment and tracking the user's pose is even more crucial, because it requires real-time registration and tracking to realize the optimal mapping between the virtual world and the real world.

Interface and Interaction. In VR/AR, the visual interface is the most important one. In addition, auditory and haptic interfaces, and even smell and taste interfaces can be used to further augment the visual interface to make the user feel fully immersed in a VR/AR environment. In terms of interaction, how the user manipulates and interacts with the virtual objects as he/she does with physical objects should be developed.

5.2   Methodologies for Assembly Simulations in VR/AR

This section reviews and discusses the state-of-the-art methodologies that enable VR/AR manufacturing assembly simulations.

5.2.1 *MAS modeling*

Creating digital models for virtual objects is one of the primary tasks in MAS. The conventional approach for building 3D models is to use commercial CAD software, such as NX,[46] SolidWorks,[25] and CATIA,[24] to create CAD models for virtual objects. Another approach is reconstruction of 3D models from real objects, which starts with data acquisition from physical objects in a real environment and ends with digital models representing these objects on the computer.[63] With this approach, the often time-consuming modeling process done by human designers can be automated, which significantly reduces the development time and cost. As shown in Fig. 5.3, the process of 3D model reconstruction includes data acquisition, data processing, positional registration, modeling, and rendering.[26,27]

Fig. 5.3. Process of 3D model reconstruction.

To create a 3D model from a real object, the first step is to acquire the digital data of the 3D object's surface. Many data acquisition techniques have been developed, and they can be categorized as mechanical and optical approaches. There are some other methods such as ultrasonography, radiography and Magnetic Resonance Imaging (MRI) for data acquisition purpose. They are not discussed here as they are costly and not commonly used for MAS applications. A classification of these techniques is illustrated in Fig. 5.4. Mechanical data acquisition is a mature and well-established method that has been used for many years in reverse engineering and industrial inspection. It utilizes a Coordinate Measuring Machine (CMM) or a robotic arm to measure the coordinates of points on the object's surface to acquire the shape. Currently, optical methods are more widely used as they can provide non-contact, relatively more efficient data acquisition. In addition to acquiring the shape, they can capture the appearance as well, which further reduces the time consumed for modeling and rendering. The optical methods can be divided into passive and active ones. Passive methods do not emit light onto the target object, and the shape of the object is estimated from the perceived images, using techniques such as shape from shading,[35] shape from silhouette,[18,50] and stereo vision.[29,30,68] Active methods often project light onto the target object before sensing. The structural light based method[66] projects a certain pattern onto the object and then retrieves the depth information by analyzing the distorted pattern from the captured image. The Time-of-Flight based method[22] measures the time taken for the light to travel from the transmitter to the object surface and back to the receiver, based on which the depth information can be calculated.[45] The light source can be a laser or a near-infrared LED.

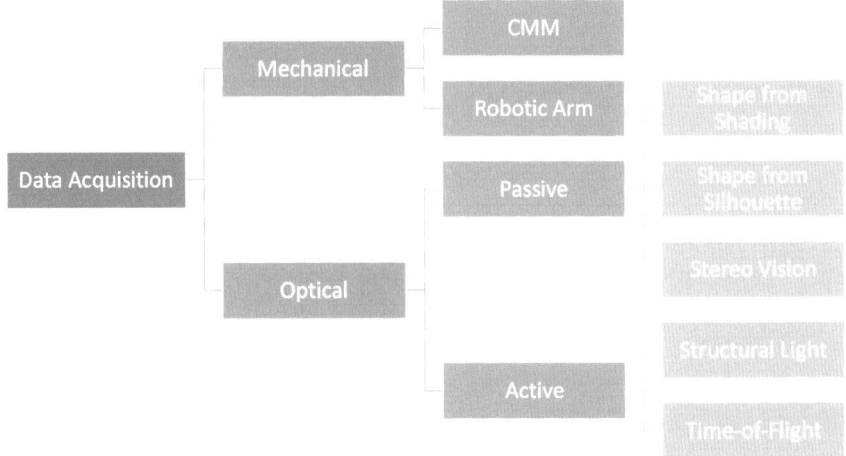

Fig. 5.4. 3D model data acquisition techniques for MAS.

After the procedure of data acquisition, the 3D model of the object can be generated by surface reconstruction, the objective of which is to determine the object's surface geometry from a given finite set of measurements. Usually, the acquired data are disorganized and noisy. Furthermore, the surface may not have a specific topological type and could be arbitrary in shape. The steps to generate 3D models from the acquired digital data include the following:[63] (i): Pre-processing: Erroneous data are removed, and the noise in the data is smoothed out; (ii) Determination of the surface's global topology; (iii) Generation of the polygonal surface; and (iv) Post-processing: Edge correction, triangle insertion, hole filling, and polygon editing are used to optimize and smooth the shape.

The data acquisition devices are usually called 3D scanners. Besides expensive industrial scanners, there are some low-cost 3D scanners in the market that are affordable and suitable for MAS development, such as Microsoft Kinect,[52] MakerBot Digitizer,[49] and 3D Systems Sense,[1] which are shown in Fig. 5.5. The 3D model reconstruction software is also provided to generate the digital models from 3D scanning.

Fig. 5.5. Example low-cost 3D scanners for data acquisition.[52,49,1]

5.2.2 Sensors and Sensing Technologies

This section reviews different kinds of sensors and sensing technologies for environment perception and human pose estimation, including marker-based and marker-less tracking technologies. Human pose estimation methods are also reviewed.

5.2.2.1. Marker-based tracking for AR

Real-time tracking is one of the crucial tasks in AR applications because the generated virtual information needs to be superimposed upon the real world with intuitive mapping in real time to avoid causing discomfort for the user. Marker-based tracking is the most widely used method for real-time tracking due to its ease of implementation and high accuracy. As illustrated in Fig. 5.6, a predefined marker is captured by a camera and it is detected and tracked on each frame. Then the position and orientation of the marker relative to the camera is estimated. Finally, a virtual model is rendered using the estimated pose. There are some commercially available tools for marker-based tracking, such as the classic ARToolKit[41] and Vuforia,[81] which will be discussed in detail in Section 5.4.1.

(a) Marker   (b) Video capturing   (c) Marker tracking   (d) Model overlaying

Fig. 5.6. Illustration of marker-based tracking for AR.

5.2.2.2. Marker-less tracking for AR

Since markers can be designed with optimal tracking patterns, marker-based methods are very accurate for camera pose estimation. However, these methods are not convenient in some cases, especially for objects with small size or uneven surface, which is not feasible to mount markers on. Furthermore, the tracking can be lost when the marker is occluded. Therefore, researchers have developed marker-less tracking methods for AR technology.[47,82] Instead of detecting a specific marker, a marker-less method extracts features from the real environment, such as intersections of walls and floors and edges of an object, then these features are used to estimate the object's position and orientation.

Simultaneous Localization and Mapping (SLAM) technology is a technology initially developed in the robotics field for self-navigation, which gets the sensing data (e.g., Lidar, odometer, GPS, visual) to construct or update a map of an unknown environment while simultaneously keeps track of an agent's location within this map.[16,71] A SLAM technique using cameras is also called visual SLAM (vSLAM) because it only uses visual information.[71] SLAM is getting increasingly attractive in recent years due to the prevalence of domestic robots, self-driving cars, and smart drones. Since it is useful for perceiving and understanding the real physical world, researchers and companies have been utilizing SLAM for AR applications. As examples, Apple released their ARKit[5] for AR developers in 2017, and Google launched ARCore[31] in 2018 to replace their previous experimental AR project Tango.[40] ARKit and ARCore both incorporate SLAM algorithms to detect and track planes such as floors and walls in the real-world scene, then the digital content can be overlaid onto these planes. At present, SLAM is an active research area with lots of new algorithms being developed.

5.2.2.3. *Human pose estimation*

Human pose estimation is very useful for human-computer interaction in the VR/AR environment. According to the sensing techniques used, human pose estimation can be classified into two categories: optical and non-optical.[45] Optical methods utilize optical cameras to capture digital images, from which the poses are estimated.

(1) **Marker-based**. Marker-based methods need specific trackable markers to be mounted on the human body to represent the positions of the body part. These markers can be passive markers, which are usually small balls coated with a retro-reflective material. The tracking area is illuminated by an Infrared (IR) light and an IR camera is used to capture the markers. Companies such as OptiTrack,[61] Vicon,[79] and ART[7] have such passive optical tracking systems that are commercially available. The markers also can be active markers, which are IR LEDs and emit IR light by themselves. An IR camera is used to capture the markers. The Wiimote controller from Nintendo uses such techniques for tracking the player's pose. These systems can use the same marker tracking algorithm as the passive marker systems but are much less expensive than the passive maker systems like OptiTrack. Zhu et al.[89-92] developed a low-cost assembly simulation system using Wiimote for tracking.

(2) **Marker-less**. A marker-based system can achieve high accuracy because the markers are designed and optimized for tracking purpose. However, it has shortcomings such as inconvenience in setting up the tracking system and

movement interference with the attached markers. Marker-less tracking provides non-invasive solutions to address these issues that marker-based methods have. Microsoft Kinect[52] falls into this category and is popularly used. It has a depth sensor to perceive the image depth, from which the skeleton-based human pose estimation is calculated. Some other depth cameras are commercially available, such as Intel RealSense[36] and Structure Sensor.[57] The recent unprecedented development in the artificial intelligence (AI) area, especially deep learning, makes it possible to accurately estimate the human pose directly from a digital image without the help of depth information. OpenPose,[17,69,84] initially released in 2017, is the first real-time multi-person system to estimate the human pose from a single image. It can detect human body, hands, and facial key points. OpenPose is a promising solution for human pose estimation because it does not need special cameras, but it is computationally intensive and relies on high-end GPUs to realize real-time human tracking, which is one of its limitations.

(3) **Non-optical**. Non-optical sensors also have been used to estimate the human pose. A magnetic tracking system, such as MotionStar developed by Ascension Technology Corp. in 1997,[8] calculates an object's position and orientation based on the earth's magnetic field. It has some drawbacks, e.g., it may be interfered by metallic objects in the tracking area. An inertia-based tracking system, such as Moven from Xsens Corp.,[87] uses accelerometers and gyroscopes to capture the human body's movement and estimate the human's pose. It does not measure positions directly, thus accumulated errors may occur. An acoustic tracking system uses the time-of-flight technique to estimate the position of the emitter relative to the receivers. The emitter is attached to the body and the receivers are mounted at known locations in the environment.

(4) **Sensor fusion**. To compensate for the shortcomings of each method, sensor fusion methods integrating different modalities have been developed. Researchers at the Missouri University of Science and Technology used a Kinect to provide skeleton information and a Myo armband to provide inertial and surface electromyography (sEMG) measurements. Then a multimodal deep learning method was used for worker behavior understanding, achieving promising results for future endeavors.[4,73]

5.2.3 *Human-computer Interface for Rendering and Interaction*

Human-computer interfaces provide the user with different visual, haptic and auditory sensations, which play a vital role in a virtual assembly system for increasing the degree of immersion in the VR/AR environment. Figure 5.7 shows a typical VR/AR system configuration with physical input and output devices that transmit information between the user and the environment. These sensing technologies are essential to the realism of the VR/AR system. The critical technologies addressed here include visual interface, auditory modeling and rendering, and haptic modeling and rendering.

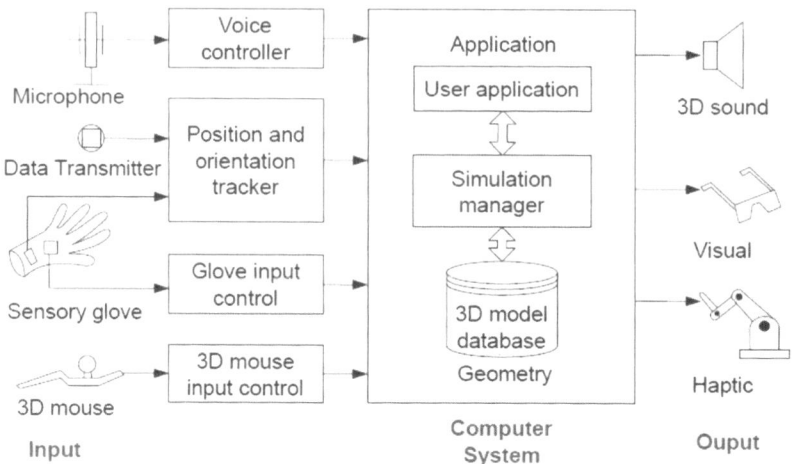

Fig. 5.7. Typical VR/AR configuration with human-computer interfaces.[45]

5.2.3.1 *Visual interface*

Visual interface is the most important interface in VR/AR. There exists different hardware providing visual interfaces, such as desktop displays, hand-held displays, projection displays, and Head Mounted Displays (HMD) that have been the mainstream due to the fully immersive experiences they provided. VR HMDs can be divided into three classes, tethered HMDs that need to be connected to a PC or console, mobile-dependent HMDs that need to attach onto a smartphone, and standalone headsets that do not need to be connected to other devices. Figure 5.8 shows three VR glasses available in the market that fall into these three classes and their costs range from $100 to $500. Some of the mobile-dependent products cost less than $100, which are affordable to most consumers. AR HMDs are relatively more expensive than VR HMDs because they require more complicated optical designs to realize the see-through ability. Figure 5.9 shows three AR HMDs in the market. The selection of visual hardware for a given application should take into consideration the resolution, update rate, field-of-view, head tracking accuracy, latency, etc.

Fig. 5.8. VR headsets of Sony PlayStation VR, Oculus Rift, and Google Daydream (from left to right).[33]

Fig. 5.9. AR headsets of Microsoft HoloLens, Magic Leap One, and Google Glasses (from left to right).[51,48,32]

5.2.3.2 *Auditory modeling and rendering*

Audio clues can be used to augment visual interfaces for assembly simulation in VR/AR. Auditory rendering is especially helpful when haptic feedback is not available. Physics-based sound modeling is too computationally expensive for real-time rendering required in virtual assembly. Synthetic sound can be used to approximate the real sound generated from the physical assembly, making the simulation more realistic. Spectral modeling can be used as the basis for sound synthesis in virtual assembly.[56,86] Sound generation using deep learning methods also can be used in this case.[78]

In the virtual environment, a sound generator can be attached to a virtual object to generate 3D audio for auditory rendering. 3D audio can provide listeners a spatial hearing experience that enables them to sense where they are relative to the sound sources, further immersing them in the virtual world.

5.2.3.3 *Haptic modeling and rendering*

Haptic devices providing force or tactile feedback to the users can further improve the realism besides visual and auditory sensations. Such devices usually are embedded with sensors and actuators to measure the user's contact position with a virtual object and apply force or other haptic feedback to the user at the contact position. The current haptic devices can be classified into three categories: (1) handheld devices such as the Touch from 3D Systems [2] that has been used widely as a force feedback device; (2) hand wearable devices such as the Sense Glove[67] which provides feedback to individual fingers to simulate how the users interact with the real objects; and (3) haptic suits such as the Teslasuit[74] which can provide haptic feedback to the body covered by the suit. These haptic devices have some drawbacks such as having strict geometry, placement and workspace requirements, and being cumbersome for wearing, which limit them from being widely used.

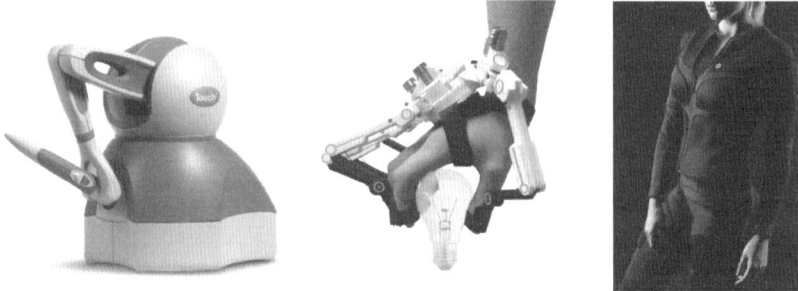

Fig. 5.10. Haptic devices of 3D System Touch, Sense Glove, and Teslasuit (from left to right).[2,67,74]

5.3 Application and Examples of MAS using VR/AR

Manufacturing assembly simulation using VR/AR can provide intuitive, immersive and interactive solutions for manufacturers to improve the capability and efficiency of the various assembly processes, covering assembly design, process verification, and workforce training.

Many companies have utilized MAS with VR/AR in their assembly processes and greatly benefitted from it.[64] For example, in the automotive area, Toyota[75] develops an interactive virtual learning system using VR technology to train their assembly line workers. The trainee is immersed in a virtual assembly line environment wearing an HTC Vive headset. During the training session, the trainee is guided by step-by-step assembly processes and interacts with the virtual object using the controllers. The Volkswagen Group, collaborated with the VR studio, Innoactive,[93] has launched a plan of bringing VR training to 10,000 employees, which includes over 30 VR training experiences covering tasks from vehicle assembly, new team member training, to customer service.[103] Other companies like Tesla,[14] Mercedes-Benz,[97] BMW,[98] Volvo,[13] Ford,[20] and Bentley[10,11] also apply VR/AR in their factories to improve the assembly workflows. Compared with traditional training methods using paper manuals, such training systems not only can benefit the trainees with more motivational, personalized and intuitive training experience but also can benefit the manufacturers with reduced training cost, improved training efficiency and excellent scalability.

In the aerospace area, Boeing has been using VR/AR in various tasks, such as wing assembly tasks, wiring tasks, and some specialized manufacturing tasks, to help improve training efficiency, reduce design errors, and speed up maintenance processes. With the help of a Microsoft HoloLens providing the assembly instructions to the trainees, Boeing showed that this approach can shorten training time by 75% per person.[6,12,42] Similarly, Airbus,[3] Rolls-Royce[100] and Lockheed Martin[99] also reported benefit from VR/AR utilization.

Almost all the leading industrial manufacturing companies, such as Siemens,[94] Bosch[95] and Dassault Systems[96] have been actively seeking opportunities to apply the VR/AR technologies to industries.

A typical MAS application in VR is shown in Fig. 5.11, which is a MAS scenario of seat mounting in VR developed by Bentley Motors and OPTIS.[10,11,60] The native CAD models are imported into the virtual environment and haptic feedback is generated when an operator's hand collides with a virtual object. The haptic feedback gives car makers a way to simulate and analyze where clashes and collisions might occur during the worker's operation, and find out the optimal possible manufacturing and installation protocols. Multiple markers are attached onto the operator's body for motion capturing and tracking.

Fig. 5.11. A operator wearing an Oculus headset for immersive VR and attached with multiple markers for motion tracking (Image courtesy of OPTIS).[11]

AR technology allows the operator to see the real environment with virtual information superimposed upon the physical world. This has been popular in AR-assisted assembly training and guidance.[65,88,83] AR also has been applied to other assembly related tasks, such as manual assembly station planning,[62] assembly workplace design,[58] and assembly constraint analysis.[59]

A typical MAS in AR developed by DAQRI[23] for workforce training and guidance is shown in Fig. 5.12, which is a control module in an assembly task.

During the assembly task, the instruction information, such as which item to pick and which tool to use, is overlaid onto the operator's view through an AR helmet. The operator can follow the instructions step by step to get familiar with the assembly sequence and acquire assembly skills. The virtual instructions can be multimedia including text, image, video, voice, etc. The task completion status is also computed and visualized.

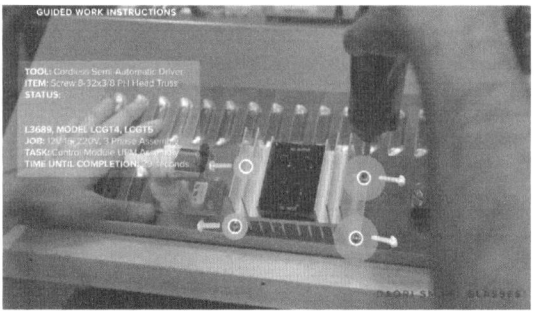

Fig. 5.12. An AR guidance scenario from DAQRI.[23]

5.4 A Case Study

This section presents a case study to provide a practical guide to implementing an AR assembly simulation application. In this case study, AR instructions are developed to guide the user in a spindle carriage installation task;[37] see Fig. 5.13. Hand interaction with virtual objects is explored using a Leap Motion Controller.[44] The performance comparison between AR guidance and traditional manual guidance is also presented.

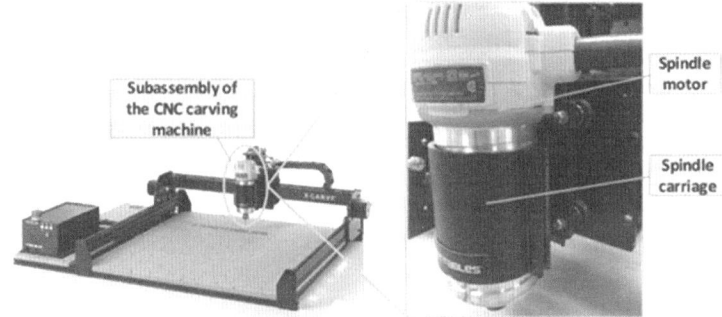

Fig. 5.13. The spindle subassembly of a CNC carving machine.

5.4.1 *Available Tools*

There are various tools that can be used for developing AR MAS applications. Some commonly used ones are introduced as follows:

Unity. Unity is a game engine developed by Unity Technologies that allows its users to develop games.[76] The engine can provide various visual effects including 2D and 3D graphics, textures, lighting and shading. The users can create a scene by importing customized CAD models with texture rendering. The engine platform supports scripting via programming languages such as C# and JavaScript.

Unreal Engine. Unreal Engine is a game engine that was first brought to the gaming platform in 1998 and has been widely used.[77] The engine is programmed in C++ and is available for different operating systems.

ARToolKit. ARToolKit is a library that can be utilized for AR application development and was originally developed by Dr. Hirokazu Kato. It is being supported by multidisciplinary institutions across the country.[41] The library can provide AR rendering through camera pose estimation and target tracking.

Vuforia. Vuforia is a Software Development Kit (SDK) for AR development.[81] It provides the functionalities of target recognition and tracking, enabling its users to superimpose 3D digital contents with respect to the world coordinates as 2D image registration for a composite view. The user can define the trackable marker for maker-based AR by importing the desired image target for augmentation with different configurations.

Wikitude. Wikitude SDK combines target recognition, tracking, and simultaneous localization and mapping (SLAM), as well as Geo-location, for various AR development engines and configurations across Android and iOS.[85]

ARKit. ARKit from Apple is a platform for building AR iOS applications. It provides object detection and mapping functions for marker-less tracking, enabling the user to directly overlay information onto the environment with different geometries.[5]

ARCore. ARCore is an AR platform from Google. It integrates three main top-notch elements, i.e. motion tracking, environmental understanding, and light estimation.[31] ARCore provides a wide variety of features and functionalities with different APIs and can be deployed on both Android and iOS devices.

In this demonstration project, the application is developed using Unity with the support of Vuforia SDK due to its fundamental usability and accessibility for AR implementation.

5.4.2 *Modeling*

In this case study, NX is chosen as the CAD software to build the 3D digital model for the spindle carriage. Figure 5.14 shows the created CAD model of the spindle carriage in NX.[101]

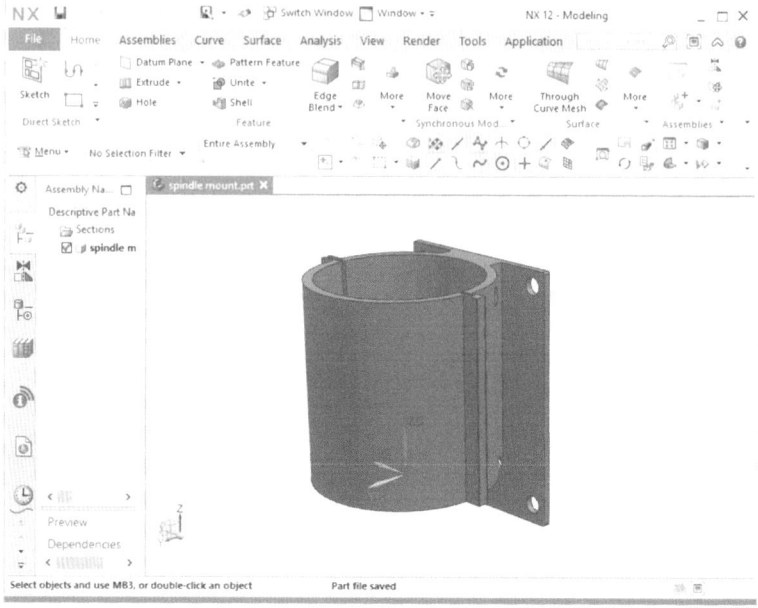

Fig. 5.14. The CAD model of the spindle carriage.

Once modeling is finished, an AR assembly scene in Unity can be created by importing CAD models into the scene as Unity game objects either through the drop-down menu as shown in Fig. 5.15 or using drag-and-drop to the "Assets" panel. The imported CAD models would then be categorized as game objects and be sorted on the hierarchy panel once they have been assigned to the scene. Multiple static and dynamic features can then be added to each of the game objects with different settings and parameters.

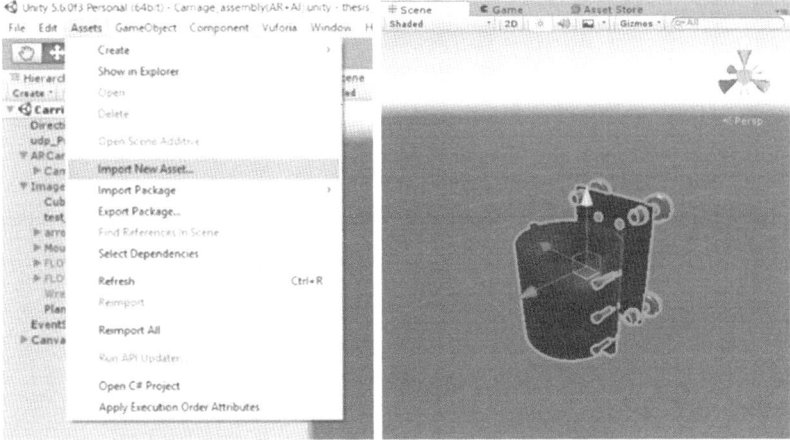

Fig. 5.15. Importing CAD model of spindle carriage to Unity.

5.4.3 *AR Realization*

The AR guidance function is achieved using Vuforia SDK in the Unity environment. The AR composite view can be realized by utilizing Vuforia prefabs and the computed target database imported from the developer portal in which the user can upload image patterns for target markers, as well as visualize the augmented contents according to the quality of the computed features. Figure 5.16 shows the workflow of Vuforia prefabs in Unity.

Fig. 5.16. The workflow of AR realization using Vuforia in Unity.

The database enables the marker-based AR by activating "ARCamera" and "ImageTarget" prefabs to recognize and track objects for data registration with a built-in algorithm, which can provide the coordinate transformation of camera pose in a real-time manner. Once the data has been loaded, the user can activate the "Image Target Behavior" of the "ImageTarget" prefab by setting the dataset and image target. After the setting is finished, the augmented view can be visualized through the display while the marker is being captured by the camera. Figure 5.17 shows the AR scene with generated CAD models superimposed.

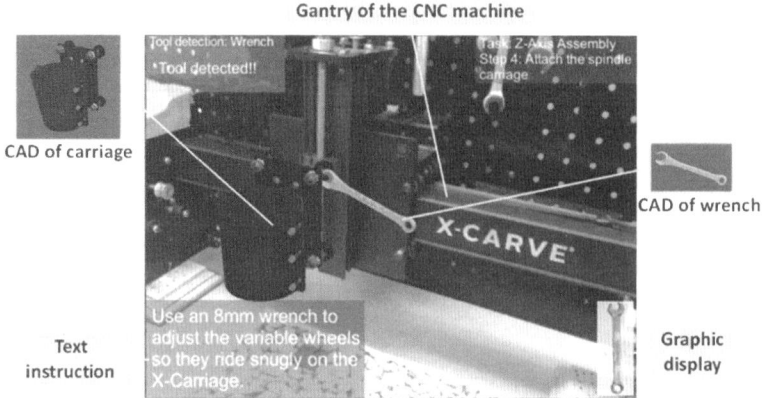

Fig. 5.17. An assembly scene runs in real time with AR instructions. Multiple types of instructions are rendered through a display including texts, graphics, and 3D animations.

5.4.4 *Hand Interaction*

A Leap Motion Controller is applied in this study to realize simple hand interactions with virtual objects. Leap Motion SDK is used to return the spatial coordinates of the real hands and Vuforia is responsible for superimposing graphic hands onto the real hands in an AR scene. To interact with virtual objects, the scripted interaction behavior and physics features for graphic hands and objects are required to simulate the real-world activities as if the user is interacting with the physical objects. Figure 5.18 shows the interaction between real hands and virtual objects with various geometries.

Fig. 5.18. Hand interaction with virtual objects in an AR scene.

5.4.5 *Experiment and Evaluation*

To evaluate the effectiveness of the AR guidance, we have applied it in an experiment to instruct users to conduct an assembly task and its performance is compared with the traditional manual guidance. Figure 5.19 shows the overall experimental setup. There are 20 subjects recruited completing the task.

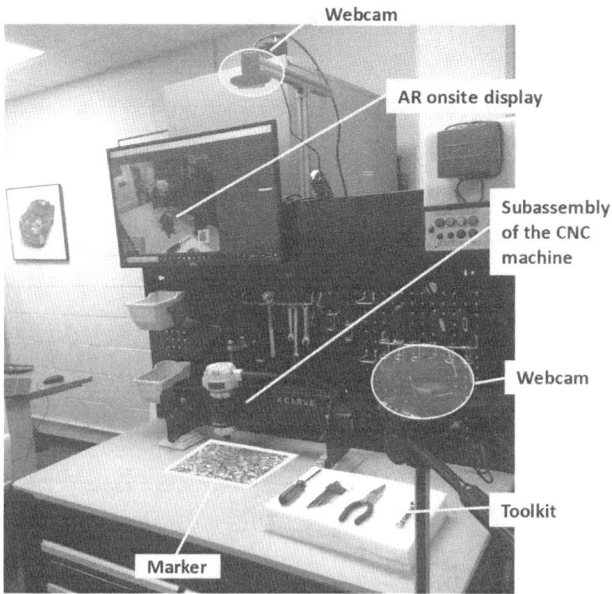

Fig. 5.19. The workstation setup for the experiment.

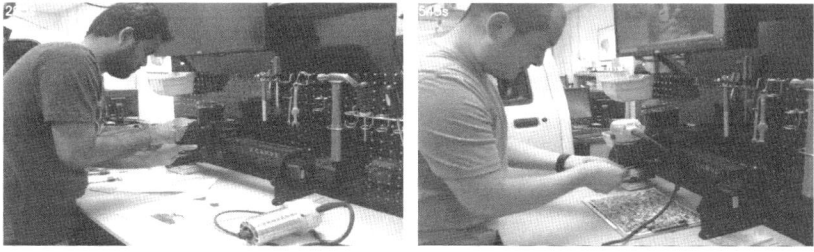

Fig. 5.20. A comparison of two subjects performing the experiment with two different methods: (left) manual and (right) AR.

The 20 subjects are divided into two groups with AR and manual instructions provided, respectively. During the experiment, each subject is asked to perform the assembly task by following the instructions step by step; see Fig. 5.20. To assess the performance, the completion time and number of errors are recorded throughout the experiment. The performance comparison is shown in Fig. 5.21; by using AR guidance, the completion time and number of errors show 33.2% and 32.4% of reduction, respectively. The considerable improvement demonstrates the great potential of applying AR technology to industries for manufacturing assembly training.

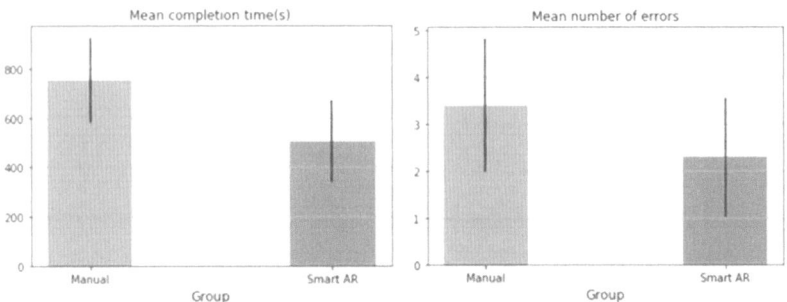

Fig. 5.21. The comparison between manual and AR guidance: (left) completion time and (right) number of errors.

5.5 Technology Limitations and Research Needs

This section discusses the limitations and challenges of current VR/AR and MAS technologies and future research needs towards MAS realism improvement, worker behavior understanding, and sharing and collaborative MAS.

5.5.1 *MAS Realism Improvement*

To further improve the realism of MAS in VR/AR environment, research and development efforts are needed to advance VR/AR technologies aimed at accomplishing the following objectives:

(1) High-fidelity and low-latency graphic visual interfaces need to be developed. For example, for head-mounted VR/AR systems, the optical system design needs to be advanced[28] for increased display resolution, update rate, and field of view, and for reduced size and weight of the headset.

(2) To enhance the visual interface for better immersive VR/AR experience, the following efforts are needed: (a) Advance the technique of 3D auditory feedback; (b) Develop multichannel haptic devices to provide users with richer touch feedback and allow them to feel the surface texture, shape, softness/hardness, and temperature of an object; (c) Further develop locomotion interface[55,70] to provide realistic walking/running experience in the virtual environment; and (d) Explore the senses of smell and taste to augment the realism of MAS applications.

(3) To realize better environment perception for AR systems, marker-less tracking methods need to be improved. The SLAM technologies have provided promising solutions for environment perception in AR. They need to be further studied for improved efficiency and robustness. Object detection and recognition techniques also need to be further developed for more advanced environment awareness.

(4) More accurate, efficient, robust, and low-cost human pose estimation approaches need to be investigated. Multi-modal motion tracking devices, advanced data fusion techniques, and deep learning methods can be exploited in this study. Motion sickness[43,54] is another challenging issue affecting the user's experience, which needs to be solved with more accurate and efficient motion tracking approaches.

(5) Currently most of the human-environment interactions are conducted with some input/output devices such as a 3D mouse or a controller. More natural ways such as voice, gaze, and gesture interaction[72] technologies need to be developed.

5.5.2. *Worker Behavior Understanding*

In a MAS task, understanding the worker's behavior can be used for quantification and evaluation of the worker's performance, as well as to provide onsite instructions in VR/AR.[73] Studies in the following aspects need to be conducted:

(1) Methods for real-time worker activity recognition need to be researched for understanding the worker's current assembly activity during a MAS task. Then the time taken for each assembly step can be analyzed for quantification and evaluation purposes.

(2) Besides activity, the worker's emotional states (e.g., stress, confusion and fatigue) should be considered in MAS, which can be estimated using sensors such as an Electroencephalography (EEG) headset, or through advanced facial recognition techniques.[39]

(3) On-demand virtual guidance for MAS should be developed based on the worker's states (e.g., activity and emotional states) to improve the interaction efficiency with minimal guidance to the worker.[102] Also, methods for online assembly quality evaluation need to be developed.

5.5.3. *Sharing and Collaborative MAS*

Due to the increasing complexities of assembly products and prevalence of global partnership in the design and manufacturing processes, sharing and collaborative MAS are needed in such contexts. It allows team members located in different geographical locations and time zones to share their knowledge and expertise and conduct cloud-based collaboration. Research opportunities in the area of sharing and collaborative MAS include the following:

(1) For MAS involving multiple users in the VR/AR environment, sharing the same virtualized/augmented world and digital contents requires more accurate, efficient and robust registration and tracking algorithms, in order to register multiple users to the same coordinate system precisely and keep synchronizing their shared contents promptly.

(2) The design interface and interaction in these situations will be more challenging because it involves not only interactions between users and digital contents, but also interactions between different users. How to enable users to have natural, effective distance collaborations in the VR/AR scenarios as they do in the real workplace is another challenge that needs to be addressed.

(3) To achieve simultaneous interfaces of VR/AR contents and concurrent interactions among collaborators in different geographical locations, advanced computing, networking, and communication architectures and methodologies, along with the necessary hardware and software, need to be developed and implemented.

5.6. Conclusion

This chapter focuses on utilizing Virtual Reality/Augmented Reality (VR/AR) technologies for assembly simulations in advanced manufacturing. First, some basic terminologies and concepts have been clarified in terms of VR, AR, and manufacturing assembly simulation (MAS). Then the state-of-the-art methodologies for developing MAS applications including modeling, sensing, and interaction that enable the VR/AR assembly simulations has been reviewed and discussed. In particular, the discussion has included how to acquire digital data from a real object and how to reconstruct a 3D model using the acquired data. This chapter also has presented different methods for AR tracking and human pose estimation. Moreover, human-computer interfaces for rendering and interaction, including visual, auditory and haptic interfaces, have been discussed. Further, this chapter has included some assembly application examples that incorporate VR/AR technologies for MAS and has demonstrated the potential of MAS systems for shortening the product design cycle, improving product quality, and enhancing worker skills. A hands-on project has been used in a case study to provide a practical guide to implementing a VR/AR assembly simulation application. Finally, the limitations and challenges of current VR/AR technologies and future research needs in terms of MAS realism improvement, worker behavior understanding, and sharing and collaborative MAS have been discussed.

References

1. 3D Systems. Sense. (2018).
2. 3D Systems. Touch. (2018). https://www.3dsystems.com/haptics-devices/touch (Accessed 16 November, 2020).
3. Airbus. Virtual Reality with real benefits. (2017). https://www.airbus.com/newsroom/news/en/2017/09/virtual-reality-with-benefits.html (Accessed November 16, 2020).
4. M. Al-Amin, R. Qin, W. Tao, and M. C. Leu. Sensor data based models for workforce management in smart manufacturing. In *Proceedings of the 2018 Institute of Industrial and Systems Engineers Annual Conference*, pp. 481-486 (2018).
5. Apple. ARKit. (2018) https://developer.apple.com/arkit/ (Accessed November 16, 2020).
6. AREA. Augmented Reality can increase productivity (2015). http://thearea.org/augmented-reality-can-increase-productivity/ (Accessed November 16, 2020).
7. ART. Homepage. (2018). https://ar-tracking.com/ (Accessed November 16, 2020).
8. Ascension Technology Corporation. Homepage. (2018). https://www.ascension-tech.com (Accessed November 16, 2020).
9. S. Aukstakalnis and D. Blatner. *Silicon Mirage: The Art and Science of Virtual Reality.* Peachpit Press (1992).
10. Bentley. Bentley reinvents the design of future vehicles with Virtual Reality. (2017).
11. Bentley. Prelude to GTC 2017: Touch and feel the pixels in your virtual car. (2017). http://www.digitaleng.news/virtual_desktop/2017/04/prelude-gtc-2017-touch-feel-pixels-virtual-car/ (Accessed November 16, 2020).
12. Boeing. Boeing tests Augmented Reality in the factory. (2018). https://www.boeing.com/features/2018/01/augmented-reality-01-18.page (Accessed November 16, 2020).
13. C. Bruce. Volvo and Microsoft partner on virtual reality and autonomous tech. (2015). https://www.autoblog.com/2015/11/20/volvo-microsoft-virtual-reality-autonomous-tech/ (Accessed November 16, 2020).
14. C. Bruce. Tesla uses augmented reality to improve EV manufacturing (2016). https://www.autoblog.com/2016/03/22/tesla-augmented-reality-factory/ (Accessed November 16, 2020).
15. G. C. Burdea and P. Coiffet. *Virtual Reality Technology.* John Wiley & Sons (2003).
16. C. Cadena, L. Carlone, H. Carrillo, Y. Latif, D. Scaramuzza, J. Neira, I. Reid, and J. J. Leonard. Past, present, and future of simultaneous localization and mapping: Toward the robust-perception age. *IEEE Transactions on Robotics* **32**(6), 1309–1332 (2016).
17. Z. Cao, T. Simon, S. E. Wei, and Y. Sheikh. Realtime multi-person 2d pose estimation using part affinity fields. In *Proceedings of the IEEE Conference on Computer Vision and Pattern Recognition*, pp. 7291–7299 (2017).
18. G. K. Cheung, S. Baker, and T. Kanade. Visual hull alignment and refinement across time: A 3d reconstruction algorithm combining shape-from-silhouette with stereo. In *Proceedings of the 2003 IEEE Computer Society Conference on Computer Vision and Pattern Recognition*, vol. 2, pp. II–375 (June 2003).

19. J. Constine. Facebook's $2 billion acquisition of Oculus closes, now official. (2014). https://techcrunch.com/2014/07/21/facebooks-acquisition-of-oculus-closes-now-official/ (Accessed November 16, 2020).

20. P. Covington. Inside Ford's Virtual Reality labs. (2017). https://www.triplepundit.com/2017/01/ford-virtual-reality-labs (Accessed November 16, 2020).

21. C. Cruz-Neira, D. J. Sandin, and T. A. DeFanti. Surround-screen projection-based virtual reality: the design and implementation of the CAVE. In *Proceedings of the 20th annual conference on Computer graphics and interactive techniques*, pp. 135–142 (September 1993).

22. Y. Cui, S. Schuon, D. Chan, S. Thrun, and C. Theobalt. 3D shape scanning with a time-of-flight camera. In 2010 IEEE Computer Society Conference on Computer Vision and Pattern Recognition, pp. 1173–1180 (Jun, 2010).

23. DAQRI. Best practices for enterprises planning to adopt augmented reality. (2017).

24. Dassault System. CATIA. (2018). https://www.3ds.com/products-services/catia/ (Accessed November 16, 2020).

25. Dassault System. SOLIDWORKS. (2018) https://www.solidworks.com/ (Accessed November 16, 2020).

26. S. El-hakim. Theme issue on imaging modeling for virtual reality, *ISPRS Journal of Photogrammetry & Remote Sensing* 53(6), 309–310 (1998).

27. E. H. Sabry. A practical approach to creating precise and detailed 3D models from single and multiple views. In *Proceedings of the XIX ISPRS Congress*, pp. 202-209, Amsterdam, The Netherlands (2000).

28. E. Elliott, K. Norton, and M. Humphreys. Freeform optics design: Optical design challenges in virtual and augmented reality. (2018).

29. A. Fusiello, V. Roberto, and E. Trucco. Efficient stereo with multiple windowing. In Proceedings of IEEE Computer Society conference on computer vision and pattern recognition, pp. 858–863 (June 1997).

30. R. C. Gonzales and R. E. Woods. Digital image processing (2002).

31. Google. ARCore. (2018). https://developers.google.com/ar/ (Accessed November 16, 2020).

32. Google. Google Glasses. (2018). https://www.x.company/glass/ (Accessed November 16, 2020).

33. W. Greenwald. The Best VR (Virtual Reality) headsets of 2018. (2018). https://www.pcmag.com/article/342537/the-best-virtual-reality-vr-headsets (Accessed November 16, 2020).

34. M. L. Heilig, inventor. Sensorama Simulator. US Patent 3,050,870. (August 1962).

35. B. K. Horn, and M. J. Brooks. *Shape from Shading*. MIT Press, (1989).

36. Intel. Intel RealSense technology. (2018). https://software.intel.com/en-us/realsense?language=ru (Accessed November 16, 2020).

37. Inventables. X-Carve instructions. (2018). http://x-carve-instructions.inventables.com/750mm/ (Accessed November 16, 2020).

38. S. Jayaram, J. Vance, R. Gadh, U. Jayaram, and H. Srinivasan. Assessment of VR technology and its applications to engineering problems, *J. Comput. Inf. Sci. Eng.* 1(1), 72–83 (2001).

39. S. E. Kahou, X. Bouthillier, P. Lamblin, C. Gulcehre, V. Michalski, K. Konda, S. Jean, P. Froumenty, Y. Dauphin, N. Boulanger-Lewandowski, and R. C. Ferrari. Emonets: Multimodal deep learning approaches for emotion recognition in video, *Journal on Multimodal User Interfaces* 10(2), 99–111 (2016).

40. J. Kastrenakes. Google's Project Tango is shutting down because ARCore is already here (2017). https://www.theverge.com/2017/12/15/16782556/project-tango-google-shutting-down-arcore-augmented-reality (Accessed November 16, 2020).

41. H. Kato. ARToolKit. (1999). https://www.hitl.washington.edu/artoolkit/ (Accessed November 16, 2020).

42. A. Kishore. Boeing: productive VR cuts training time by 75%. (2017). https://www.lightreading.com/video/video-services/boeing-productive-vr-cuts-training-time-by-75-/d/d-id/733756 (Accessed November 16, 2020).

43. D. J. Lang. For virtual reality creators, motion sickness a real issue. (2016). https://phys.org/news/2016-03-virtual-reality-creators-motion-sickness.html (Accessed November 16, 2020).

44. Leap Motion. Homepage. (2018). https://www.leapmotion.com/ (Accessed November 16, 2020).

45. M. C. Leu, H. A. ElMaraghy, A. Y. Nee, S. K. Ong, M. Lanzetta, M. Putz, W. Zhu, and A. Bernard. CAD model based virtual assembly simulation, planning and training, *CIRP Annals* **62**(2), 799–822 (2013).

46. M. C. Leu, W. Tao, A. Ghazanfari, and K. Kolan. *NX 12 for Engineering Design*, Missouri S&T (2018).

47. J. P. Lima, R. Roberto, F. Simões, M. Almeida, L. Figueiredo, J. M. Teixeira, V. Teichrieb. Markerless tracking system for augmented reality in the automotive industry, *Expert Systems with Applications* **82**, 100–114 (2017).

48. Magic Leap. Homepage. (2018). https://www.magicleap.com/ (Accessed November 16, 2020).

49. MakerBot. Digitizer. (2018). https://www.makerbot.com/stories/news/makerbot-digitizer-desktop-3d-scanner-order-today/ (Accessed November 16, 2020).

50. W. N. Martin and J. K. Aggarwal. Volumetric descriptions of objects from multiple views. *IEEE Transactions on Pattern Analysis and Machine Intelligence* (2), 150–158 (1983).

51. Microsoft. HoloLens. (2018). https://www.microsoft.com/en-us/hololens (Accessed November 16, 2020).

52. Microsoft. Kinect. (2018). https://www.xbox.com/en-US/xbox-one/accessories/kinect (Accessed November 16, 2020).

53. P. Milgram and A. F. Kishino. A Taxonomy of Mixed Reality Visual Displays, *IEICE Transactions on Information and Systems* **E77-D** (12), 1321–1329 (1994).

54. J. Munafo, M. Diedrick, and T. A. Stoffregen. The virtual reality head-mounted display Oculus Rift induces motion sickness and is sexist in its effects, *Experimental Brain Research* **235**(3), 889–901 (2017).

55. M. Nabiyouni, A. Saktheeswaran, D. A. Bowman, and A. Karanth. Comparing the performance of natural, semi-natural, and non-natural locomotion techniques in virtual reality. In *2015 IEEE Symposium on 3D User Interfaces (3DUI)*, pp. 3–10 (2015).

56. Q. Niu, X. Chi, M. C. Leu, and J. Ochoa. Image processing, geometric modeling and data management for development of a virtual bone surgery system, *Computer Aided Surgery* **13**(1), 30–40 (2008).

57. Occipital. Structure Sensor (2018). https://structure.io/ (Accessed November 16, 2020).

58. S. Ong, Y. Pang, and A. Y. Nee. Augmented reality aided assembly design and planning, *CIRP Annals* **56**(1), 49–52 (2007).

59. S. K. Ong and Z. B. Wang. Augmented assembly technologies based on 3D bare-hand interaction, *CIRP Annals* **60**(1), 1–4 (2011).

60. OPTIS. Improving production time with Virtual Reality. (2017).

61. OptiTrack. Homepage. (2018). http://optitrack.com/ (Accessed November 16, 2020).

62. G. Reinhart and C. Patron. Integrating augmented reality in the assembly domain-fundamentals, benefits and applications, *CIRP Annals* **52**(1), 5–8 (2003).

63. F. Remondino and S. El-Hakim. Image-based 3D modelling: A review, *The Photogrammetric Record* **21**(115), 269–291 (2006).

64. J. Resnick. Virtual assembly lines are making the auto industry more flexible. (2016). https://arstechnica.com/cars/2016/09/virtual-assembly-lines-are-making-the-auto-industry-more-flexible/ (Accessed November 16, 2020).

65. J. Sääski, T. Salonen, M. Hakkarainen, S. Siltanen, C. Woodward, and J. Lempiäinen. Integration of design and assembly using augmented reality. In *International Precision Assembly Seminar 2008*. Springer (2008).

66. J. Salvi, J. Pages, and J. Batlle. Pattern codification strategies in structured light systems, *Pattern Recognition* **37**(4), 827–849 (2004).

67. Sense Glove. Homepage. (2018). https://www.senseglove.com/ (Accessed November 16, 2020).

68. L. S. Shapiro and J. M. Brady. Feature-based correspondence: an eigenvector approach, *Image and Vision Computing* **10**(5), 283–288 (1992).

69. T. Simon, H. Joo, I. Matthews, and Y. Sheikh. Hand keypoint detection in single images using multiview bootstrapping. In *Proceedings of the IEEE conference on Computer Vision and Pattern Recognition*, pp. 1145–1153 (2017).

70. F. Steinicke, Y. Visell, J. Campos, and A. Lécuyer. *Human Walking in Virtual Environments*. New York: Springer (2013).

71. T. Taketomi, H. Uchiyama, and S. Ikeda. Visual SLAM algorithms: A survey from 2010 to 2016, *IPSJ Transactions on Computer Vision and Applications* **9**(1), 16 (2017).

72. W. Tao, Z. H. Lai, M. C. Leu, and Z. Yin. American sign language alphabet recognition using leap motion controller. In *Proceedings of the 2018 Institute of Industrial and Systems Engineers Annual Conference* (2018).

73. W. Tao, Z. H. Lai, M. C. Leu, and Z. Yin. Worker activity recognition in smart manufacturing using IMU and sEMG signals with convolutional neural networks, *Procedia Manufacturing.* **26**, 1159–1166 (2018).

74. Teslasuit. Ultimate tech in smart clothing. (2018). https://teslasuit.io/ (Accessed November 16, 2020).

75. Toyota. Toyota assembly line VR training – The training center of the future. (2017). http://realitymatters.eu/project/virtual-assembly-line-training/ (Accessed November 16, 2020).

76. Unity. Homepage. (2018). https://unity3d.com/ (Accessed November 16, 2020).

77. Unreal Engine. What is unreal engine 4. (2018). https://www.unrealengine.com/en-US/what-is-unreal-engine-4 (Accessed November 16, 2020).

78. A. V. Oord, S. Dieleman, H. Zen, K. Simonyan, O. Vinyals, A. Graves, N. Kalchbrenner, A. Senior, and K. Kavukcuoglu. Wavenet: A generative model for raw audio. arXiv preprint arXiv:1609.03499 (Sep, 2016).

79. Vicon. Homepage. (2018). https://www.vicon.com/ (Accessed November 16, 2020).

80. Visbox. CAVE. (2018). http://www.visbox.com/products/cave/ (Accessed November 16, 2020).

81. Vuforia. Homepage. (2018). https://www.vuforia.com/ (Accessed November 16, 2020).

82. X. Wang, S. K. Ong, A. Y. Nee. A comprehensive survey of augmented reality assembly research, *Advances in Manufacturing* **4**(1), 1–22 (2016).

83. S. Webel, U. Bockholt, T. Engelke, N. Gavish, M. Olbrich, and C. Preusche. An augmented reality training platform for assembly and maintenance skills, *Robotics and Autonomous Systems* **61**(4), 398–403 (2013).

84. S. E. Wei, V. Ramakrishna, T. Kanade, and Y. Sheikh. Convolutional pose machines. In *Proceedings of the IEEE conference on Computer Vision and Pattern Recognition*, pp. 4724–4732 (2016).

85. Wikitude. Wikitude homepage. (2018). https://www.wikitude.com/ (Accessed November 16, 2020).

86. Wu, S., Tao, W., Leu, M.C. and Suzanna, L., Engine sound simulation and generation in driving simulator. In *Proceedings of the 2018 IISE Annual Conference*, pp. 60–65 (2018).

87. Xsens Corporation. Homepage. (2018). https://www.xsens.com/ (Accessed November 16, 2020).

88. J. Zhang, S. K. Ong, and A. Y. Nee. RFID-assisted assembly guidance system in an augmented reality environment, *International Journal of Production Research* **49**(13), 3919–3938 (2011).

89. W. Zhu, A. Chadda, M. C. Leu, and X. F. Liu. Real-time automated simulation generation based on CAD modeling and motion capture, *Journal of Computer Aided Design and Applications* PACE (1), 103-121 (2011).

90. W. Zhu, C. P. Daphalapurkar, S. C. Puthenveetil, M. C. Leu, X. F. Liu, A. M. Chang, J. K. Gilpin-Mcminn, P. H. Wu, S. D. Snodgrass. Motion capture of fastening operation using Wiimotes for ergonomic analysis. In *ASME/ISCIE 2012 International Symposium on Flexible Automation*, pp. 663-669, St. Louis, Missouri, USA (June 2012).

91. W. Zhu, A. Chadda, A. M. Vader, M. C. Leu, X. F. Liu, and J. B. Vance. Low-cost versatile motion tracking for assembly simulation. In *Proceedings of 2010 International Symposium on Flexible Automation,* Tokyo, Japan (2010).

92. W. Zhu, A. M. Vader, A. Chadda, M. C. Leu, X. F. Liu, and J. B. Vance. Wii remote–based low-cost motion capture for automated assembly simulation, *Virtual Reality* **17**(2), 125–136 (2013).

93. Innoactive GmbH. (2019). https://innoactive.de/ (Accessed November 16, 2020).

94. Siemens PLM. Digital Mockup, Virtual & Augmented Reality. (2018).

95. Bosch Sensortec GmbH. Augmented & Virtual Reality. (2018). https://www.bosch-sensortec.com/bst/applicationssolutions/ar_vr/overviewarvr# (Accessed November 16, 2020).

96. R. Hills-Duty. Dassault Systems SOLIDWORKS 2019 Introduces VR and AR Functionality. (2018). https://www.vrfocus.com/2018/10/dassault-systemes-solidworks-2019-introduces-vr-and-ar-functionality/ (Accessed November 16, 2020).

97. R. Claassen. AR and VR in Manufacturing: Being There. (2018). https://www.smart-industry.net/ar-and-vr-in-manufacturing-being-there/ (Accessed November 16, 2020).

98. G. Nica. BMW Used Virtual Reality to Set Up Workstations for 3 Series Assembly. (2018). https://www.bmwblog.com/2018/11/20/video-bmw-used-virtual-reality-to-set-up-workstations-for-3-series-assembly/ (Accessed November 16, 2020).

99. E. Winick. NASA is using HoloLens AR headsets to build its new spacecraft faster. (2018). https://www.technologyreview.com/s/612247/nasa-is-using-hololens-ar-headsets-to-build-its-new-spacecraft-faster/ (Accessed November 16, 2020).

100. S. Castellanos. Find out how Rolls-Royce is utilising virtual reality to train engineers. (2017). https://blogs.wsj.com/cio/2017/09/21/rolls-royce-enlists-virtual-reality-to-help-assemble-jet-engine-parts/?mod=djemlogistics (Accessed November 16, 2020).

101. M. C. Leu, W. Tao, A. Ghazanfari, and K. Kolan. *NX 12 for Engineering Design*. Missouri University of Science and Technology (2017).

102. W. Tao, Z. H. Lai, M. C. Leu, Z. Yin, and R. Qin. A self-aware and active-guiding training & assistant system for worker-centered intelligent manufacturing, *Manufacturing Letters* **21**, 45–49 (2019).

103. B. Carlton. Volkswagen will train 10,000 employees using VR this year. *VR Scout* (March 5, 2018). Available at https://vrscout.com/news/volkswagen-employee-training/ (Accessed November 16, 2020).

Chapter 6

Virtual Environment Applications for Front-End Design and Manufacturing Planning Applications

James Ritchie, Theodore Lim, Aparajithan Sivanathan, Avery Read,
Sam Harper, Scott Mcgibbon,
Hugo I. Medellin-Castillo, and Germanico Gonzalez-Badillo,

6.1 Introduction

Virtual environments are coming to the fore in both applied research and industrial applications, particularly due to the reduction in technological costs and the realization that this can substantially enhance the front-end design and design for manufacture and assembly (DFMA) aspects of the product life cycle. At the core of this often neglected product development front-end is the ability to ensure that products can be effectively designed to suit manufacturing processes and planned in ways which are more intuitive and rapid with the added bonus of capturing and formalizing engineering knowledge with a view to training and educating engineers.

Current CAD/CAM tools often limit front-end design, manufacturing planning and DFMA; most notably in the lack of active design-analysis assistance, full plan generation and inadequate human-computer interaction.[1,2] This is to be expected since the primary purpose of CAD/CAM systems is to codify geometrical concepts, support analysis and simulate limited production methods, particularly those associated with, say, computer numerical control (CNC) machining. However, where manufacturing planning is involved virtual environments can be generally designed to address much broader design and manufacturing planning activities by utilizing product design information and production process knowledge.[3,4] Indeed surveys and reviews on computer-aided process planning (CAPP) plateau in 2014 with many reiterating the need to deliver CAPP systems which are intuitive and capable of greater collaboration and distributive planning to meet the needs of globalized manufacturing and mass customization.[5,6] What is notable from these surveys is that the evolution of products and manufacturing systems focuses on new digital product development methods and technologies as reported by Choi et al.[4]

Virtual reality (VR) for design, manufacturing planning and DFMA strives to impact on and support engineers in their ability to organize knowledge, incorporate experience into methods and capture and formalize these as they interact with information relating to a product and/or a process, including objects, actions, and theoretical constructs. Further benefits are in terms of supporting intuitive, creative engineering functions, potentially shorter stage lead times and the output of more generalized engineering information. There are two primary research pathways: firstly, the drive for full automation and, secondly, that associated with the human-in-the loop. It is in the latter area that this chapter emphasizes and addresses.

Besides visualization and ergonomic interaction, another significant asset of VR is its impact analysis on "what-if scenarios." This is where the greatest gains can be potentially obtained in the management of time and resources to address complex planning challenges frequently occurring in globalized manufacturing as well as other sectors such as urban planning and, even, finance.

With dedicated hardware and software, VR immerses the user in their engineering experience, enabling them to reciprocate knowledge and assimilate actions with newly acquired information in an interactive schema that generates cognitive understanding. Haptics for example is one VR technology that brings multisensory benefits in assembly planning.[7,8] The resulting effect helps build a mental structure or model of the design and its associated manufacturing processes to generalize novel product and/or process solutions. This is essentially a knowledge-based perspective on product design analysis and information modelling, and one that has not been addressed extensively by current research. Early work by Ritchie et al.[9] and Robinson et al.[10] demonstrated the potential of knowledge capture and deployment in a virtual design planning environment. More recent trends have been reported by Lyu et al.[11]

The rise of Industry 4.0 is paving the way for smarter manufacturing planning through the use of discreet digital technologies, blurring the boundaries between the physical and digital dimensions of production systems. Indeed, VR used in the way outlined in this chapter can be used as a means of capturing and formalizing expertize to support the development of AI within Industry 4.0 systems. In this vein, such technology impacts on production, especially in the way it exerts itself on the workforce to deliver products and services. One such virtual-physical continuum is cyber-physical-enabled mixed reality, aiming to improve, collaborate and accelerate product design and development, analysis and production planning. Industrial IoT have provided challenging research issues;[12,13] however, a common thread with VR manufacturing is data exchange, including how, what, why and where individuals and manufacturing can benefit from this technology and how data can be reused.

This chapter highlights four examples of engineering VR manufacturing planning systems researched by the authors. The applications cover VR assembly planning, VR manufacturing (material removal) process planning, haptic-VR DFMA assembly and a cyber-physical mixed reality planning system. Some aspects of designing for and planning within virtual environments are presented along with other considerations, such as opportunities for knowledge capture. As well as the case studies included in this chapter, the implications for the wider application of VR in other design and manufacturing domains are discussed.

6.2 Assembly Planning

The nature of assembly planning is such that interactive human-in-the-loop and operational capabilities of VR technologies are ideal for practicing and implementing the movement of selection, deselection and manipulation of objects whilst assembling them intuitively. Indeed, there are numerous examples of assembly planning in the literature[14] and many of these have provided very different approaches to defining and generating assembly sequences.

In this chapter, the examples of virtual assembly given revolve around the early fundamental assembly planning work carried out in.[15]

In this research, an assembly planning system called UVAVU (Unbelievable Vehicle for Assembling Virtual Units) incorporated human-in-the-loop interaction via a head mounted display and a non-haptic 3D mouse allowing the planner to assemble virtual products. During this study, a significant gap was identified in CAAP (Computer Aided Assembly Planning) systems where there was a distinct lack of generic applications in this domain for real industrial products and it was felt that VR could address this by providing an intuitive interface for this purpose. This approach also differed from mainstream VR CAAP work in that it used chronological logging and log file inference to generate assembly plans comprising detailed stage-by-stage instructions for the assembly of a specific product. Since this was a non-haptic approach, the system used proximity snapping of parts into their final positions. Its early prototype was initially tested and validated using models of children's toys which, most importantly, showed planners did not break assembly sequence precedence when using it even though at the time there were no barriers to them doing this. The planners therefore tended to follow the known assembly procedures associated with these particular 'products' and felt that this novel approach was an intuitive and useful means of assembly.[15,16] Once the system prototype was tested, a full VR-based CAAP system was implemented. Different industrially-based planners each developed the assembly plans for a printer assembly on UVAVU and feedback obtained on their practical application on the shop floor by providing the product planning build instructions and components to shop floor operators who — not knowing how the plans were generated — successfully built their assemblies.

This capability to log planners in this way, generate planning instructions, including temporally, and test the system formed the foundation for the work outlined in the rest of this section and chapter. Indeed, a key feature of all of the applications discussed is the combination of unobtrusive user logging, an ergonomic interface reducing activity interrupts and plan inference from a time-phased logged data file.

This also provided the first example of VR being used as a formal knowledge capture tool when it was realized that the plans themselves were an expression of the planners' tacit planning knowledge. Further knowledge capture work was developed because of this.

The next area in which VR-based CAAP was studied was in the domain of cable harness design. Using the same basic technology as UVAVU, this research was carried out to provide the first detailed fundamental comparison of VR and computer aided design (CAD) systems for a specific design task;[17] in this case cable harness design routing within electro-mechanical equipment. Using the HMD and 3D mouse, an interface was developed which allowed the user to route and follow cable harnesses throughout the product using "artist pallet-based" menus. This demonstrated that significant productivity gains were achieved when using immersive HMD VR for cable routing when compared to a number of CAD packages. A further benefit using this VR approach was extending this research into a similar system called Co-Star which used chronological and log file post activity analysis[10,18] to capture and formalize cable harness design methods, engineering knowledge and design intent. Using lessons learnt from the earlier assembly planning work, this system was subsequently extended to facilitate the generation of assembly plans for cable harnesses within electro-mechanical equipment.[19] Some associated product geometry interactions and examples of the final plans generated are shown in Fig. 6.1 and Fig. 6.2 respectively.

The assembly plans produced from the chronological log file were threefold. Firstly, by interactively highlighting the bulkhead connectors in the proper sequence a bulkhead connector assembly plan was output from the associated XML log file. Secondly, the cables were then highlighted in turn with the connectors — again in the relevant sequence — so that the cable assembly harness could be constructed and a cable harness assembly plan generated. Finally, by sequentially and interactively choosing the relevant order of bulkhead connectors and associated cables, a harness installation plan could be output.

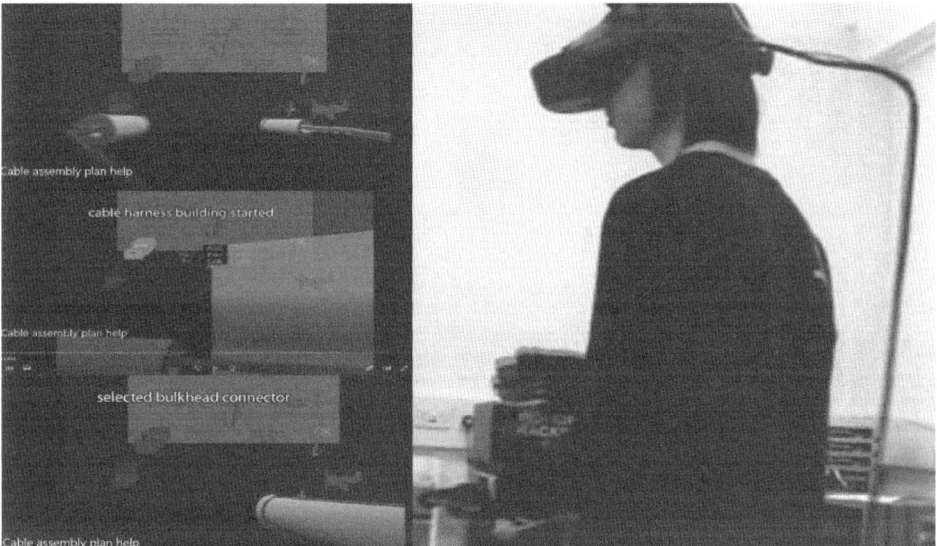

Fig. 6.1. COSTAR operation and interaction.

With a traditional 2D CAD user interface for manual routing, performing an assembly or disassembly is not as intuitive as in real-life and, via interface interrupts, the interface can also be disruptive to the user's creative process. Therefore, using the COSTAR system immersive 3D user interface, the planners experience was improved by allowing them to ergonomically mimic real-life assembly tasks.

This planning approach also set two other important precedents for both VR-based assembly/process planning with user logging. First, it was possible to map the virtual movements onto real world movements; therefore, real world assembly times could be applied or mapped onto these motions; showing that such an ergonomic VR interface enables the inference of real manufacturing times.

Secondly, it became apparent that the times taken to carry out the virtual moves to plan the assembly when totaled up gave the total planning time. This could be compared to other planning methods for similar assemblies or for other planning domain applications.

Bulkhead Connector Installation Plan

Op Num	W/ Centre	Assembly Instructions	Tooling	Assembly Time (s)
10	Cable Bench	Connect bulkhead connector CON01 (Type: plug Shell size: 1 Number of poles: 2) to bulkhead 3250 located at position (3250, -500, 3725) and Orientation (0, -0, 0.707107, 0.707107)	Hand Assembly	7.8
20	Cable Bench	Connect bulkhead connector CON04 (Type: plug Shell size: 1 Number of poles: 2) to bulkhead 2250 located at position (2250, -500, 325) and Orientation (-0, -1, -0, 4.37114e-08)	Hand Assembly	19.9
30	Cable Bench	Connect bulkhead connector CON05 (Type: plug Shell size: 2 Number of poles: 7) to bulkhead 1750 located at position (1750, -500, 325) and Orientation (-0, -1, -0, 4.37114e-08)	Hand Assembly	17.70
40	Cable Bench	Connect bulkhead connector CON10 (Type: plug Shell size: 2 Number of poles: 7) to bulkhead 2250 located at position (2250, -500, 2175) and Orientation (-0, -1, -0, 4.37114e-08)	Hand Assembly	29.6

Cable Harness Assembly Plan

Op Num	W/ Centre	Assembly Instructions	Tooling	Assembly Time (s)
10	Cable Bench	Connect cable CAB02(Type: CONTROLCY Number of Cores: 7 Core Cross-Section: 1 Colour (RGB): 225,125,0) to inline connector CON23 (Type: plug Shell size: 2 Number of poles 7)	Hand Assembly	10.3
20	Cable Bench	and inline connector CON24 (Type: socket Shell size: 2 Number of poles 7)	Hand Assembly	27.18
30	Cable Bench	Connect cable CAB01(Type: SINGLECORE Number of Cores: 1 Core Cross-Section: 4.8 Colour (RGB): 255,0,0) to inline connector CON22 (Type: plug Shell size: 1 Number of poles 2)	Hand Assembly	15.70
40	Cable Bench	and inline connector CON21 (Type: socket Shell size: 1 Number of poles 2)	Hand Assembly	14.24

Fig. 6.2. Cable harness plans (adapted from Ritchie et al.[19]).

Cable Harness Installation Plan

Op Num	W/ Centre	Assembly Instructions	Tooling	Assembly Time (s)
10	Assy Station	Connect inline connector CON21 (Type: socket Shell size: 1 Number of poles 2) to bulkhead connector CON01 (Type: plug Shell size: 1 Number of poles 2) located at position (3250,- 500,3725) and Orientation (0,-0,0.707107,0.707107)	Hand Assembly	7.17
20	Assy Station	Connect inline connector CON22 (Type: plug Shell size: 1 Number of poles 2) to bulkhead Connector CON04 (Type: socket Shell size: 1 Number of poles 2) located at position (2250,-500,325) and Orientation (-0,-1,-0,4.37114e-08)	Hand Assembly	6.75
30	Assy Station	Connect inline connector CON23 (Type: plug Shell size: 2 Number of poles 7) to bulkhead connector CON05 (Type: socket Shell size: 2 Number of poles 7) located at position (1750,-500,325) and Orientation (-0,-1,-0,4.37114e-08)	Hand Assembly	4.58
40	Assy Station	Connect inline connector CON24 (Type: socket Shell size: 2 Number of poles 7) to bulkhead connector CON10 (Type: plug Shell size: 2 Number of poles 7) located at position (-2250,-500,-2175) and Orientation (-0,-1,-0,4.37114e-08)	Hand Assembly	7.69

Fig. 6.2. (*Continued*).

These early 3D visualization assembly planning approaches proved the key principle that it was possible to use interactive VR-based systems to unobtrusively monitor and log assembly planners and generate plans from well-structured log files. As VR technology evolved, the success of this human-in-the-loop work then posed the question: "What benefits would there be in enhancing such systems by stimulating other human senses?" Therefore, the next stage of this work was to focus on the next technological advance in the VR domain: the use of haptics.

6.2.1 *Haptic Assembly, Machining, and Manufacturing System*

A haptic assembly, machining and manufacturing system (HAMMS) approach offers a more natural, free-from counter to virtual assembly systems that often rely on pre-defined assembly associations to automate the generation of assembly plans. Consequently, this obscures data relating to associated procedural and final operational assembly information. The loss of such precise details and fitting operations has implications downstream, for example, when robotic assembly instructions or manual instructions are required. The HAMMS application is coded in C++ and comprises three key modules as seen in the schematic of Fig. 6.3.

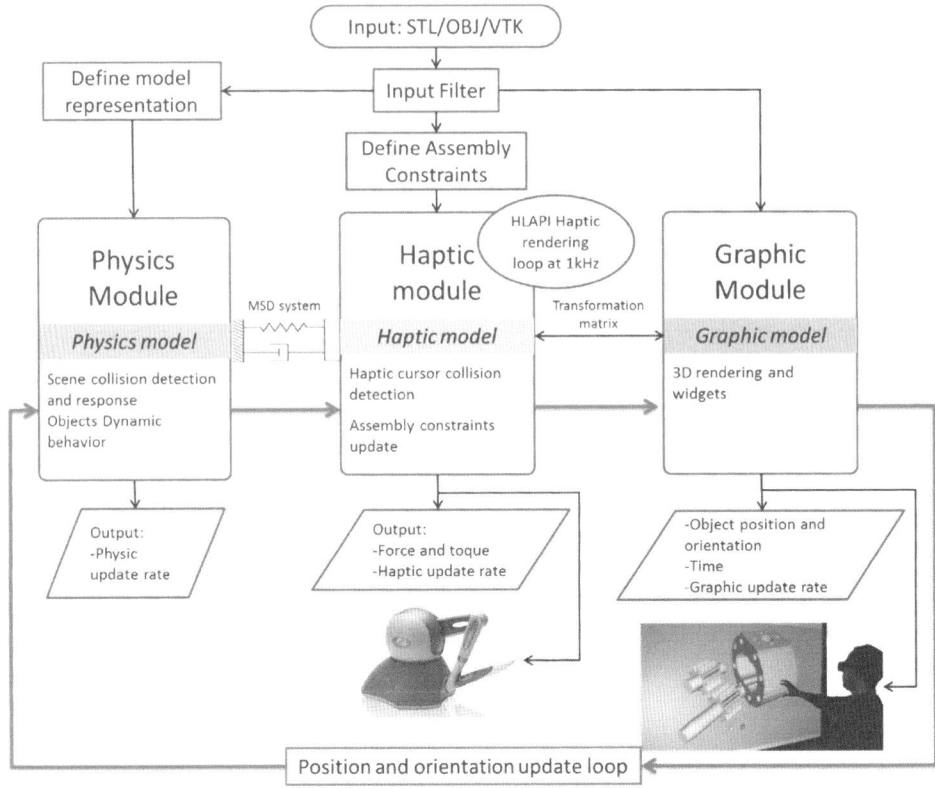

Fig. 6.3. HAMMS schematic.

Seth et al.[14] identified the two most common methodologies used in virtual assembly as constrained-based modeling and physics-based modeling. Constrained, based modelling uses defined positional or geometric constraints to place parts in their final position and orientation, typically integrated into auto alignment-proximity snapping assembly simulation. HAMMS introduces the use of dynamic assembly constraints to enhance the virtual assembly performance. It features automatic design for manufacturing and assembly (DFMA) analysis including manual definition of assembly constraints within the virtual assembly system, widgets to modify simulation parameters and evaluate its influence on simulation performance at run time; assembly data logging such as trajectories, forces and update rates for post-processing, further analysis or its presentation in the form of chronocyclegraphs to graphically analyze the assembly process. In HAMMS the physics engine implemented offers convex and concave capabilities which allow the user to feel more precise collisions when virtual objects are being manipulated (e.g. weight/gravity perception, fit tolerance, and friction).

To automate assembly procedures an understanding of the cognitive insight of the human operator is beneficial. A method is to track user-object interaction and plot this in a time-dependent manner describing motion together with position, orientation, and velocity. Therbligs are a set of symbols developed by Frank Gilbreth[20] during the early 20th century to study assembly motions, where each symbol represented the mental and physical processes involved during an assembly task. The 18 therblig units in Fig. 6. were implemented into HAMMS. As therbligs map onto each individual operation task associated with a process, it directly supports DFA analysis. For example, when numerous "delay" therbligs associated with a particular assembly operation is evident, that specific task will have to be improved or to rethink the product's design.

GROUP OF ACTIVITIES		NAME OF ACTIVITY	SYMBOL	COLOUR	
1.	EFFECTIVE OPERATION	USE	∪	PURPLE	
		ASSEMBLE	#	VIOLET	
		DISASSEMBLE	#	LIGHT VIOLET	
2.	MANUAL OR VISUAL IDENTIFICATION	SEARCH	⊂⊃	BLACK	
		FIND	⊂◯⊃	GREY	
		SELECT	→	LIGHT GREY	
		INSPECT	◯	BURNT OCHRE	
3.	CONTROL ACTIVITY	GRASP	∩	RED	
		RELEASE LOAD	⌐	CARMINE RED	
		HOLD	⌒	GOLD OCHRE	
4.	PRECISE MOVEMENTS	POSITION	9	BLUE	
		PRE-POSITION	ß	PALE BLUE	
5.	GENERAL MOVEMENT	TRANSPORT LOAD	⌣	GREEN	
		TRANSPORT EMPTY	⌣	OLIVE GREEN	
6.	DELAY	PLAN	ℙ	BROWN	
		RESET FOR OVERCOMING FATIGUE	ℛ	ORANGE	
		UNAVOIDABLE DELAY	⌢	YELLOW	
		AVOIDABLE DELAY	⌣o	LEMON YELLOW	

Fig. 6.4. Gilbreth's Therblig symbols.

Gilbreth also devised chronocyclegraphs for motion studies.[20] Using a light source mounted on the hands of a person performing an assembly task and long-exposure photography of the whole assembly process, revealed the trajectories that helped identify areas of inefficient movement by the user. By letting the light source flash at a known frequency, it also helped to determine the velocity and acceleration of the hand movements. There is much to be gained from Gilbreth's seminal work to study assembly processes and planning. However, there is no literature that shows that these have been applied in any VR and/or haptic engineering environment.

6.2.2 *Case Study*

To demonstrate the effectiveness of HAMMS, a group of 34 participants were tasked to carry out both physical and virtual assembly of a gear pump comprising five components (a housing, two bushes, a large cog and a small cog, see Fig. 6.5). The overall dimensions of the pump are 14.5 × 11 × 17 cm.

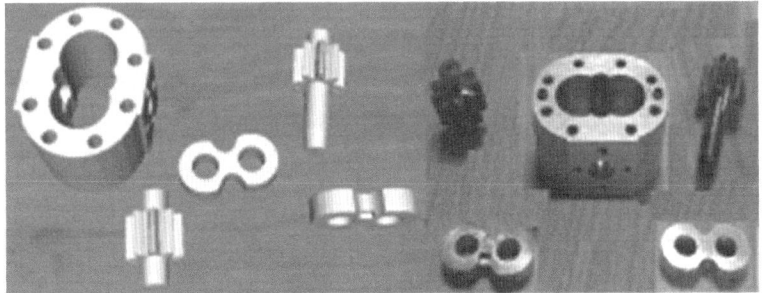

Fig. 6.5. Pump components, a) virtual and b) actual. Geometric dimensions and tolerances were faithfully replicated in the 3D models.

HAMMS is an unconstraint virtual assembly environment thus uploaded CAD models may not be well-ordered before the assembly. Additionally, HAMMS does not rely on proximity snapping, object-object co-alignment or other forms of programmatically assisted assembly functions. Instead HAMMS relies on the physical connotation that once a component is assembled, its geometry is constrained by the surroundings, as in the real world. As the rigid body comes to rest its dynamics are altered to "kinematic" forming the "joint" associated to the subassembly.

Eight levels of weight, measured in Newtons (N), are defined for each pump component, L1 to L8, where L1 is the minimum weight and L8 the maximum weight in the virtual scene. The virtual and real weights are presented in Fig. 6.6. These virtual weights were obtained by scaling the density of the virtual objects.

The maximum force supported by the Sensable Omni Device (3.3 N) was considered when assigning the weight level 8 to the heaviest manipulated object, the big cog. The housing is not considered because during the assembly process, real and virtual, it is the base part and remains static.

Level	Housing	Big Cog	Small cog	Bearings
L1	0.02	0.02	0.02	0.02
L2	1.3	0.17	0.13	0.1
L3	3.34	0.41	0.34	0.29
L4	>4	0.82	0.66	0.51
L5	>4	1.11	0.9	0.69
L6	>4	1.64	1.31	1.01
L7	>4	2.23	1.81	1.34
L8	>4	3.24	2.71	1.47
Real	16.7	6.7	5.2	1.6

Fig. 6.6. Levels and weights (N) of pump components.

Precise information of the assembly process is logged accordingly:

(1) Data related to the manipulated object position, orientation, trajectories, name, haptic interface point (HIP position) and time is logged.
(2) Data related with torque and force applied to manipulated objects is logged.
(3) Data related to the system performance such as haptic, physics, and graphics update rates.

Once the assembly is completed the logged data can be exported in *.TXT or *.CSV file formats.

Table 6.1 Graphic representation of user movements with respect to Therbligs.

Spheres		Modality
	Green	Wandering (search) mode, scene recognizing.
	Blue	Touching (inspect) mode, virtual object recognizing.
	Red	Controlling (grasp) mode, virtual object manipulation.
	Distance	Movement (transport) speed

Chronocyclegraphs of user movements are represented by colored spheres which represent the modality of the virtual assembly (Table 6.1) with the distance between spheres representing the speed of the movement (Fig. 6.7).

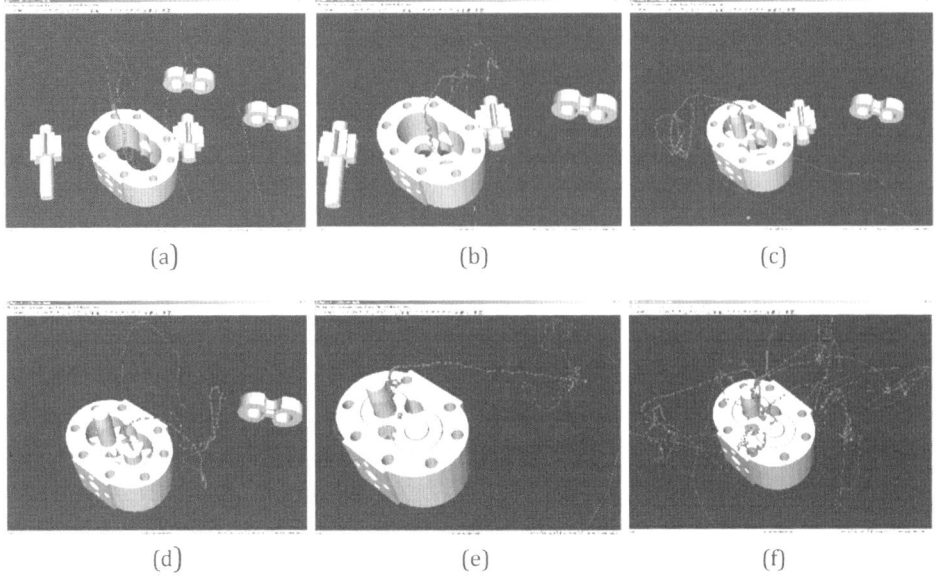

Fig. 6.7. Virtual assembly: (a) reposition housing (b) assemble bush (c) assemble large cog (d) assemble small cog (e) assemble bush (f) complete assembly chronocyclegraph.

The logged data from the virtual assembly is processed to extract and generate the assembly plan. Fig. 6.8 details the assembly of the small cog part. The results

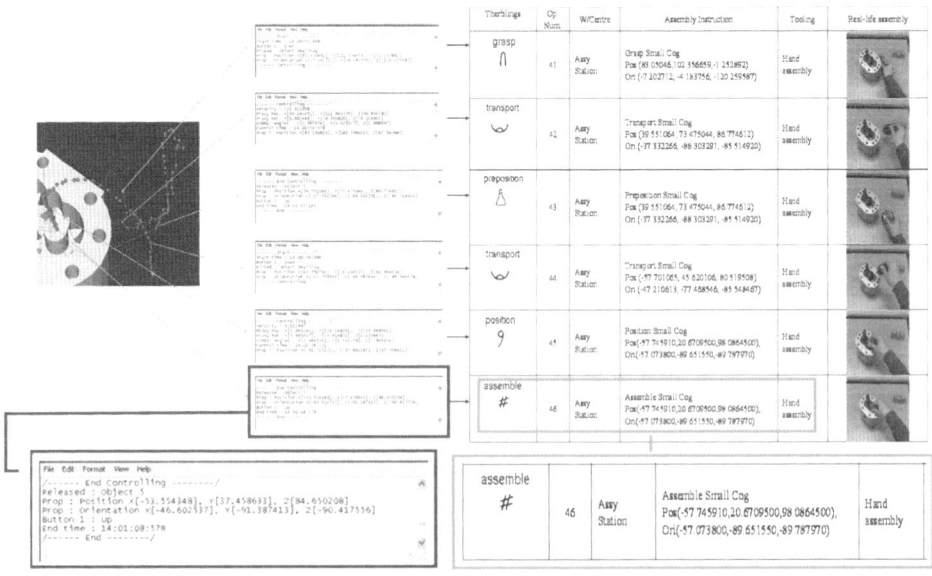

Fig. 6.8. Identification, extraction, and mapping of assembly operations from virtual assembly planner logging against manual assembly.

clearly show that both the chronocycle data and the logged file can be used to identify individual assembly tasks and motions performed by the user during the assembly. These assembly details can further be used to automatically generate assembly plans associated to physical operations. Figure 6.8 also shows the correlation between the virtual and physical assembly operations as extracted by the parser.

A general process plan generated from the logged data (Fig. 6.9) contains the assembly time obtained during the manual assembly process of the gear pump. Although the assembly times in real-world is faster, each operation timing is relatively well mapped in the virtual environment.

HAMMS TRIAL ASSEMBLY PLAN

Op. Num.	W Centre	Assembly Instruction	Tooling	Assembly Time Virtual (s)	Assembly Time Real (s)
10	Assy Station	Assemble Housing Pos(58.4883300,57.9209000,203.717230), Ori(-45.441740,-63.667560,-67.873010)	Hand assembly	6.961	3.0
20	Assy Station	Assemble Bushing Pos(-38.544190,22.1121600,42.7273800), Ori(55.8205900,-89.920540,89.9831100)	Hand assembly	14.672	12.0
30	Assy Station	Assemble Large Cog Pos(-45.852190,19.6320600,74.7069200), Ori(-24.664120,-86.972570,-89.210800)	Hand assembly	9.672	5.0
40	Assy Station	Assemble Small Cog Pos(-57.745910,20.6709500,98.0864500), Ori(-57.073800,-89.651550,-89.787970)	Hand assembly	12.719	6.0
50	Assy Station	Assemble Bushing Pos(43.4192370,75.5965990,157.523040), Ori(-55.059900,83.3759800,-95.860880)	Hand assembly	17.797	9.0

Fig. 6.9. Assembly plan automatically generated from the virtual assembly logged data.

Three techniques were used to quantify the performance of the HAMMS code: sampling, instrumentation, and manual timing using a high-resolution clock. Sampling and instrumentation performance tests were achieved using the profiler included in the Premium edition of the Visual Studio 2010 development environment. Figure 6.10 illustrates HAMMS haptic rendering performance while assembling a "figure eight" component of the pump.

The geometric precision of the model does effect the overall performance of HAMMS. The times measured for each call to the physics calculation function in Fig. 6.10(a) – when the "Fig. 6.8" component is dropped in – indicate that until measurement number 2770 the pieces are far enough apart to avoid the narrow phase collision detection. Therefore, no call to the physics calculation takes longer than 16.7ms (the target rate for the physics calculation is 60Hz), although 65% of physics engine calls do take longer than 1ms with the average time-per-call being

2.7ms. From measurement number 2770, the two pieces are close enough to cause substantial work in the narrow phase collision detection within the physics library, causing 72% of calls to the physics calculation to take longer than 1/60th of a second and all of them now taking longer than 1ms with the average time-per-call being 21ms.

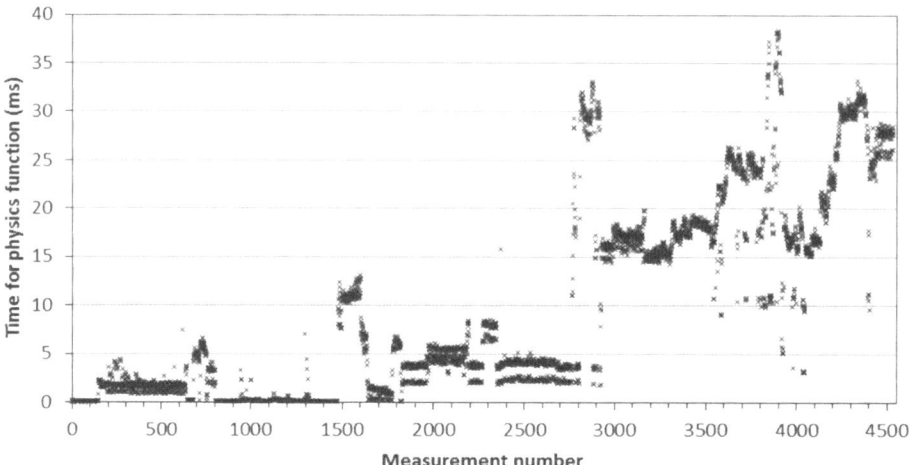

(a) Time per call to the physics calculation function for the scenario where the "figure eight" piece is *dropped* into the housing piece.

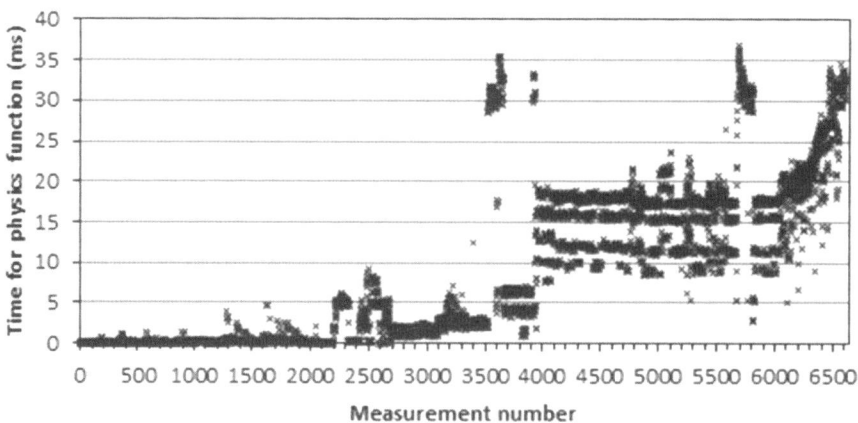

(b) Time per call to the physics calculation function for the scenario where the "figure eight" piece is *pushed* into the housing piece.

Fig. 6.10. Time per call to the physics calculation function for "figure eight" piece manipulation and assembly.

Similarly in Fig. 6.10(b), when the "Fig. 6.8" component is pushed in, up until measurement number 3520, the pieces are far apart enough to avoid the narrow phase collision detection and no call to the physics calculation takes longer than one 60th of a second, although 34% take longer than 1ms with the average time-per-call being 1.1ms. From measurement number 3520, the two pieces are close enough together to cause substantial work in the narrow phase collision detection within the physics library, causing 56% of physics calculation calls to take longer than a 1/60th second and 100% to take longer than 1ms with the average time per call being 17ms.

The target frequency for the haptic device component is 1000Hz. To achieve this rate requires that every call to the physics component must take less than 1ms, given that some time must remain for the haptics and graphics operations in the loop. This requirement is never met when narrow phase collision detection is active. Even if the component updates were decoupled, the target frequency for the physics component is 60Hz, which requires that calls to the physics function take no longer than 17ms. Even this less stringent requirement is not met for the majority of calls where narrow phase is active.

The timing of the physics engine showed that even for the relatively small systems investigated, it is close to the performance limits of a single CPU, and parallelism within components is required. To overcome these issues, a more flexible architecture is needed to endure that the three key components – haptics, graphics, and physics – run concurrently, for example using multiple threads. This would also trivially allow applications to take advantage of multi-core CPUs available in modern computer systems for increased performance in human-haptic interactions.

Despite the physics engine being a performance bottleneck, all the previous planning examples set a number of precedents with regard to manufacturing planning methods which, as the research evolved, demonstrated the potential for VR-based human-in-the-loop CAAP to be both practical and applicable to generic assembly solutions for products. Such an approach would be considerably beneficial for engineers and manufacturers if integrated into current CAD/CAM and CAE package offerings.

However, inspired by the previous work, another important aspect of product development and manufacturing was identified that could combine assembly planning and a novel haptic VR machining planning paradigm. This investigated if haptic VR could be used for human-in-the-loop component machining process planning by incorporating both work centre set-up (using VR-based CAAP) and virtual material removal.

6.3   VR Process Planning (Machining and Jigs and Fixtures)

Process planning is the phase in the product development process that takes place between design and actual product manufacture. It is the point at which all decisions are made regarding how a product will be produced, critical decisions made which can have a significant impact on cost and quality.[21,22]

When looking at manufacturing applications within computer aided engineering (CAE) systems and the traditional product engineering functions carried out, it is interesting to note that one of the most neglected areas is holistic process planning for material removal processes. There is a distinct lack of integrated computer aided process planning (CAPP) systems that incorporate all of the tools required to support and simulate the creation of a product's planning sequence from its raw material state to its production to the finished drawing or model state.

Although many proprietary computer aided design/computer aided manufacturing (CAD/CAM) systems include some kind of component planning capability this usually takes the form of computer numerical control (CNC) sequencing and part programming. Within such systems, significant gaps exist in their application across the whole process planning cycle, such as setting up/tear down, manufacturing time analysis, upstream and downstream non-CNC operation incorporation/simulation, etc.

To help address some of these issues Computer Aided Process Planning (CAPP)[23] systems have been developed, although these tend not to be integrated into CAD/CAM systems. Such approaches used within this field generally tend to be either generative or variant.[13] However, these tend to be interactive text-based systems separated from any model simulation and interaction. They are not necessarily intuitive because they do not involve the planner in a human-in-the-loop experience, which can enhance and support natural process planning cognition. Specific gaps in this area of process planning may include some or all of the following: the lack of setting up/tear down analysis, full operation manufacturing time analysis, CNC operation programming (for variant systems), the need for plan "finishing" (for generative systems), full sequence simulation, etc.

Because of these gaps and the inherent inflexibility and lack of integration in current CAPP systems, manual process planning is very much still traditionally used. Experienced process planners carry this out by developing full production process plans based on their personal experience of production processes, tooling, and manufacturing systems. Although manual process planning addresses many of the information requirements and operational gaps associated with current

CAD/CAM and CAPP, it is clerically time consuming, inconsistent with regard to methods optimization, is much slower and invariably does not allow a proper visual evaluation of the full sequence before a product hits the shop floor.

Recent studies have found that in large manufacturing organizations a mix of CAPP systems is used, often requiring expert process planner intervention, even if the systems under consideration are described as generative[24]; however, small to medium size enterprises (SMEs) still very much depend on traditional manual methods.[25]

In order to address these shortfalls in CAE, CAPP systems, VR potentially provides an opportunity to develop an integrated CAE approach to process planning which would address many of the current shortfalls as well as perhaps providing other advantages. Supporting the interactive simulation of a component's production, generating downstream process plans and time estimates and capturing tacit planning intent and making it explicit could provide a paradigm shift in the technology support of CAPP and the capture of expert planning knowledge.

VR is previously demonstrated in this chapter and elsewhere as an ideal human-in-the-loop planning tool for assembly[26,27] with many of the lessons from this domain being applicable to virtual machining. This includes using an algorithm to infer a planning sequence from chronological, time-phased logged data.

For the virtual machining environment outlined in this chapter, each planning simulation provides a clearer understanding of a component's manufacturing requirements through properly scaled and visual feedback. It also covers the whole range of planning requirements from set up through to machining and tear down. The application of haptics is particularly relevant to material removal as there a need to accurately pick up and manipulate the virtual materials and tools and a need to differentiate different machining methods for different processes and materials depending on the relevant machining parameters,[28] Such interfaces could stimulate the planner's intuitive sense of understanding by providing a higher degree of interaction when experienced in conjunction with vision, providing a more convincing – but not necessarily very realistic – interactive virtual experience.[29] This is facilitated by haptic rendering algorithms[30,31] that generate forces within the haptic device allowing the operator to feel vibrations or collisions between complex objects, e.g. cutters and materials during machining operations.

Of course, carrying out such a planning function interactively does require a familiarity with the associated materials, processes, and cutting methods. However, the intuitive VR interface provides a novel means for generating process planning sequences by monitoring the user in real time and inferring operations and associated planning sequences by analyzing — in real time or post activity —

the user's interactions with the virtual environment and any associated objects, whether they be components, fixtures, or cutting tools. This is demonstrated later in this chapter via a case study given in 6.3.2.

Current haptic VR "machining" research tends to be focused on training for very specific and limited processes. In the case of generic process planning, there is a need for an approach where multiple operation machining can be defined from which process plans are automatically generated. Within virtual machining, haptics provide a more user-friendly interface when interacting with 3D graphics whilst capturing human programming expertise specifically relevant to a 5-axis milling machine tool path.[32] A haptic device to emulate milling was developed[33] using a haptic sculpted model output as an STL file used to develop and generate a tool path for carving an object.[34,35] Haptic VR has also been applied to fixture planning a work holding requirement of a process planning system[36] but was not integrated with any form of material removal operation.

However, no haptic or non-haptic VR process planning system was apparent in the literature permitting: (i) the integration of the whole process planning activity including set up, machining, and tear down; (ii) the output of a time-estimated process planning document and sequence; (iii) user evaluation of the system's operation with user feedback; and (iv) validation of the plans by machining them in a real-world manufacturing environment.

6.3.1 *Haptic Aided Process Planning*

The VR-based system developed and tested for multi-operation material removal process planning is HAPP (Haptic Aided Process Planning). Fig. 6.11 illustrates the virtual machining environment showing a work surface, selection of cutting tools, a vice, and an inspection probe.

A combined VR/haptic interface was preferred since it provided a potential technological solution that would be intuitive; naturally interactive with a user-friendly interface requiring minimal menu interrupts to support continuous cognition as well as the ability to generate formalized downstream planning information and knowledge from the user's tacit input.

The hardware comprises a standard desktop PC, shutter glasses and 3D Systems Phantom Omni with 6DoF input and 3DoF feedback. All process planning systems software is developed in C++ using OpenSceneGraph (OSG)[37], osgModelling,[38] ODE physics engine,[39] and Openhaptics.[40] Further details re also vailable on the system set up and associated experimentation.[41]

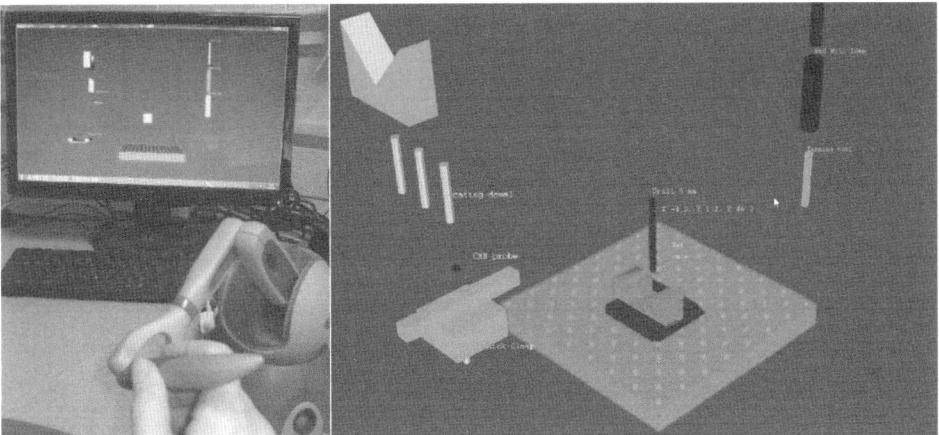

Fig. 6.11. HAPP system and interface [from Fletcher[41]].

It is necessary for a process planning system to integrate all of the manual process planning functionalities as well as generate the plan itself.[21,22] HAPP addresses this by providing a new technology paradigm shift in the field of CAPP.

Within the system, the planner can set up and clamp a billet, set up the tooling, an inspection probe and operation tear down for a combination of milling, drilling, and/or turning. Set up times are generated by mapping the haptic movement of objects and fixtures onto work study empirical data whereas machining times are calculated using standard formulae.[22] Component machining visualization and feature datum and machining choice is aided by presenting the finished component model embedded in a translucent virtual billet with the machining parameters fixed according to the material type.

While logging in real time all user interactions and VR environment changes are temporally gathered and stored in a time-stamped log file for processing (Table 6.2).

Table 6.2 Sample HAPP log file [from Fletcher[41]]

Time(s)	Tool	Tool State	L_Force(x)	L_Force(y)	L_Force(z)	L_Position(x)	L_Position(y)	L_Position(z)
39	5mm drill	OFF	0.1181	0.4909	0.07674	12.51	-20.04	0.003492
39	5mm drill	OFF	0.1181	0.4909	0.07673	12.51	-20.04	0.003492
39	Stop Manipulation							
0	Start Manipulation							
0	5mm drill	ON	0	0.04129	0	12.51	-20.04	0.003492
0	5mm drill	ON	-5.76E-05	-0.2853	0.008751	12.51	-20.04	7.503
0	5mm drill	ON	-4.76E-08	0.1367	0.09855	12.51	-20.04	7.503
0	5mm drill	ON	1.39E-05	0.2561	0.09644	12.51	-20.04	7.503
0	5mm drill	ON	2.77E-05	0.5972	0.09434	12.51	-20.04	7.503
0	5mm drill	ON	0.000184	0.898	0.07059	12.51	-20.04	7.503

As in the previous assembly planning examples, when planning is completed the log file of the user's interactions within the virtual machining environment is parsed into a range of process planning outputs (see case study in 1.3.2). These include: (i) a Route Sheet, (ii) an Operation Sheet with feeds and speeds along with machining times, (iii) a Tool List, and (iv) a manufacturing Cost Sheet.

Operationally, within HAPP all objects can be classed as either "manipulated" or "static"; however, in addition to these cutting tools are classed as "machining". Therefore, within the machining virtual environment the physics modelling contextualizes individual object interactions as well as their dynamic/static conditions. During logging and associated object identification, e.g. a tool or a material, once a cutting tool is grasped collisions are switched off, object penetration switched on and the haptic device commanded to generate vibrations associated with material cutting. At the same time, temporal recording of the Phantom using Openhaptic libraries supports the capture of its position, velocity and rotation, and embeds them within the log file. One key aspect of a typical CAD/CAM package approach adopted within HAPP was that any milling and turning operations were haptically "machined" using a routing methodology whereby the cutting tool moves rather than the machine table, i.e. the user, via the haptic device, holds and moves the tool to simulate the cutting action. If required, any cutting tool can be set orthogonally and zeroed as required against any component or material surfaces or features as a datum or as starting and finishing points for cutting operations.

However, there is an important and novel output from the operation of HAPP building on the planning work described for virtual assembly systems. Embedded within the log file is a representation of the planner's tacit manufacturing intent or knowledge. By parsing these data, not only can it produce a process plan but also the plan itself represents the planner's explicit knowledge associated with the component's manufacture; potentially from this, ontologies could be automatically produced. Therefore, as well as generating the final instructions, tool lists, operation instructions, set up sheets and operation set up and machining times, HAPP is the first interactive CAPP system that can dynamically capture, from a user, material removal planning know-how.

6.3.2 *Case Study*

In order to validate the effectiveness of the system a number of previously designed components were process planned by a range of subjects using the system.[41] In addition to this extensive analysis, feedback was obtained via questionnaires and interviews to evaluate the effectiveness operationally and as a process planning tool. A comparison was made with the currently most commonly used means of material removal process planning methodology used in industry, manual process planning.

By way of a case study the HAPP outputs for the component in Fig. 6.12 are outlined along with a brief summary of some of the general user feedback on the system's effectiveness and a process planning tool. This mild steel component has a range of features including slots, steps, and holes as well as a requirement for the production of datum surfaces. The full component set up and interaction is also shown in Fig. 6.11. Within the interaction via the haptic device, the planner picked up and manipulated the tools in the order required to manufacture the part by cutting the virtual material. The planner being guided by the finished component model geometry embedded within a translucent raw material; subsequently using the routing approach to remove the material after positioning the tools, for finish cuts, against the relevant component model features. Various operation stages and sub-stages could be deleted and amended as required as the production sequence is defined. One specific rule was that any change in the component set up detected would imply a new operation, even if it is on the same machine.

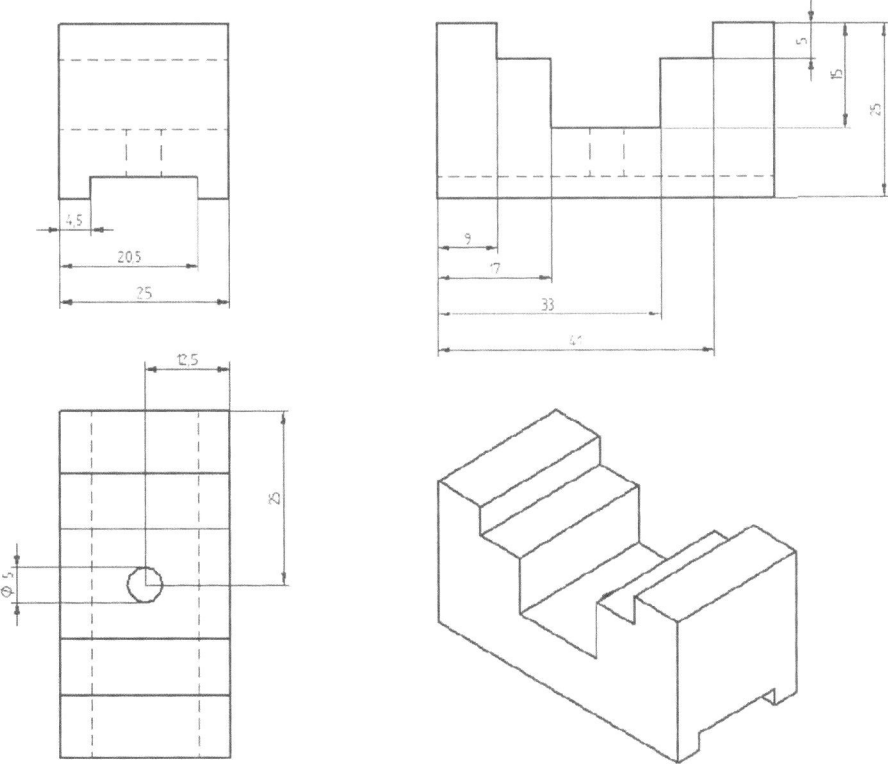

Fig. 6.12. Case study component [from Fletcher[41]].

Once the sequence was finalized and the planner satisfied with the simulation of the setup, machining, and tear down for each operation, key manufacturing information was generated automatically by inferring the production sequence from the system log file as well as other production information. The outputs obtained at this stage for the case study part are shown in Fig. 6.13 with the full range of components machined given in Fig. 6.1.

To evaluate HAPP from a user's perspective a SUS questionnaire[42] helped determine their impressions of the system and its operation. The score is rated from 0 to 100 with 100 being the best usability level and 0 being the worst (Table 6.3); these results along with further extensive experimental outputs are also detailed.[41]

Extensive feedback was obtained from the system trials.

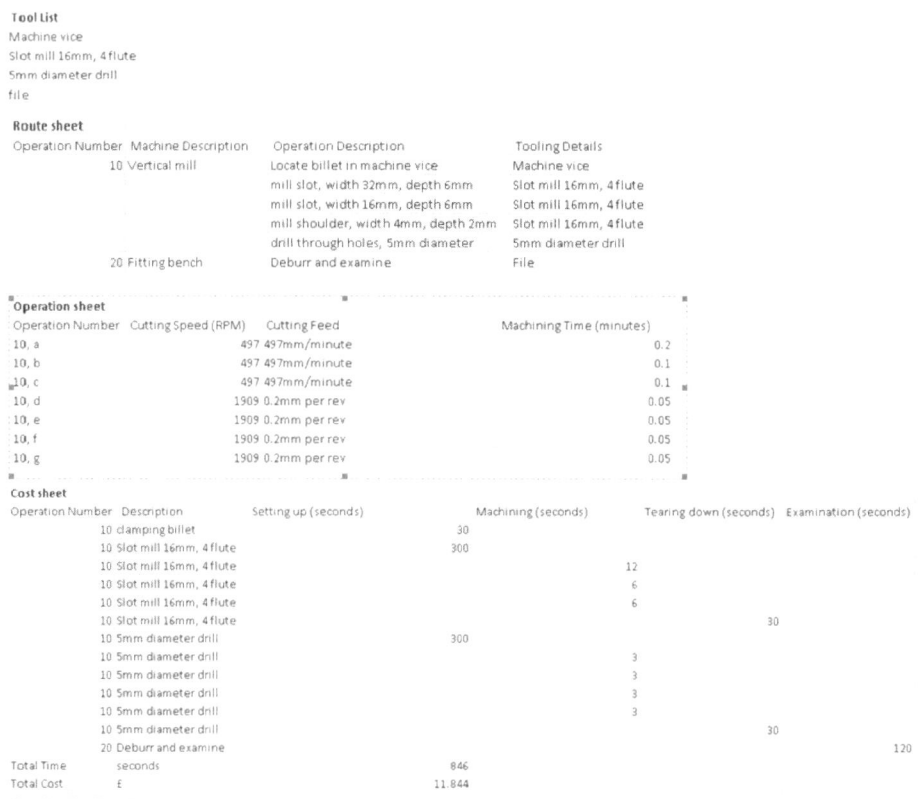

Fig. 6.13. HAPP outputs (Tool list, Route Sheet, Operation Sheet and Cost Sheet) [from Fletcher[41]].

Table 6.3 SUS process planning system comparison results [from Fletcher[41]].

User Group	Sample size	SUS score (mean)	
		Traditional process planning approach	HAPP
All	16	43	70
Expert planners	6	64	57
Novice planners	8	35	78
High level of computer gaming experience	7	41	73
Low level of computer gaming experience	9	44	67

Table 6.4 SUS process planning system learnability results [from Fletcher[41]].

User Group	Sample size	SUS score (mean)	
		Traditional PP approach	HAPP
All	16	46	67
Expert planners	6	60	56
Novice planners	8	30	75
High level of computer gaming experience	7	38	71
Low level of computer gaming experience	9	53	64

The users would have preferred to use HAPP more frequently than their current systems, it was less complex and the functions better integrated. The operators also felt HAPP would be quicker to learn (Table 6.4) and less cumbersome to use as evidenced by the experimentation.

They were also more confident in its operation and felt more immersed in the environment as well as feeling that their mental workload reduced using HAPP.

The quality of the plans generated using HAPP was compared against traditional process plans. In general, the HAPP process plans were found to be of a much higher quality, more standardized and judged as being consistent and accurate in providing enough information to carry out full component production. All the process plans generated were validated by giving them to an experienced machine operator with the drawings;[41] note that the operator did not know from where the plans came. In all cases the parts were successfully machined (Fig. 6.1).

Fig. 6.14. HAPP system process plan validation [from Fletcher[41]]. Note the operator using a generated plan for validation purposes.

In addition to machining, the general skilled operator feedback on the quality of the plans was very positive, he was able to follow the instructions given and stated that they were comprehensive and accurate enough to be easily understood when accompanied with the part drawing.

This study demonstrated the potential for haptic VR to support machining process planning by providing a tool that interactively allows planners to virtually machine and visualize component machining for a combination of traditional material removal operations. This includes full set up and tear down, machining time estimation, material processing and automated process planning generation; the latter using the time-phased capability of user logging within VR to capture all of the relevant data for post processing.

Through VR, this novel approach extends CAPP into a more multi-functional and integrated environment addressing the significant gaps identified in current systems and the literature. In addition, the capture of expert knowledge provides the potential to generate data, which can inform the automation of some or all of a machining sequence as well as other potential applications within the CAD/CAM field, such as automatic CNC part program generation after virtual simulation. HAPP was validated via rigorous user and follow-up real world machining trials; also providing a novel formalized methodology for the evaluation of future CAPP systems of all kinds.

This and previous virtual assembly work showed VR's potential as a tool in product design for the evaluation of DFMA (Design for Manufacture and Assembly); this is focus of the next section in this chapter.

6.4 Sketch based Haptic DFMA

Design for manufacture and assembly (DFMA),[43] a subset of concurrent engineering, could be significantly enhanced through VR and haptics. The sketch-based haptic design for assembly (DFA) methodology introduced herein enriches and expands future human-in-the-loop DFMA capability.

An analysis of the literature[44-52] suggests that a front-end sketch based DFMA applications should comprise the following within an integrated system:

- Sketch based model creation and editing capabilities.
- Haptic feedback.
- 3D input space.
- Real-time design for assembly analysis.
- Real-time design for manufacture analysis.
- Design improvement suggestions and real-time feedback.

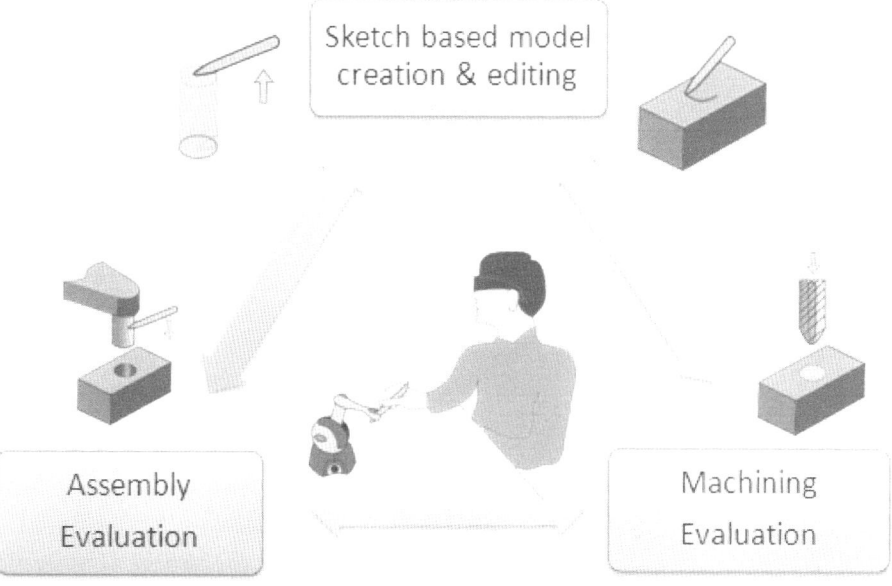

Fig. 6.15 A framework for haptic sketch based DFMA.

To our knowledge, none of the sketching systems investigated support any of the last three functionality criteria even though they are central to DFMA. The seamless real time aspect of such an approach is important in minimizing both user interrupts and distractions as well as overall design lead times. This approach provides an opportunity to establish a novel means of creating and testing an integrated real-time human-in-the-loop DFMA system based on haptic VR including haptic sketching (Fig. 6.15) and DFMA analysis with real-time feedback.

The planned virtual DFMA approach comprises three integrated modules:

I.   Sketch based model creation and editing module:
- Haptic enabled sketching for modelling operations
- Quickly edit features in response to information gathered from other modules

II.   Assembly Evaluation module:
- Haptic enabled interactive model assembly in the virtual space
- Assembly plan generation with features from modelling module
- Use DFA metrics to inform the user (in the form of suggestions to improve the design e.g. consider combining these parts)
- Store history of part assembly for future reference in case of geometry being modified in ways that would prevent assembly (both in the final assembly and in the assembly process)

III.   Machining evaluation module (will also share some functions with modelling):
- Allows the user to use machine tools to create the model from raw material
- Provide DFM metrics and feedback to the user
- Creates a process plan using features in the modelling module

Table 6.5 DFMA Criteria[43] and final output generated by each module.

Module	DFMA Criteria	Final Output
Modeler	Volume Bounding box Mass Axis and types of symmetry Tangling potential Potential for jams & hang-ups Ease of insertion	Models of parts
Assembly	Order of assembly Assembly reorientations Ease of assembly Time for each operation Cost of assembly	Assembly plan
Machining	Number of operations Time to machine Ease of machining Cost of machining	Process plan

The use of a sketch-based interface for modelling provides several advantages over more traditional WIMP-based CAD modelling interfaces. They are more intuitive to use, take less time to learn, allow for faster modelling times and do not distract the user's attention with menus.

Within this DFMA system, sketch-based modelling module allows the user to create or import geometry via the sketching and extrusion of profiles. Once completed a DFMA criteria (Table 6.5) is automatically generated. The user can edit within the module during initial geometry creation and after subsequent DFMA analysis. The final output being the parts' and subassemblies' geometry comprising the final model assembly. This approach is analogous to the FEA (finite element analysis) informed design tool mentioned by Masry and Lipson[53] where FEA details are available to the designer as they alter their model using a sketch-based interface.

The assembly module presents the user with all of the parts in the model and allows the user to fit them together using proximity snapping and haptics to form the final assembly. While the user is completing this task the system logs the data needed to create the assembly plan in addition to capturing relevant factors necessary to perform the Boothroyd and Dewhurst DFA (design for assembly) analysis[43] such as the number of times the assembly needs to be re-oriented and the potential for certain parts to be combined. The DFA criteria are defined in Table 6.5.

The machining module presents the user with a billet of raw material in a manner similar to the haptic process planning system outlined in 6.3.1 with the final model embedded in within it along with a range of work holding options and tools for machining. The user can test and compare different work holding setups and cutting methods to find and determine the optimum machining set up. They can also test and compare different machining sequences with the system automatically capturing information needed for the DFM (design for machining) analysis and, once complete, process planning. The DFM criteria are defined in Table 6.5.

The inclusion of the machining module in this way integrates the full VR-based DFMA capability within the system.

6.4.1 *Sketch based Haptic DFA Analysis*

The haptic-sketching system is implemented with UNITY. While useful for gaming, its underlying physics engine is not sufficient for handling shape concavity which is commonly represented within real-world mechanical parts; for this reason, the convexFT technique[54] was applied.

Upon uploading an assembly or parts, the system automatically gathers their key features, computes assembly operations and machining processes ready for performing DFMA analysis. The DFMA values are computed based on the criteria in Table 6.5. All of the parts contained within the assembly can be viewed alongside the number of each part required and whether this part has been identified as a candidate for merging or deletion. An example part and an interface is shown in Fig. 6.16. The center panel contains the modelling environment where the user can create, alter, and merge parts using sketch-based modelling techniques. As the user receives feedback, they are free to make changes to the design and, as they do this, the parameters are automatically updated and feedback provided to the engineer which allows them to immediately assess the impact of their design changes.

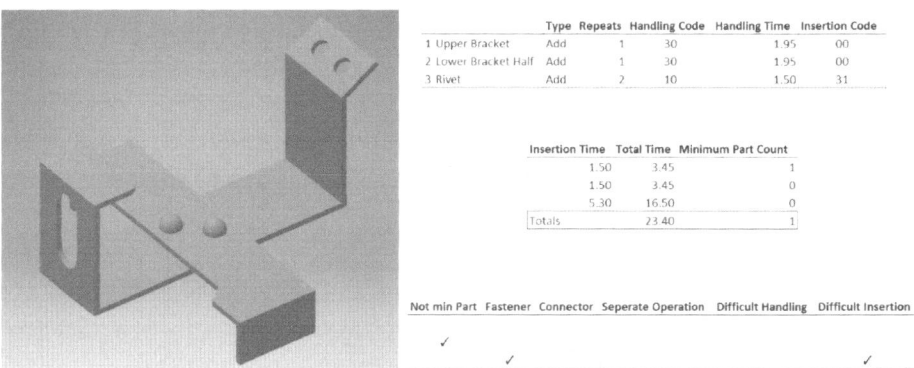

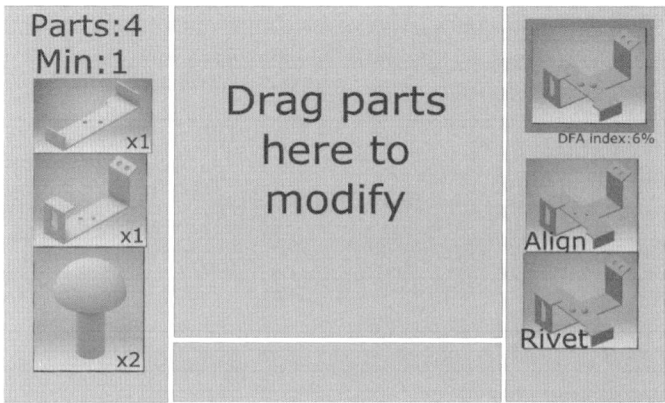

Fig. 6.16 Example of a design analysis and auto-generated assembly parameter values based on the DFA criteria. A part modification user interface allows any alterations to be made.

As the parts are modified, the DFA algorithm gathers changes in both the geometry of the individual parts and the way in which the user assembles the parts. Using this information, the DFA operators compute the time taken for each operation. Additionally, parts to be combined are identified and the theoretical minimum part count calculated. Suggestions for design improvement to the part depicted in Fig. 6.16 are:

- Lower Bracket does not meet criteria for minimum parts:
  - Consider combining it with Upper Bracket.

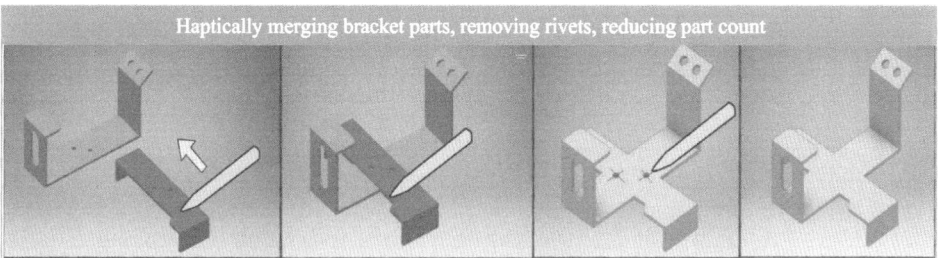

	Type	Repeats	Handling Code	Handling Time	Insertion Code
1 Merged Bracket	Add	1	30	1.95	00

	Insertion Time	Total Time	Minimum Part Count
	1.50	3.45	1
Totals		3.45	1

Not min Part Fastener Connector Seperate Operation Difficult Handling Difficult Insertion

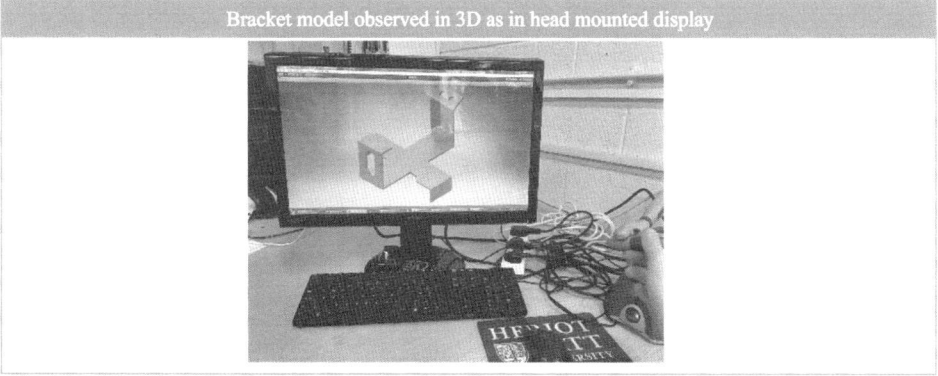

Fig. 6.17 Sheet metal bracket model undergoing part modification through haptic sketching process. Part modification and optimization via DFMA analysis. Merging process to erase rivets. DFA values computed and displayed to user.

- Rivet does not meet criteria for minimum parts as its primary function is to connect other parts.
  - ○ Consider merging other parts to eliminate need for Rivet.
- Rivet is difficult to fix to the assembly:
  - ○ Consider adding self-locating features.
  - ○ Consider redesign to eliminate the need for tools.

Fig. 6.17 shows the haptic sketch DFA system to finalize the bracket assembly. The parameters associated with any merged or deleted parts are updated and the DFMA metrics revaluated and displayed with respect to the design change. Timings for each operation are reported back to the engineer and any parts with potential to be merged highlighted. The real-time visualization and DFMA feedback enable the process of engineering and optimizing design to be more easily understood and appreciated.

6.4.2 *Case Study*

A controller assembly[43] comprising 16 parts and 21 assembly operations was used for this case study. Fig. 6.18 shows the assembly tree and time line of the original assembly. The bill of materials (BOM) table is derived from part information from the model and the DFA algorithm computes a *Functional Score* for each component's assembly. These results are comparable to the ones obtained using manual DFA analysis.

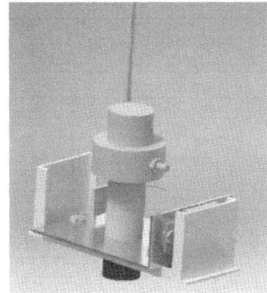
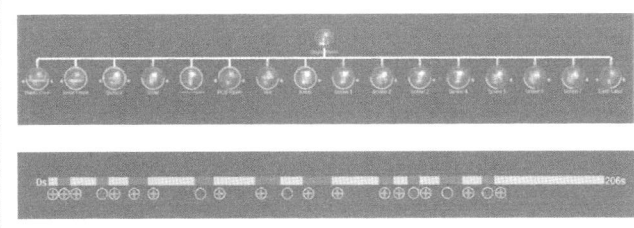

	Handling Code	Insertion code	Function Score	Total Assembly Time (mins)
Pressure Regulator	30	00	1	3.45
Metal Frame	30	02	1	4.55
Nut	00	31	0	9.33
Reorient	-	61	-	4.50
Sensor	30	03	1	7.15
Strap	20	03	0	7.00
Screw x2	11	31	0	17.10
Apply Tape	-	62	-	7.00
Adapter Nut	10	51	0	15.10
Tube Assembly	42	10	0	9.30
Screw Fasten	-	60	-	8.10
PCB Assembly	42	03	1	10.80
Screw x2	11	31	0	17.10
Connector	30	05	0	5.25
Earth Lead	42	05	0	8.90
Reorient	-	61	-	4.50
Knob	30	03	1	7.15
Screw Fasten	-	60	-	8.10
Plastic Cover	30	03	0	7.15
Reorient	-	61	-	4.50
Screw x3	11	51	0	40.4

Fig. 6.18 The controller assembly, its assembly tree, and time line to assembly. The accompanying BOM lists the results of the DFA algorithm's analysis.

Eleven part modifications were recommended by the DFA analysis algorithm pertaining to the functionality of the assembly parts. These include merging of the metal frame with the plastic cover (Fig. 6.19), eliminating the strap holding the sensor onto the frame, removing the tube connecting the sensor to the pressure regulator, an alternative way of attaching the PCB to the frame/cover, removing the earth lead, knob nut, and all the screws.

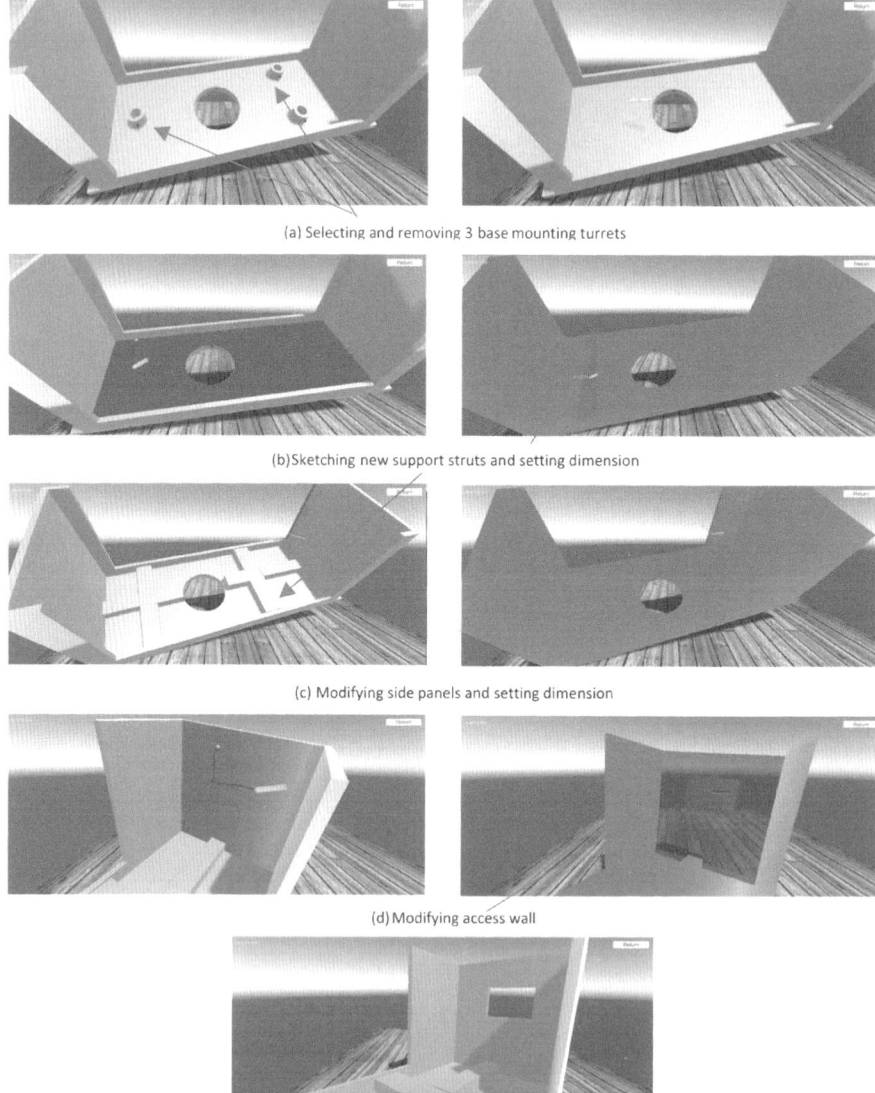

(a) Selecting and removing 3 base mounting turrets

(b) Sketching new support struts and setting dimension

(c) Modifying side panels and setting dimension

(d) Modifying access wall

(e) Redesigned cover

Fig. 6.19 Part redesign as recommended by the DFA analysis.

The resulting design changes to the cover in Fig. 6.2 follows the DFA advice. The original design had a DFA index of 7% and took 206 seconds to assemble while the final design has a DFA index of 19% and took only 78 seconds to assemble.

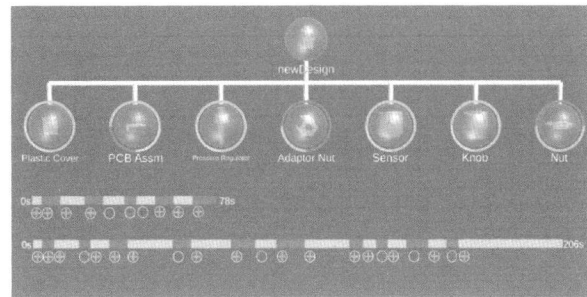

	Handling Code	Insertion code	Function Score	Total Assembly Time (mins)
Pressure Regulator	30	00	1	3.45
Plastic Cover	30	03	1	7.15
Nut	00	31	0	9.33
Knob	30	03	1	7.15
Screw fastening	-	60	-	8.10
Reorientation	-	61	-	4.50
Apply tape	-	62	-	7.00
Adapter nut	10	51	0	15.10
Sensor	30	31	1	7.25
PCB Assembly	42	05	1	8.90

Fig. 6.20 Overview of analysis for controller assembly redesign. The timeline shows the comparison between the optimized designs against the original.

The controller case study was a baseline to validate that a sketch-based haptic DFMA system was both intuitive and could conduct robust DFMA analysis. The controller assembly included flexible parts and cables modelled as solid inflexible parts. Though simplified for haptic rendering it still provided sufficient information to correctly assign DFA codes to the parts. The results were similar to those calculated in Boothroyd et al.[43] using manual methods, validating the accuracy of the DFA analysis of the system. The ease of modelling within the system demonstrates that the sketch-based modelling environment is a viable way of carrying out design modifications for the purpose of DFMA analysis.

6.5 Cyber-physical Mixed Reality Planning

Building on the previously described DFMA and planning work further studies in these domains were carried out in the context of digital construction using virtual reality and augmented reality (AR). There is a close similarity between the construction industry and manufacturing with regards to use of computer integrated environments (CIE).[55, 56] CIE is central to a Digital Construction strategy aimed at streamlining building design and project processes. Besides modernizing for efficiency it is also to address skills shortage in UK construction sector,[57,58] which stem from inadequate vocational training through to the volatile nature of construction work. What is clear is that the UK government has recognized this and recently put in place a £64m investment for digital and construction training to support people to re-skill.[59] Despite the increasing interest by academics and practitioners in CIE for construction, evidence suggests its leverage into integrating construction vocational training is comparatively less than industrial manufacturing.[60-63]

The role of VR presented here is to modernize vocational education and training (VET), in particular specialist trades such as stonemasonry and for on site assessment and training (OSAT). Modern stonemasonry often requires operating hand and power tools, as such this vocation is exposed to potentially fatal accidents throughout the course of using the tool. One tool in particular is the portable power grinder.[64]

The work focuses on engineering cyber-physical mixed reality environments to create more meaningful and authentic/purposeful experience while addressing the all too flimsy worlds between education and work.[60] It is also to address vocational qualifications through a CIE for construction such as the heritage sector, and the past lack of training opportunities.[65]

6.5.1 *Cyber-Physical Systems (CPS) and Game Technology*

Cyber-physical systems (CPS) network physical and computational components enabling feedback loops of physical processes to affect computations and vice versa. In manufacturing, this offers flexible production arrangements according to affordances or constraints within a production system without the need for direct intervention by workers. From a VET and workplace training perspective such a platform allows more authentic, realistic training and process/operations planning, and configurable for intra-operative guidance as required.

Research in creating VR and AR systems to address construction safety is increasing.[66] However, studies have also indicated many construction firms have yet to fully exploit the potential of VR/AR. The findings indicate system level integration and interestingly, perception, are of the main obstacles.[66-68]

To intensify engagement and participation, gaming and gamification techniques are now being considered more seriously. In the last decade there has been an explosion of game-based implementations in both manufacturing and the construction applications.[66,69-72] Gaming has made VR mainstream and as the technology has matured and branched out VR/Gaming should be viewed more a tool than a toy. Producing immersive media is still a black art and none more so as interaction today includes wearables and IoT.[73,74]

Figure 6.2 illustrates the CPS mixed reality environment for training and assessing stonemasonry developed as part of the EU H2020 BEACONING project.[a] Designed for anywhere, any time learning the BEACONING approach is to enable transactions of knowledge across formal, informal and workplace learning spaces. The transitional mechanisms needed call upon ubiquitous computing, geolocation context awareness, pervasive and ambient environments through to procedural content generation and AI, all seamlessly working to deliver a learning/training solution. Mixed reality implementation is via Hololens and Unity3D game engine.

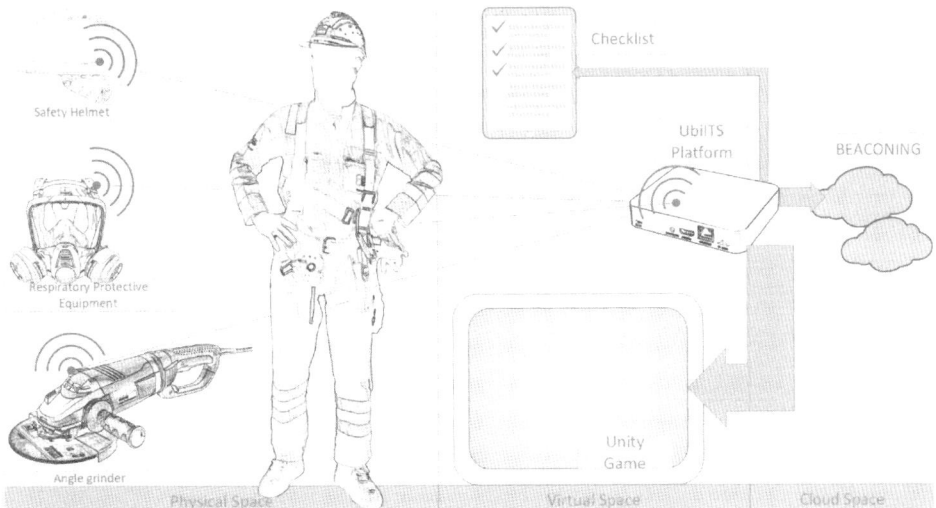

Fig. 6.21 Cyber-physical game based mixed reality setup configured for stonemasonry vocation developed for the EU H2020 BEACONING project.

---

[a] http://beaconing.eu/

Bespoke devices have been developed and configured to function as a body area network, including IoT interfacing with power tools (Fig. 6.22). The proprietary devices contain sensors (accelerometer, gyroscope, and magnetometer), a micro-processor, wireless transmission components, built-in storage and power supply. The sensors record limb motion (speed, displacement, joint angles, inclination, even force, and torsion) and characterize them with regard to their severity in terms of body health. Multimodal data capture/synchronization and communications across the virtual environment and server provided through the UbilTS framework[63,75] forming a closed-looped CPS network.

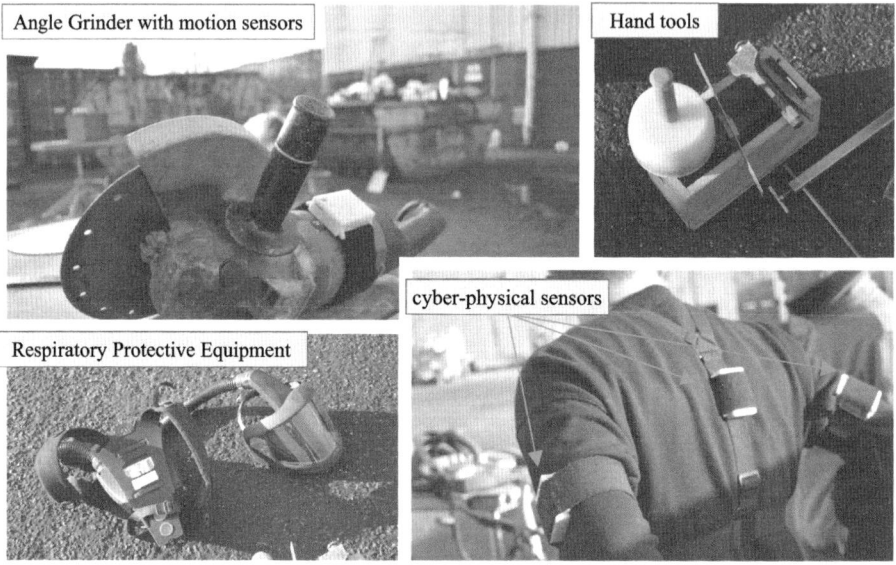

Fig. 6.22 Sensors and their configuration for human-in-the-loop cyber-physical systems based mixed reality for stonemasonry.

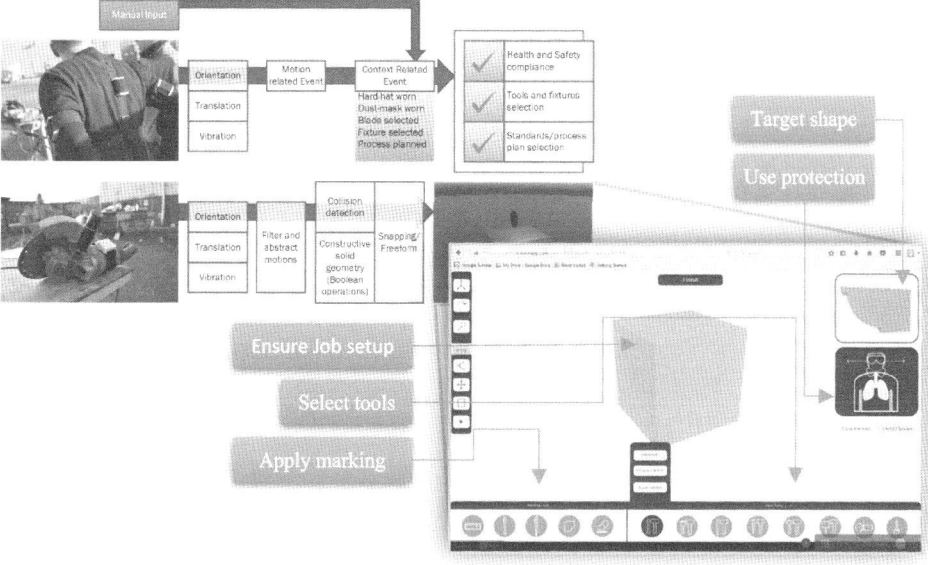

Fig. 6.23 Conventional virtual environment for planning stone waste material removal and shaping preparation.

With Unity3D, a conventional virtual environment and an AR environment which serves also for Hololens mixed reality was also developed. Fig. 6.2 shows the menu and game-based elements of the VET serious game as viewed on a PC or immersively with a VR headset. Functions to conduct planning and manipulation of virtual objects are provided. These are indexed and assigned values which are used by backend processes such as a learning management system or a procedural content generator.

Under a CPS setting, data from the body area network and other sensors replace the virtual tool selection and manipulation properties. Motion sensors track the user and the power tool during a physically simulated (or real) planning operation and material removal processes. Recorded data are similarly utilized for competency assessment but more importantly for post activity feedback and reflection sessions to develop manufacturing operations and planning thinking.

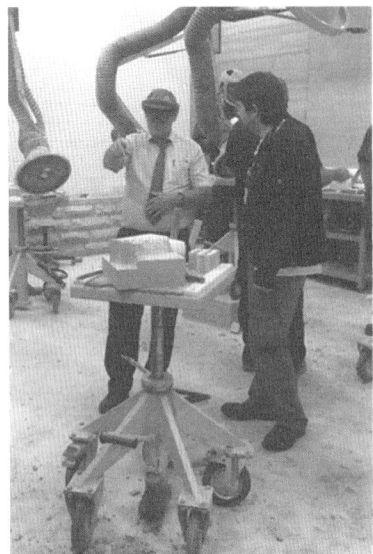

Fig. 6.24 Hololens in different workshop settings. Augmented reality mode (left) and CPS Mixed reality mode (right).

The augmented reality version functions rather similarly to the PC/immersive environment but for two major differences – its use in workplace or shop floor settings and image-based object tracking (Fig. 6.2). Tracking is through Vuforia[76], creating a "tangible interface" grinder that is used to cut into a virtual stone block. It was determined that placement of the image target on top of the blade allowed for the greatest operating range before the target disappears from camera view and tracking ceases to operate. Real grinding operations produce physical vibration in the grinder, which cannot currently be replicated, however other aspects such as dust and sound are reproduced to provide some tangible feedback to the operator. This is also where the chosen grinding blade comes into effect, as an incorrect choice of blade for the stone will cause the grinder to fail.

6.5.2 *Manufacturing Planning*

In contrast to process planning for manufacture with shop floor machine tools, e.g. CNC, there is no CAD/CAM equivalent when it comes to planning for onsite heritage restorative work. Much of the restoration process requires stonemasons to use both power and hand tools, as such fine motor cognitive skills are directly associated to spatial acuity, i.e., the ability to develop a compartment-based mathematical model of geometry, form fit, and function. Effective and efficient DFMA in stonemasonry process planning also requires knowledge about the fabrication techniques with respect to the type of stone as well as an understanding about the types of tools that can be used interchangeably for executing different tasks.

Table 6.6 shows a typical plan and a planning procedure that involves transferring a 2D detail into a set of templates to produce a series of 3D structures, selecting the right tool, and ensuring that its associated operation is conducted safely, effectively, and efficiently. Indeed, mental planning the route of a power cutting tool is critical as this is has severe personal and collateral consequences should an accident occur. The dimensions of interactivity include human factors as much as knowledge of material science and geometry. Therefore, training muscle memory of machine (power tool) handling is equally paramount for save machining handling and a well-organized manufacturing plan.

Both the augmented reality and PC/immersive versions for stonemasonry training include gamification mechanics in its learning and assessment OSAT framework. Game-play controls for the virtual environment were also implemented in both instances.

Under a training or assessment scenario, trainers and trainees are able to view the status and state of process planning to obtain the required geometric shape. All cutting operations are captured including feed rate, depth of cut, number of cuts,

Table 6.6 Simplified process plan for the use of an angle grinder in on-site stonemasonry practice.

Protocol for 9" Angle Grinder in stone cutting use		
Activity	Description	Example
1. Identify required templates	Create appropriate templates to enable production of replacement stone. Common templates are joint, bed, face and reverse.	
2. Apply 2D template	Using templates mark out the whole of the work from the datum surface prior to commencing. Scribe on working lines of template	
3. Waste removal	Identify the areas where most waste can be removed, e.g. cutting circular work scribe 10mm above finished working line. Follow pre-scribed lines with angle grinder to full depth of blade.	
4. Completed work	Care must be taken not to go below template guidelines.	

the type of abrasive blade chosen, and even the tool motion/path taken. The choice of personal protective equipment is also logged. It should be noted that the plan is manually generated before the task and automatically assessed post task. The eventual aim is to automatically generate a plan by monitoring the physical task using the cyber-physical system. However, the mixed reality system now described in serves as an intermediate step to capture and understand the human DFMA strategy used by the stonemasons.

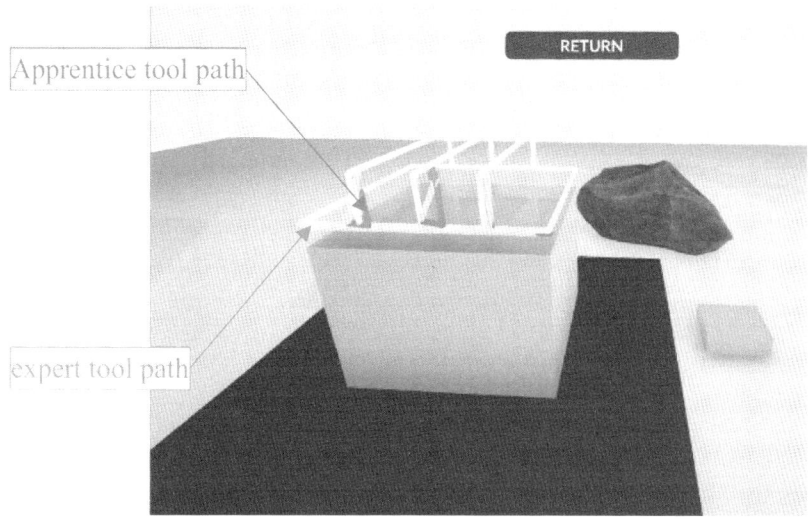

Fig. 6.25 Apprentice planned tool path compared with expert/optimum tool paths.

Figure 6.25 shows optimum tool paths superimposed over that planned by an apprentice. This functionality allows trainer and trainee to check progress, discuss approaches and conduct analysis. At this point it is useful to state that both VR and CPS mixed reality versions are still under testing. Results from initial small pilot groups (n = 27; 20 students, 5 vocational academics, 2 experts) have indicated a preference for the CPS mixed reality version, with over 70% participants indicating that such systems would offer enhanced connectivity and learning to the vocation compared to current VET delivery. A playback function included in the conventional VR environment was cited as one of the most beneficial tools and will be incorporated in the Holoens CPS mixed reality environment as development continues. The results thus far are encouraging.

6.6 Discussion

The integration of DFA combined with the ability to actually virtually assemble the product and take advantage of the already proven benefits of haptic interaction during such an assembly process points to significant potential benefits for more intuitive product design tools in the future.

While mixed reality could theoretically be the primary means of communicating manufacturing and planning content, its modern application should consider higher orders of dimensions. For example, in digital construction there is currently limited understanding of how virtual immersion of onsite personnel might impact the construction performance. A well-structured, unifying OSAT framework has been missing in the stonemasonry vocation. The VET CPS-enabled mixed reality case study illustrates a strategic sustainable development under digital construction could help address specialist trade skills shortage. It represents a holistic systems approach applied effectively within VET to instigate a change in OSAT leadership practice, with prospects of the system being embedded within the present construction industry. Based on the experiences of the CPS case study, a systems level thinking is required to achieve the desired goal. Literature evidences that interactivity in communicating design and technology are highly multifaceted thus research in designing immersive media suitable across a spectrum of reality-virtuality continuums is needed.

6.7 Conclusion

The examples reported in this chapter have a common thread - technological innovations through VR always raise questions on the effects of operational production, users/workers and their working life. In terms of human and mechanical capacities, VR technological change affects organizations both at the level of existing skills and with regard to their knowledge assets. It can also be seen that VR along with peripheral sensors can provide a layer of "experience authenticity" not offered by other media. All of the systems described demonstrate that through human-in-the-loop time-phased logging substantial metadata and information can be generated and output which can support engineering tasks throughout the whole product life cycle, e.g. particularly in design improvement, planning and knowledge capture and inference. Until such capabilities are embedded within proprietary CAD/CAM and CAE systems it is unlikely that we will see the substantial opportunities for productivity gains exploited within both product design/development and downstream manufacturing.

Future work on some of the systems discussed will focus on more substantial integration. The haptic planning work can be taken forward into other domains such as construction, project planning, surgical planning, and training. The DFMA work will be further extended by closely merging design for manufacture machining planning (DFM) within the DFMA system to provide more rapid machining feedback and will be tested using rigorous industrial-based trials.

The final vision of cyber-physical systems foresees digitalization to have direct influence on work tasks and processes. From an educational/training perspective, the individual level of workers is of particular relevance since they serve as flexible resources within an organization. As work processes change, workers must adapt and learn. Depending on the changes, a need for onsite vocational education and training arises. It is unknown if the demands of digitalized construction work will require a higher or a lower level of qualification and capabilities. Probably both, as guaranteeing safety in work processes requires information autonomy while interaction between workers and digital systems must maintain a closed-loop, proactive arrangement.

Another key aspect of future work is to investigate how such systems can be used in collaborative DFMA or manufacturing planning environments as well as supporting products and processes throughout the whole product life cycle. One possibility is their integration with discrete event modelling systems such that the effects of product design and planning changes on manufacturing systems and associated supply chains can be evaluated as a part of an overall DFMA approach; a real game changing application and something which will be essential to Industry 4.0.

Overall, this work has shown that with the considerable and continuing reductions in costs of VR technologies there is huge scope for VR-based engineering systems for design and planning. However, this is only the beginning and it is hoped that the applications demonstrated in this chapter will act as both an incentive and a useful foundation to take VR forward in all of its forms throughout the product life cycle. With the proper investment and by continuously enhancing people's work experience and capabilities, it has the potential to provide huge productivity gains across the engineering and other sectors, not just manufacturing.

Acknowledgments

This research work is supported by the EPSRC grant GR/R35285/01, EPSRC/IMRC grant GR/S12395/01, and the following industrial partners: BAE Systems, C.A. Models, Pathtrace and Renishaw. The work presented herein is also partially funded under the European H2020 Programme BEACONING project, Grant Agreement nr. 687676. Authors also acknowledge the financial support from CONACYT (National Science and Technology Council of Mexico) and from SIP-UASLP (Research and Postgraduate Secretariat of Universidad Autonoma de San Luis Potosi, Mexico).

References

1. A. Y. Nee, S. K. Ong, G. Chryssolouris and D. Mourtzis, Augmented reality applications in design and manufacturing, *CIRP Annals-Manufacturing Technology* **61**(2), 657–679 (2012).

2. Z. Kosmadoudi, T. Lim, J. Ritchie, S. Louchart, Y. Liu and R. Sung, Engineering design using game-enhanced CAD: The potential to augment the user experience with game elements, *Computer Aided Design* **45**(3), 777–795 (2013).

3. K. I. Lee and S. D. Noh, Virtual manufacturing system—A test-bed of engineering activities. *CIRP Annals* **46**(1), 347–350 (1997).

4. S. Choi, K. Jung and S. D. Noh, Virtual reality applications in manufacturing industries: Past research, present findings, and future directions, *Concurrent Engineering*, **23**(1), 40–63 (2015).

5. Y. Yusof and K. Latif, Survey on computer-aided process planning, *The Intl. J. of Adv. Manuf. Tech.* **75**(1–4), 77–89 (2014).

6. M. M. R, Isnaini and K. Shirase, Review of computer-aided process planning systems for machining operation—Future development of a computer-aided process planning system, *Intl. J. of Auto. Tech.* **8**(3), 317–332 (2014).

7. T. Lim, J. M. Ritchie, J. R. Corney, R. G. Dewar, K. Schmidt, and K. Bergsteiner, Assessment of a haptic virtual assembly system that uses physics-based interactions. In *Proc. IEEE Intl Sym. on Assembly and Manuf. (ISAM)*, pp. 147–153 (2007).

8. G. Gonzalez-Badillo, H. I. Medellin-Castillo and T. Lim, Development of a haptic virtual reality system for assembly planning and evaluation. *Procedia Technology* **7**, 265–272 (2013).

9. J. Ritchie, J. Simmons, R. Dewar and I. Carpenter, A methodology for eliciting expert knowledge in virtual engineering environments. In *Proc. IEEE Management of Eng. and Tech. (PICMET)*, pp. 285–290 (1999).

10. G. Robinson, J. M. Ritchie, P. N. Day R. G. Dewar, System design and user evaluation of Co-Star: An immersive stereoscopic system for cable harness design, *Computer Aided Design*, **39**(4), 245–257 (2007).

11. G. Lyu, X. Chu and D. Xue, Product modeling from knowledge, distributed computing and lifecycle perspectives: A literature review, *CIM* **84**, 1–13 (2017).

12. A. Haroon, M. A. Shah, Y. Asim, W. Naeem, M. Kamran and Q. Javaid, Constraints in the IoT: The world in 2020 and beyond. *Intl. J. of Adv. Comp. Sci. and App.* **7**(11), 252–271 (2016).

13. Z. Wu, Z. Meng, and J. Gray, IoT-Based techniques for online M2M-interactive itemized data registration and offline information traceability in a digital manufacturing system, *IEEE Trans. on Industrial. Information* **13**(5), 2397–2405 (2017).

14. J.A. Seth, J. Vance and J. Oliver, Virtual reality for assembly methods prototyping: A review, *Virtual Reality* **15**(1), 5–20 (2011).

15. J. M. Ritchie, R. G. Dewar, J. E. L. Simmons, The generation and practical use of plans for manual assembly using immersive virtual reality, *Proc. of the IMechE Part B: J. of Engr. Manuf.* **213**, 461–474 (1999).

16. R. G. Dewar, Assembly plans from virtual environments, PhD thesis, Heriot-Watt University, Edinburgh, UK (1998).

17. Ng F. M., Virtual reality and computer based tools for cable harness design, PhD thesis, Heriot-Watt University, Edinburgh, UK (1999).

18. R. C. W. Sung, J. M. Ritchie, G. Robinson, P. Day, J. R. Corney, T. Lim, Automated design process modelling and analysis using immersive virtual reality, *Computer Aided Design* **41**(12), 1082–1094 (2009).

19. J. M. Ritchie, G. Robinson, P. N. Day, R. G. Dewar, R, C. W. Sung and J. E. L. Simmons, Cable harness design, assembly and installation planning using immersive virtual reality, *Virtual Reality* **11**(4), 261–273 (2007).

20. M. P. Price, Frank and Lillian Gilbreth and the motion study controversy, 1907-1930, *Critical Evaluations in Business and Management* **2**, 455 (2003).

21. P. Scallan, *Process Planning: The Design/Manufacture Interface.* Butterworth-Heinemann (2003).

22. J. Ritchie and G. Simpson, *Engineering Applications: A Project-Based Approach.* Butterworth-Heinemann (1998).

23. H-P Wang, J. K. Li, *Computer Aided Process Planning.* Elsevier Science (1991)

24. F. Zhao, V. R. Murray, K. Ramani and J. W. Sutherland, J.W., Toward the development of process plans with reduced environmental impacts, *Frontiers of Mech. Engr.* **7**, 231–246 (2012).

25. B. Denkena, M. Shpitalni, P. Kowalski, G. Molcho and Y. Zipori, Knowledge management in process planning, *CIRP Annals: Manuf. Tech.* **56**(1), 175–180 (2007).

26. A. Abdul Kadir, X. Xu and E. Hammerle, Virtual machine tools and virtual machining: A technological review, *Robotics and Computer-Integrated Manufacturing* **27**, 494–508 (2011).

27. R. C. W. Sung, J. M. Ritchie, T. Lim and H. Medellin Assembly planning and motion study using virtual reality, In *Proc. ASME-AFM 2009 World Conf. on Innovative VR (WINVR)*, pp. 31–38 (2009).

28. M. A. Srinivasan, *What is Haptics?, Laboratory for Human and Machine Haptics*, The Touch Lab, Massachusetts Institute of Technology, Cambridge, MA, USA (1995).

29. M.C. Whitton, Making virtual environments compelling, *Comm. ACM* **46**, 40–47 (2003).

30. D. C. Ruspini, K. Kolarov and O. Khatib, The haptic display of complex graphical environments, In *Proc. 24th Annual Conf. on Comp. Graph. & Inter. Techniques*, pp. 345–352 (1997).

31. S. Laycock, A. Day, A survey of haptic rendering techniques, *Comp. Graphics Forum* **26**, 50–65 (2007).

32. M. Balasubramaniam, S. Ho, S. Sarma and Y. Adachi, Generation of collision-free 5-axis tool paths using a haptic surface, *Computer Aided Design* **34**, 267–279 (2002).

33. Z. Yang and Y. Chen, Haptic rendering of milling, In *Proc. of EuroHaptics*, pp. 206–217 (2003).

34. W. Zhu and Y-S Lee, Dexel-based force–torque rendering and volume updating for 5-DOF haptic product prototyping and virtual sculpting, *Computers in Industry* **55**(2), 125–145 (2004).

35. W. Zhu and Y-S Lee, Five-axis pencil-cut planning and virtual prototyping with 5-DOF haptic interface, *Computer Aided Design* **36**(13), 1295–1307 (2004).

36. T. Liu, M. Y. Wang, Haptic simulation of fixture loading planning, In *Proc. IEEE Intl Conf. on Robotics and Biomimetics (ROBIO)*, pp. 190–194 (2005).

37. OpenSceneGraph. Available at: www.openscenegraph.org/ (Accessed June 26, 2018).

38. osgModeling. Available at: http://code.google.com/p/osgmodeling/ (Accessed June 26, 2018).

39. Open Dynamics Engine. Available at: http://www.ode.org/ (Accessed June 26, 2018).

40. 3D Systems (2018). Available at: http:// https://www.3dsystems.com/scanners-haptics/ (Accessed June 26, 2018).

41. C.A. Fletcher, The evaluation of a novel haptic machining VR-based process planning system using an original process planning usability method, PhD Thesis, Heriot-Watt University, Edinburgh, UK (2014))

42. A. Bangor, P. Kortum and J. Miller, Determining what individual SUS scores mean: adding an adjective rating scale, *Usability Studies* **4**(3), 114–123 (2009).

43. G. Boothroyd, P. Dewhurst and W. A. Knight, *Product Design for Manufacture and Assembly, Second Edition*, CRC Press (2001).

44. A. S. Forsberg, J. LaViola and R. Zeleznik, ErgoDesk: A framework for two-and three-dimensional interaction at the ActiveDesk. In *Proc. 2ⁿᵈ Intl. Immersive Projection Technology Workshop (IPTW)*, pp. 11–12 (1998).
45. O. Bimber, L. M. Encarnacao and A. Stork, A multi-layered architecture for sketch-based interaction within virtual environments, *Comp. & Graph.* **24**(6), 851–867 (2000).
46. G. Wesche and H. P. Seidel, FreeDrawer: A free-form sketching system on the responsive workbench, In *Proc. ACM Symp. VR Software and Technology*, pp. 167–174 (2001).
47. S. Schkolne, M. Pruett and P. Schröder, Surface drawing: creating organic 3D shapes with the hand and tangible tools. In *Proc. ACM Conf. on Human factors in Computer Systems (SIGCHI)*, pp. 261–268 (2001).
48. T. Fleisch, G. Brunetti, P. Santos and A. Stork, Stroke-input methods for immersive styling environments, In *Proc. IEEE Shape Modeling Applications (SMA)*, pp. 275–283 (2004).
49. H. Kaufmann and D. Schmalstieg, Designing immersive virtual reality for geometry education, In *IEEE Virtual Reality Conference (IEEE VR)*, pp. 51–58 (2006).
50. H. Perkunder, J. H. Israel and M. Alexa, Shape modeling with sketched feature lines in immersive 3D environments, In *Proc. 7ᵗʰ Sketch-Based Interfaces and Modeling Symposium*, Eurographics Assoc., pp. 127–134 (2010).
51. R. Bruno, G. Casiez, J. A. Jorge and M. Hachet, Mockup Builder: 3D modeling on and above the surface, *Comp. & Graph.* **37**(3),165–178 (2013).
52. B. Milosevic, F. Bertini, E. Farella and S. Morigi, A SmartPen for 3D interaction and sketch-based surface modeling, *International Journal of Advanced Manufacturing Technology* **84**(5–8), 1625–1645 (2016).
53. M. Masry and H. Lipson, A sketch-based interface for iterative design and analysis of 3D objects. In *Proc. Special Interest Group on Computer Graphics and Interactive Techniques Conference (SIGGRAPH'07)*, pp. 31 (August 2007).
54. G. Gonzalez, H. I. Medellin, T. Lim, J. M. Ritchie and R. C. W. Sung, 3D object representation for physics simulation engines and its effect on virtual assembly tasks, In *Proc. ASME Conference IDETC/CIE*, pp. 1449–1459 (2012).
55. V. E. Sanvido and D. J. Medeiros, Applying computer-integrated manufacturing concepts to construction, *Construction Engineering and Management* **116**(2), 365–379 (1990).
56. W. Pan and M. Arif, Manufactured construction: Revisiting the construction-manufacturing relations, In *Proc. Association of Researchers in Construction Management 27ᵗʰ Annual Conf. (ARCOM)*, vol. 1, pp. 105–114 (2011).
57. S. Mackenzie, A. R. Kilpatrick and A. Akintoye, UK construction skills shortage response strategies and an analysis of industry perceptions, *Const. Mgmt. & Econ.* **18**(7), 853–862 (2000).
58. M. Mohamed, E. A. Pärn and D. J. Edwards Brexit: measuring the impact upon skilled labour in the UK construction industry, *Intl. J. of Building Pathology and Adaptation* **35**(3), 264–279 (2017).
59. Policy Paper: Industrial strategy: Building a Britain fit for the future, Department for Business, Energy and Industrial Strategy (Revised June 2018).
60. R. Y. K. Ng, R.Y.S. Lam, K. K. Ng and I. K. W. Lai, Identifying the needs of flexible and technology enhanced learning in Vocational and Professional Education and Training's (VPET) workplaces. In *New Ecology for Education—Communication X Learning*, Will W.K. Ma, Chi-Keung Chan, Kar-wai Tong, Heidi Fung and Cheuk Wai Rose Fong (eds). Springer (2017).

61. A. Wilke and J. Magenheim, Requirements analysis for the design of workplace-integrated learning scenarios with mobile devices: Mapping the territory for learning in industry 4.0. *Global Engineering Education Conference*, EDUCON, pp. 476–485 (2017).

62. R. Hämäläinen, M. Lanz and K. T. Koskinen, Collaborative systems and environments for future working life: Towards the integration of workers, systems and manufacturing environments. In *The Impact of Digitalization in the Workplace*, Christian Harteis (ed). Springer (2018).

63. A. Sivanathan, S. Mcgibbon, T. Lim, J. Ritchie and M. Abdel-Wahab, A cyber-physical gaming system for vocational training. In *Proc. ASME IDETC/CIE*, pp. V001T02A063-V001T02A063 (2017).

64. L. P. Andersen, L. Nørdam, T. Joensson, P. Kines and K. J. Nielsen, Social identity, safety climate and self-reported accidents among construction workers, *Const. Mgmt. and Econ.*, **36**(1), 22–31 (2018).

65. S. McGibbon and M. Abdel-Wahab, Stonemasonry skills development: Two case studies of historic buildings in Scotland, *Structural Survey* **34**(3), 218–241 (2016).

66. X. Li, W. Yi, H. L. Chi, X. Wang and A. P. Chan, A critical review of virtual and augmented reality (VR/AR) applications in construction safety, *Automation in Construction* **86**, 150–162 (2017).

67. S. Woksepp, Virtual reality in construction: tools, methods and processes, PhD Thesis, Luleå tekniska universitet, Sweden (2007).

68. G. Armstrong and C. Gilge, Global Construction Survey 2016 | Building a technology advantage, KPMG International Cooperative, pp. 1–32 (2016).

69. W. Yan, C. Culp and R. Graf, Integrating BIM and gaming for real-time interactive architectural visualization, *Automation in Construction* **20**(4), 446–458 (2011).

70. K. Y. Lin, J. W. Son and E. M. Rojas, A pilot study of a 3D game environment for construction safety education, *Information Technology in Construction* **16**(5), 69–84 (2011).

71. A. Pedro, Q. T. Le and C. S. Park Framework for integrating safety into construction methods education through interactive virtual reality, *Prof. Issues in Eng. Education and Practice* **142**(2), p.04015011 (2015).

72. F. M. Dinis, A. S. Guimarães, B. R. Carvalho and J. P. P. Martins, Virtual and augmented reality game-based applications to civil engineering education, In *Proc. Global Engineering Education Conference (EDUCON)*, pp. 1683–1688 (2017).

73. C. Salter, Disturbance, Translation, Enculturation: Necessary research in new media, technology, and the senses, *Visual Anthropology Review* **34**(1), 87–97 (2018).

74. J. C. K. Tham, Interactivity in an age of immersive media: Seven dimensions for wearable technology, internet of things, and technical communication, *Technical Communications* **65**(1), 46–65 (2018).

75. A. Sivanathan, Ubiquitous Integration and Temporal Synchronisation (UbilTS) framework: a solution for building complex multimodal data capture and interactive systems, PhD Thesis, Heriot-Watt University, Edinburgh, UK (2014).

76. Vuforia Augmented Reality SDK. Available at: https://www.vuforia.com/ (Accessed June 26, 2018).

.

Chapter 7

Virtual Reality Applications for Computer Aided Design and Advanced Manufacture of Medical Devices

Hugo I. Medellin-Castillo, Jorge Zaragoza-Siqueiros, Eder H. Govea-Valladares
James Ritchie, Theodore Lim, and Aparajithan Sivanathan

7.1 Introduction

Modern design and manufacture engineering technologies, such as Computer-Aided Design (CAD), Computer-Aided Engineering (CAE), image processing and 3D reconstruction, reverse engineering (RE), robotics and computer vision, virtual reality (VR) and augmented reality (AR), and advanced manufacturing systems such as additive manufacturing (AM), have been created and developed to assist industry. However, the use of these modern engineering technologies in medical applications for the delivery of human healthcare has significantly increased in the last three decades. As a consequence, Engineering Assisted Surgery (EAS) has been introduced as a new research and development field and is defined as the application of engineering and manufacturing technologies in the delivery of healthcare.[1] EAS comprises data acquisition from computer tomography (CT), magnetic resonance imagining (MRI), 3D scanners, CAD systems, and Finite Element Analysis (FEA). The aim is to enhance healthcare processes through digital technologies and systems. Typical applications of engineering technologies in medicine include the visualization and reconstruction of human anatomy; organ and tissue modelling; surgical simulators for planning and training; robotic surgery; locomotion and gait analysis; and the design and manufacture of prosthesis, ortheses, implants, biomodels, scaffolds, training models, and surgical aids and tools.

CAD and computer-aided manufacturing (CAM) have been incorporated into virtual systems to allow the design and manufacture of medical assistance tools and implants.[2] Others have applied integrated engineering techniques for the design and manufacture of tools, surgical guides, prosthesis and implants for medical applications.[3-5] However, commercial systems with integrated engineering tools can be very expensive. For this reason, medical specialists have decided to use CAD/CAM tools independently; however, this practice requires engineer specialists or the training of surgeons in the use of engineering techniques, which increase the time and cost of the surgery planning process.

Research works have focused on the development of specific purpose computer systems. For instance, a CAD technique for the design of multiple surgical splints was developed in Ref. 6. More recently a system to allow the generation of surgical splints from previously repositioned virtual models of the maxilla was developed in Ref. 7. Recent studies have also validated the use of commercial software (Materialize®) to design and fabricate 3D occlusal splint for orthognathic surgeries.[8-10] The generation of a set of surgical templates for the segmentation and bone repositioning of maxillary bones by using commercial software Geomagic® was investigated in Ref. 11.

Virtual reality design and manufacturing techniques can enhance traditional medical procedures by providing an equivalent of model base design and production information modelling, all in an immersive environment. One of the main applications of VR in medicine has been the development of computer assisted surgery and simulation systems.[12,13] Virtual environments are created to enable the interaction with the human body anatomy and reduce the risk and cost of surgical procedures.[14] However, a main issue of VR applications is the design and development of the virtual environment, which comprises the modelling of the virtual objects, including their geometry, and surface characteristics such as colours, textures, etc. As the level of realism (LoR) of the virtual environment increases, the amount of data needed to be processed by the VR application will increase, affecting its performance.[15] Thus, the key compromise is between the largest amount of data required to increase the accuracy of the results and the minimum use of computer resources within a practical LoR. Sometimes it is necessary to sacrifice the level of realism to prioritize the data processing and time response of the system. For this reason, some research works have focused on determining the appropriate LoR and immersion required for the particular VR application.[16] Advances in modelling software, high performance computing and measurement devices have contributed to the developments of high-performance virtual scenarios. However, these tools can be very expensive and limited to a minority of users with financial capability to such tools. Few works in the literature have focused on reducing the costs of developing virtual environments.[15] In addition, medical applications can be enhanced by enabling the sense of touch to the computer user interface by means of haptic technologies, adopting many lessons from virtual design and advanced manufacturing research.

This chapter presents a review of the use of virtual reality technologies for the delivery of human healthcare. The aim is to demonstrate how advanced design and manufacture technologies can be incorporated into a virtual environment for human healthcare. For this purpose, a general methodology to develop VR applications for the design and manufacture of medical devices is presented. The proposed methodology is validated by a case study related to the development of a haptic-enabled VR application for the design and manufacture of surgical templates in maxillofacial surgery. This case study brings together surgical planning and the design and manufacture of surgical guides in a single virtual environment created using open-source software and haptics. The results show that the automation of medical device design and manufacturing processes is possible using a parametric modelling approach within a haptic-enabled VR environment combined with advanced additive manufacturing technologies.

7.2 Virtual Reality in Medicine

Virtual reality can be described as a set of technologies that enable people to interact with a virtual environment beyond reality.[17] It is also defined as a synthetic environment, generated by the computer and other external devices, that allows the user to interact with a 3D virtual world in which the objects behave and look like they are real. The fundamental concept behind VR is the illusion.[18] VR takes advantage of both computer technological development and scientific visualization to create a virtual world where the user can interact with the virtual objects.[19] It offers a high level of realism and immersion but requires advanced computing technologies capable to process large amounts of scientific data and graphics.[20] Computer virtual reality applications with high levels of immersion and interaction are being developed to analyze, speed up, and optimize engineering activities such as product design, manufacturing planning, and simulation. However, the development of VR applications is not limited to engineering areas. There have been several VR and haptics applications in the area of medicine, rehabilitation, architecture, psychology, entertainment, astronomy, archaeology, art, etc.

The efficacy of a virtual environment depends on the level of realism and the level of immersion.[15,21,22] The level of realism depends on the amount of data that requires processing by the VR application, which affects the performance of the application. Since medical models are usually obtained from CT and MRI images, they comprise large amounts of data, which are difficult to process in VR systems. Therefore, a compromise among the accuracy of the model, the system's response and the level of realism is necessary and will depend on each particular application. On the other hand, the level of immersion refers to the level of visual and touch interaction.[23] It also refers to the level of how deeply the user is sensorially involved inside the virtual environment, i.e. how much the user can see, hear, feel and even smell or taste the virtual objects. There are different immersion levels; for instance, at the highest immersion level the user would be fully isolated from the real world and would be using his/her five senses to interact with the virtual environment. To date, there is not any virtual environment able to fully immerse the user. On the other hand, a low immersion level involves only one or two senses, being the sight the most common. The use of haptic devices that allow feeling the shape, texture, weight and inertia of virtual objects, is more common every day. According to Ref. 18, VR systems be classified into three main types: 1) non-immersive (desktop systems), 2) semi-immersive, and 3) fully-immersive. Table 7.1 presents the classification of the VR systems and their characteristics including input and output devices, resolution, level of immersion and interaction, and cost. It is important to mention that these features are continuously evolving.

Table 7.1. Classification and features of Virtual Reality systems.[18]

Features	VR Systems		
	Non-immersive	**Semi-immersive**	**Fully-immersive**
Input devices	Mice, keyboard, joysticks, and track balls	Joysticks, space balls, and data gloves	Gloves and voice commands
Output devices	Standard high-resolution monitor	Large monitor, large screen projector system, and multiple television projection systems	Head Mounted Displays (HMD), and visualization room-size systems (CAVE)
Resolution	High	High	Low-Medium
Sense of immersion	Non-low	Medium-high	High
Interaction	Low	Medium	High
Cost	Lowest	Expensive	Very expensive

The visual sense is the principal sensorial modality to provide users with the real-world sensation in a virtual environment. However, different methodologies allowing the graphical representation of anatomical parts for medical applications have been proposed.[23-25]. These methodologies are based on computer graphics and the 3D reconstruction of medical images such as CT and magnetic resonance imagining (MRI). On the other hand, sensing touch is an important characteristic of a medical virtual environment because it allows the interaction of the user with virtual objects, for example in medical training.[26]

Haptics can be considered within different concepts such as: 1) haptic perception, referring to the process of object perception via the sense of touch; 2) haptic feedback, i.e. the process of receiving a force or external signal to stimulate the sense of touch; and 3) the haptic interface, referring to the devices used to generate the haptic feedback signals. Touch sensing is possible by means of haptic feedback, the combination of sensory input through the tactile receptors in the skin and the kinesthetic receptors in the muscles, tendons and joints.[27] On the other hand, haptic rendering is the name given to the general process of feeling or touching virtual objects. This comprises tactile feedback, to feel properties such as the superficial texture, and the kinesthetic feedback, to feel the shapes, sizes, and weight of virtual objects. Like graphic rendering, haptic rendering provides interactive projections of virtual objects to the user, but with the key difference that virtual objects can be touched. Haptic interfaces are commonly used to enable the user with the sense of touch and kinesthesia when manipulating virtual objects in a VR system. They can also be used for the remote manipulation of real objects; for example, to control a robotic arm that manipulates hazardous materials or performs rehabilitation therapies. Haptic devices behave as a small robot that exchanges mechanical energy with the user. Although haptic devices could be designed to be in touch with any part of the user's body, hand devices have been the most developed and used haptic interfaces. Currently, there are several types of haptic devices: the Geomagic Touch (formerly known as the Phantom Omni and Phantom desktop from Sensable), the Falcon from Novint, the Virtuose from Haption, among others. The advances in haptic technologies have been focused on the development of haptic devices for force/torque feedback and for tactile feedback. Force/torque haptic devices are oriented to detect the kinesthesic reactions during the interaction with the virtual objects, whereas tactile haptic devices are oriented to detect sensations related to the skin receptors (e.g. the surface temperature, the surface roughness, etc.).[23]

Haptic technologies have been integrated in VR applications to increase contextual connections with virtual entities. This has been shown to be highly beneficial in medical contexts where VR and haptic technologies enrich surgical simulators for planning and training of surgical procedures in areas such as otolaryngology, gastroenterology, urology, and pulmonology.[28] The main architecture of a virtual reality system with visual, auditory, and haptic rendering comprises the following basic elements[29]:

- *Simulation engine*, responsible for computing the physical behaviour of virtual objects in the virtual environment.
- *Visual, audio, and haptic rendering*, responsible for calculating the graphics, audio, and force feedbacks of the virtual environment.
- *Transducers or interfaces*, responsible for converting the visual, audio, and force feedback signals from the computer to the user.

The practice of medicine is a complex decision making process that requires knowledge, experience and manual abilities;[30] practitioner abilities are acquired through experience and training, which is a slow process that may take several years. In order to get experience and abilities, a student of medicine must be the protagonist of his/her training whilst considering as a main priority the avoidance of risks and unnecessary inconveniences for the patient[31]. Consequently, the use of virtual reality and computer technologies in medicine has become an important tool for students and practitioners to understand and confirm concepts, and to improve skills in surgical practice, e.g. for experienced surgeons to plan and make more precise diagnosis.[32,33]

During the last two decades, the use of VR in medical applications have focused on the following areas:

- Surgical planning[34-36]
- Surgical simulation and training[23,37-40]
- Medical education[41-42]
- Virtual and augmented reality surgery[43,44]
- Patient evaluation and diagnosis[45-47]
- Rehabilitation[48-50]
- Disability solutions[51]
- Human and organ modelling[14,52-54]
- Virtual design and manufacture of medical devices[1,5,55]

Numerous VR systems have been developed and reported in the literature with the aim of improving the learning and outcomes of different medical procedures and to increase the surgical planning performance.[56-61] Some of these VR systems and their key features are summarized in Table 7.2.

Table 7.2. Virtual medical systems and their key features.

References	Type of VR system	Application	Key features
Ref. 62	NI-VR	Surgical simulator for angiology and vascular surgery	• Employ computational fluid dynamics (CFD) to simulate blood flow. • Available preloaded arterial models and surgery instruments controlled by a simple PC-mouse.
Ref. 63	SI-VR	Surgical planning for liver surgery	• Haptic feedback. • 3D liver and vascular tissue reconstruction from CT data. • Deformable 3D model according liver mechanical properties. • 3D model segmentation.
Ref. 64	NI-VR	Surgical planning for orthodontic and orthognathic surgery	• Patient 3D model visualization. • Model segmentation and reposition. • Wafer generation using CAD. • Report generation for maxilla repositioning.
Refs. 65,66	SI-VR	Surgical training for vascular surgery	• Contains preloaded 3D anatomic structures for vascular surgery. • Integrates haptic feedback by means of two haptic devices.
Ref. 67	SI-VR	Surgical training for dental procedures	• Dental virtual models obtained from CT. • Haptic feedback. • Virtual drilling and milling of dental structures.
Ref. 68	SI-VR	Surgical simulator for paranasal surgery	• Model created based on a high-resolution CT. • Soft tissues added manually. • Model manipulation with virtual surgical tools controlled by a haptic device. • Visualization, haptic rendering, and tissue removal are represented.
Ref. 69	SI-VR	Surgical training for orthopaedics	• Data acquisition from CT and magnetic resonance MRI. • Haptic feedback. • Virtual drilling simulation by means of a haptic device.
Ref. 70	SI-VR	Simulation (Ultrasonic simulation)	• CT data extraction and 3D reconstruction of models. • Integrates haptic feedback by means of two haptic devices.
Ref. 71	SI-VR	Surgical training for laparoscopy	• Contains pre-loaded 3D anatomic structures for laparoscopic surgery, gynaecology, and general surgery. • Integrates haptic feedback. • Haptic device based on the real laparoscopic instruments.

References	Type of VR system	Application	Key features
Ref. 72	SI-VR	Surgical simulator for neurosurgery	• Patient data obtained from CT. • Haptic feedback. • Includes the kinematic and dynamic simulations of the surgical instruments. • Soft tissues are three-dimensional reconstructed.
Ref. 73	NI-VR	Surgical planning for spine surgery	• Virtual model reconstruction from CT. • The system proposes pre-created 3D templating tools adapted to each patient to define the new vertebral position. • 3D templating tools exported as STL file to be manufactured using additive manufacturing.
Ref. 36	SI-VR	Surgical training for endoscopy	• Contains pre-loaded 3D gastrointestinal structures. • Haptic feedback. • Simulation of the cutting and removal of soft tissue structures by means of a haptic device.
Ref. 38	NI-VR	Surgical training for endourology	• Includes a torso mannequin. • Contains pre-loaded 3D structures. • Graphics simulation of the cutting of soft tissue structures.
Ref. 74	SI-VR	Surgical simulator for endoscopy	• Force-feedback human computer interface. • The VR system receives the movements of the haptic device and calculates in real-time the motion of the virtual flexible endoscope. • The system integrates navigation, clipping, and cutting and diathermy virtual tasks.

NI-VR: Non-immersive VR, SI-VR: Semi-immersive VR, FI-VR: Fully immersive VR.

In the area of maxillofacial surgery, in particular orthognathic surgery (OGS), the traditional surgical planning process started to evolve with the use of computer methods to carry out 2D cephalometric analyses.[75] Since then, several systems for Computer-Aided cephalometry have been developed and are commercially available. The next evolution involved 3D scanning and engineering technologies, allowing the 3D reconstruction and visualization of the patient skull, the segmentation of the patient's virtual model, the displacement and relocation of bone fragments, and the design and fabrication of surgical guides to assist the real surgical procedure.[76-81] These modern OGS planning systems integrate engineering tools such as Computer-Aided Design and Computer Aided Manufacture (CAD/CAM) with model surgery to enable the inclusion of advanced fabrication techniques such as additive manufacturing (AM). Moreover, the integration of the sense of touch and force feedback into a virtual environment for OGS planning eases the bone sectioning and alignment, allowing users to explore anatomic features and reduce the skill learning curve for novice surgeons.[82-84]

7.3 Development of Virtual Reality Medical Applications

Figure 7.1 shows a proposed general architecture for the development of virtual reality systems for medical applications and comprises the following five main modules:

(1) *Model reconstruction module*

This module is responsible for the generation of the patient's 3D models from medical images such as CT, MRI, or 3D scanning. Several commercial and open-source systems have been developed to carry out the 3D reconstruction of medical images; examples are 3DSlicer,[85] ITK-SNAP,[86] TurtleSeg,[87] and Dolphin Imaging.[88] In addition, some methodologies and algorithms for the reconstruction of 3D scanning data have been proposed. These reconstruction methodologies are based on approximating the geometry from a set of 3D points or cloud points to generate a mesh that represents the external shape of the patient's anatomy.[89] Other algorithms include internal information of the patient such as internal tissue properties or bone density;[90] these are based on graphical representation using voxels, marching cubes or octrees to represent the patient anatomy in the virtual environment.[91,92]

(2) *Visualization module*

This module is responsible for the graphics rendering of objects in the virtual environment. The quality of the graphical representation of virtual objects defines the level of realism. Various technologies to immerse the user into the virtual environment in order to increase the level of realism have been developed. Some of these technologies comprise head mounted displays (HMD),[93] monitors with stereoscopic projection or virtual reality rooms (CAVE).[94] The visualization in VR medical systems not only refers to the projection of virtual models to the user, but also to the projection of medical procedures, the manipulation of anatomical models, medical tools, and results. Thus, the visualization module works in conjunction with the model reconstruction module, the manipulation module, and the simulation module.

(3) *Manipulation module*

This module allows the interaction of the user with the objects in the virtual environment. A main requirement of medical VR applications is that the user must be able to interact with the patient's anatomy by means of visual, tactile, and sound sensations. These sensations can be produced in graphics displays or monitors, haptic devices and sound systems, respectively. The sensation of manipulating virtual objects is possible by adding physical behaviour to the objects in the virtual environment, and by rendering the forces to the user by means of a haptic device. In this module it is also possible to incorporate CAD tools to allow the design of surgical templates, implants or prostheses from the existing virtual objects.

(4) *Simulation module*

This module allows the simulation of medical operations and procedures, such as cutting, drilling, and milling of bone, among others. The simulation module must integrate the mathematical modelling of the physical phenomenon that occurs during the virtual medical procedure. It is also possible to incorporate computer-aided manufacturing tools to enable the simulation of the fabrication process of the surgical assistance tools, implants, or prostheses needed in the real surgical process.

(5) *Medical data analysis module*

This module is responsible for the analysis and exporting of the medical data generated in the VR system. Data processing is fundamental to carrying out training, simulation, or planning tasks in the virtual environment. In virtual surgery, the VR system must be able to extract medical information relevant to the surgeon during the real operation, such as the sequence of operations, bone displacement, position of sutures, surgical templates, among others. In the case of virtual training, the system must be capable of extracting data to measure and evaluate the trainee's performance, skills, and progress. All of which are analogous to manufacturing planning and training applications.

Although there have been several research works reported in the literature focusing on the development and analysis of Computer-Aided VR applications in medicine, few have addressed the development of virtual environments.[95,96] Virtual environments have a significant impact on the performance of the application and the level of realism; however, again, sometimes it is necessary to sacrifice the level of realism to prioritize the data processing and time response of the system.

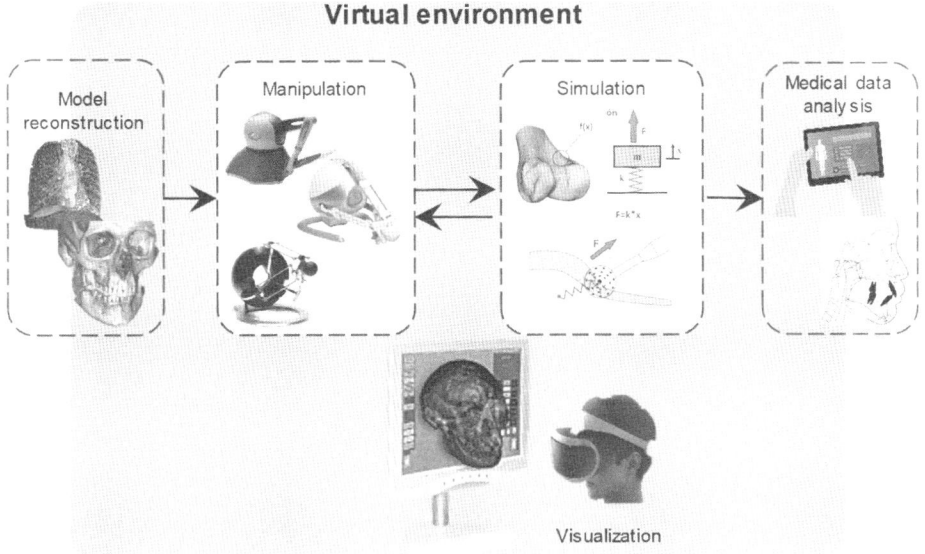

Fig. 7.1. General architecture of virtual reality systems for medical applications.

In Fig. 7.2, a proposed methodology to create virtual reality environments is shown. Although this has been implemented using the open-source software Blender 2.49,[97] visualization toolkit VTK 5.6,[98] and Python 2.7 programming language,[99] it can be used with any other software or programming language. The main steps of the proposed methodology are:

1. *Create a scenario.* Modelling starts by creating the virtual models placed on the stage. 3D models can be reconstructed from 3D scanning, CT or MRI, or can be created using the conventional CAD modelling techniques.
2. *Materials and textures.* Textures are assigned to each element of the models and must correspond to the type of material as well as the visual aspect they have in the real world. This process of adding textures can be carried out using standard images or by assigning colour to each part.
3. *Surface characteristics.* To boost realism, it is necessary to provide the virtual environment with visual features like lighting, shadows, reflections, transparencies, and more.
4. *Get data model.* Once the scene is completed, the next step is to extract the information corresponding to orientation, rotation, and location of each virtual object in the scene.
5. *Generate VTP.* In this step, the virtual scenario is converted into a VTP file. The VTP (VTK Polygonal Data) is a VTK file that contains the polygonal data of the 3D model.

6. *Export to VTK window.* Finally, a VTP file is used to import all the elements of the scene into a VTK window in the external application being developed.

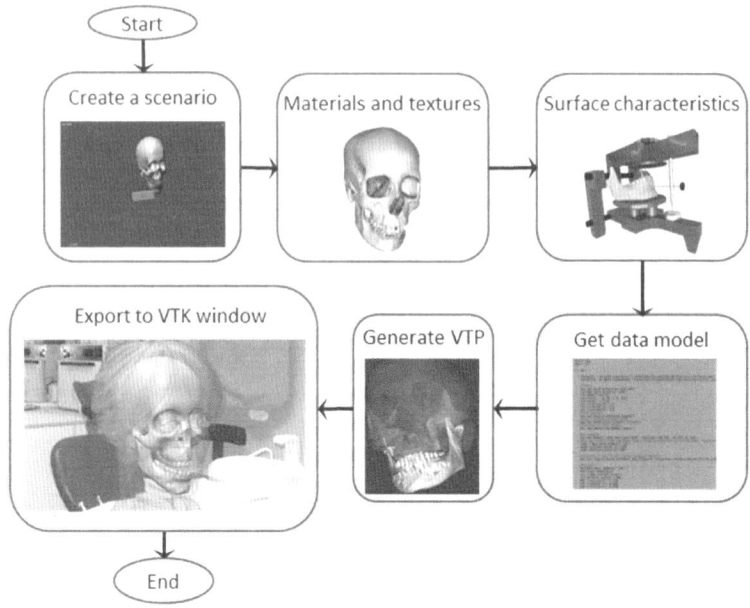

Fig. 7.2. Methodology to create virtual environments.

In order to show the level of realism obtained using the proposed methodology, two virtual scenarios were developed. The first corresponds to an orthognathic surgery simulator to perform dental surgeries or procedures in a virtual dental office environment, Fig. 7.3(a). Textures, lights and images were added to increase the level of realism. Transparency was used to observe internal details such as the bone structure, Fig. 7.3(b). Dental tools, such as mills or drills were modelled, Fig. 7.3(c), and added to the virtual scenario to perform virtual cuts on the patient mandibular bone, Fig. 7.3(d). The second virtual scenario corresponds to a dental articulator, which is a mechanical device used in dentistry and maxillofacial surgery to simulate and record positions of the mandible in relation to the maxilla. Figure 7.4(a) shows the real articulator used as the modelling reference and Fig. 7.4(b) shows the virtual articulator in the virtual scenario corresponding to a hospital. A 3D model of a mandible was obtained from medical image reconstruction and imported into the virtual scenario where the articulator was created. An image type texture was also added to simulate real bone texture. Finally, a smoothing filter was applied to obtain a smooth surface without imperfections due the mesh elements.

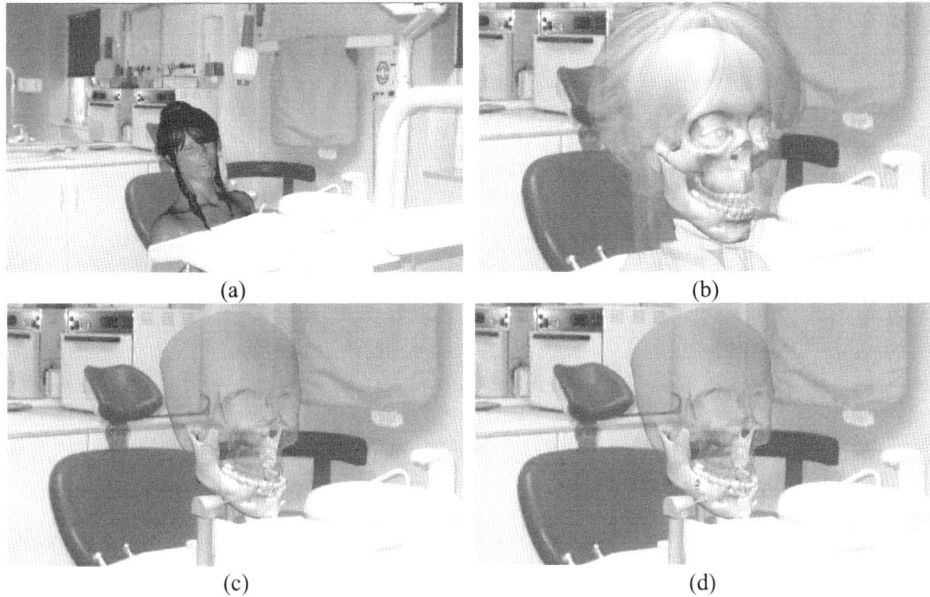

Fig. 7.3. Medical surgical simulator: a) dental room, b) transparent layers of virtual patient, c) virtual tool for bone cutting, d) results of virtual bone cutting.

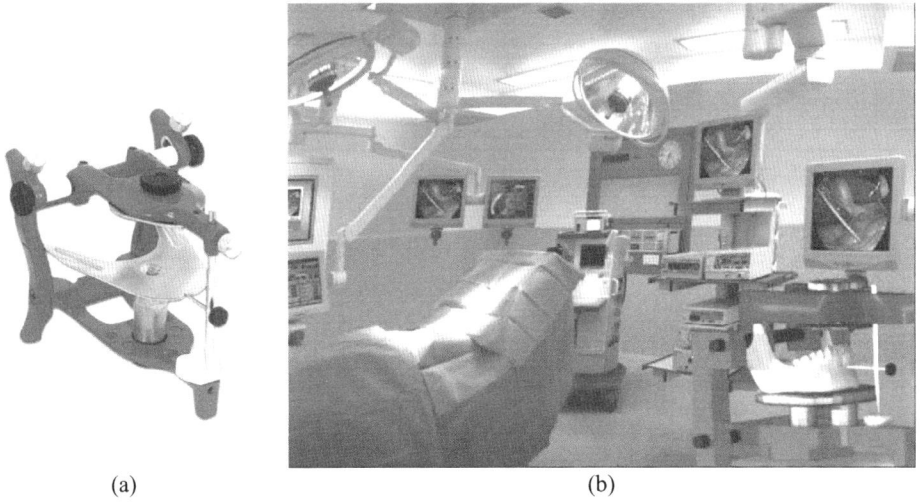

Fig. 7.4. Dental articulator: a) real articulator, b) virtual scenario.

7.4 Virtual Computer Aided Design and Manufacture of Medical Templates: A Case Study in Orthognathic Surgery

The conventional procedure for orthognathic surgery (OGS) planning is shown in Fig. 7.5. This traditional OGS planning process begins with the analysis of the patient's facial harmony (1), which is carried out on a patient's photography. From this facial study, a previous diagnosis identifies the required mechanical, orthodontics or surgery correction procedure. Subsequently, a bone cephalometric analysis (2) is performed on a patient's sagittal skull X-ray image. In the cephalometric analysis, the bone dimensions and the cephalometric values are calculated. The results are compared with the predefined anatomical standards defined according to the patient's ethnic group in order to identify the patient's condition and define the correcting treatment. Once the cephalometric analysis is completed, the patient's dental casts are obtained and mounted on a dental articulator that simulates the patient's dental occlusion. On the cast models, a model surgery process (3) is performed to get the patient's new occlusion by cutting and realigning the cast models. Once the new dental occlusion of the patient is obtained, a surgical template (4) corresponding to the desired dental occlusion is fabricated. This template is used during the real surgical procedure (5) to guarantee the correct position of the maxilla and mandible.[100,101]

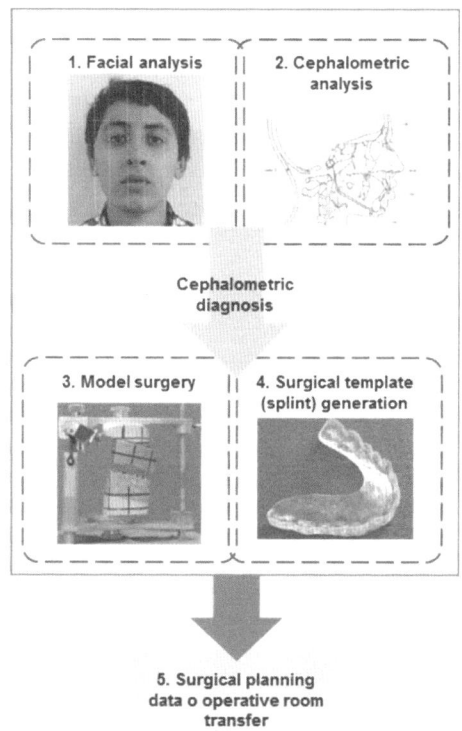

Fig. 7.5. Traditional orthognathic surgery planning process.

Based on the proposed architecture for medical VR systems and the conventional procedure for orthognathic surgery planning, a new virtual haptic-enabled system for planning orthognathic surgeries has been developed. The architecture of the proposed system is shown in Fig. 7.6, and comprises the following five modules:

1. *Medical data input module.* This module incorporates tools to import 3D models as STL or OBJ formats, and previously generated from the reconstruction of medical images such as CT, MRI, or 3D scanning. It also integrates tools to import medical information from the patient such as medical history, X-ray images, and photographs as standard image files (*.jpg, *.png and *.tiff).

2. *Visualization module.* This module is responsible for generating the graphic scene of the virtual environment and generating the visual feedback of the virtual object manipulation. The visualization module is supported by VTK graphic libraries.[98]

3. *Manipulation module.* This allows users to manipulate virtual objects with force feedback and sense of touch during the virtual interaction and by means of a haptic device. This module also integrates collision detection between virtual objects and bone fragments. To integrate the haptic technology and collision detection the H3DAPI[102] and the Bullet physics engine[103] are used, respectively.

4. *Simulation module.* This module allows the segmentation of 3D models using the haptic device and cutting planes defined by the user. In addition, CAD tools for the aided design of surgical templates from patient models are integrated. The module works in conjunction with the manipulation and visualization modules, providing haptic and graphic rendering to the user during the cutting and manipulation of bone fragments.

5. *Medical data output module.* This module extracts the results of the facial and cephalometric analysis, providing a diagnosis of the patient's disease. In addition, the system automatically generates the maxillary repositioning report and allows exporting the surgical template as an STL file enabling its fabrication using additive manufacturing.

The implementation of the proposed virtual orthognathic surgery planning system was carried out in C++ using the Microsoft Foundation Class (MFC) and the VTK libraries[98] for the graphic rendering of the virtual environment. In order to enable the haptic feedback, the H3DAPI libraries[102] were also integrated together with an Omni haptic device from Sensable® and a Falcon haptic device from Novint®. The graphic user interface of the system is rendered in a computer monitor as shown in Fig. 7.7.

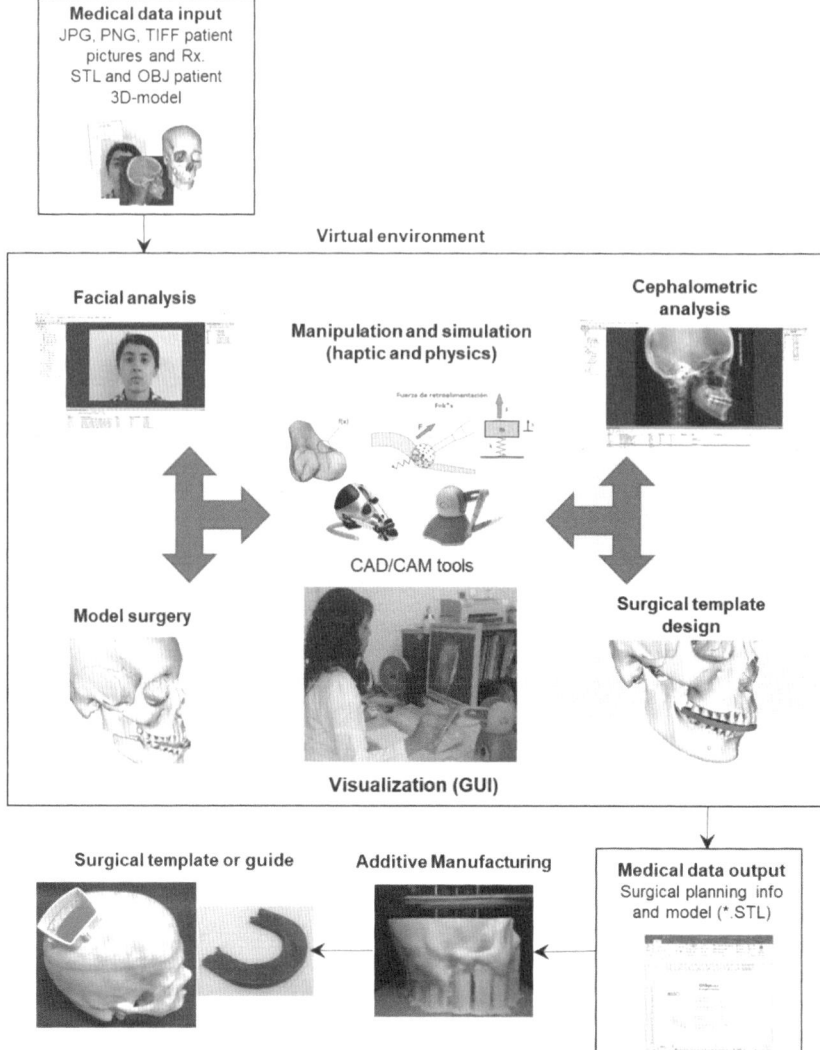

Fig. 7.6. Architecture of the virtual orthognathic surgery planning system.

7.4.1 *Haptic-enabled Segmentation, Manipulation, and Repositioning of Skull Fragments*

In orthognathic surgery planning, model surgery is a crucial procedure because it represents the surgical outcome for patients requiring the correction of a dentofacial deformity.[104] A comparison between the traditional model surgery process and the virtual model surgery process is shown in Fig. 7.8. In the virtual process, the patient's model replaces the traditional dental casts, eliminating errors due to shrinkage of the plaster during the curing process, and preventing misalignments during the assembly of the casts on the articulator. To allow the virtual model surgery process, CAD/CAM tools and functionalities are developed and integrated in the haptic-enabled virtual OGS planning system.

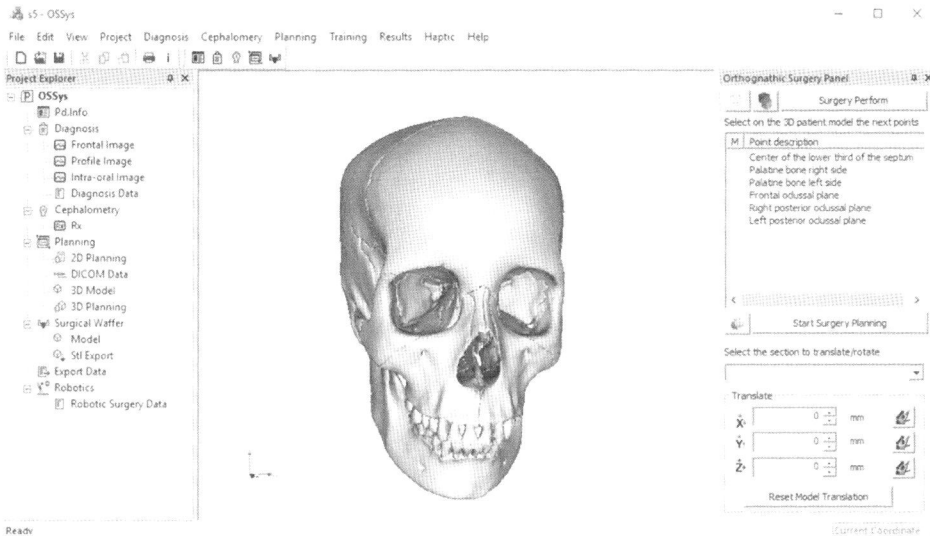

Fig. 7.7. User's graphic interface of the virtual OGS system.

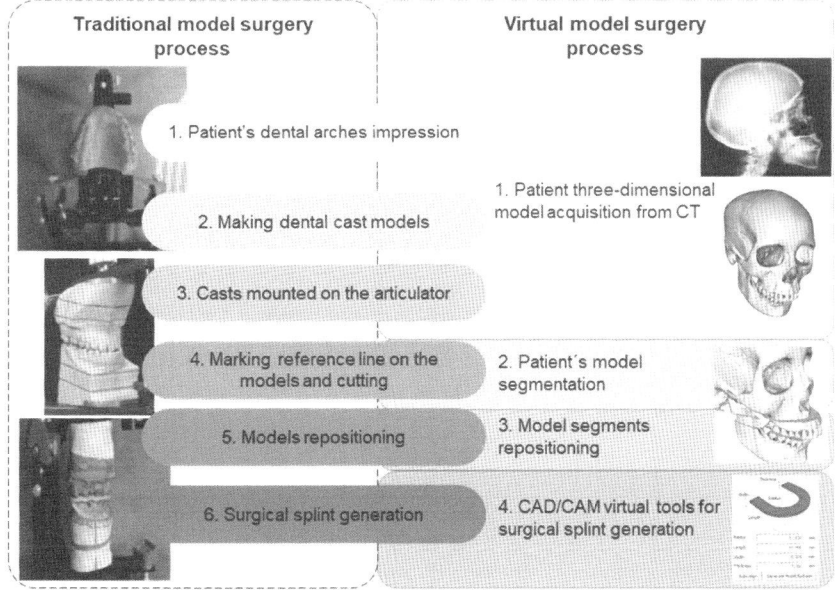

Fig. 7.8. Traditional model surgery process vs. virtual process.

The OGS planning virtual process starts by importing the patient's 3D model as OBJ or STL file formats. This model is rendered to the user as a graphical model, Fig. 7.9(a). From the graphical model, the manipulation module generates a haptic model using axis aligned bounding boxes (AABBs), Fig. 7.9(b). The graphical and haptic models overlap to enable the haptic feedback to the user during the virtual model manipulation. Next, the surgeon must select the OGS procedure and identify the landmarks that define the cutting plane in the 3D model. The model is segmented automatically by means of a CAD Boolean operation. Each bone fragment can be freely manipulated in 6 degrees of freedom (DoF) by means of the haptic device, the PC's mouse, or the PC's keyboard. In addition, to increase the accuracy of the repositioning movements, the system allows the user to customise the DoF during the manipulation process. Once the virtual bone segments are repositioned to define the new patient's occlusion, the new positions are automatically computed, and a report generated; this specifies the rotations and displacements of the maxillary and mandibular models in each direction; i.e. the projection, impact, lifting, yaw, roll, and pitch movements.

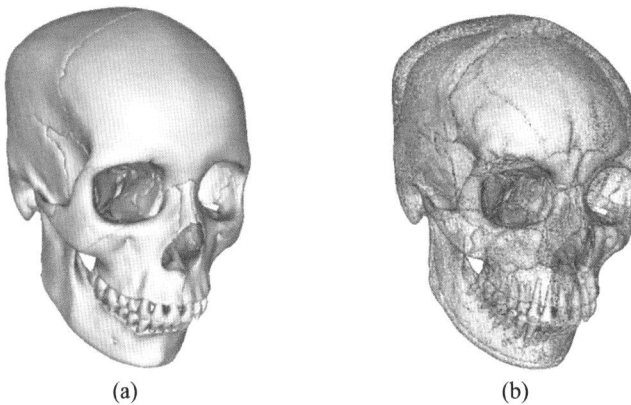

(a)   (b)

Fig. 7.9. Three-dimensional patient's models: (a) graphic model, (b) haptic model.

In the traditional model surgery process when the dental casts are mounted on the articulator, reference lines are marked. These lines are used as a reference to generate the segmented maxillary and mandibular models. In the virtual OGS planning system the reference lines are not needed; the model segmentation and repositioning is carried out by means of the haptic device and according to the orthognathic procedure shown in Fig. 7.10. The OGS procedures implemented in the virtual system include the mandibular surgical repositioning (BSSO, bilateral sagittal split osteotomy), the maxilar reposition (LeFort I and LeFort II), and the chin reposition (Geonioplasty). The user is able to select these procedures in the graphical user interface (GUI), Fig. 7.11(a). The user must identify and mark the anatomical points on the patient's 3D model according to the selected OGS procedure and the order requested by the system, Fig. 7.11(b). Anatomical points are identified by touching and feeling anatomical features on the patient's 3D model by means of the haptic device. To mark a point the user locates the haptic cursor at the desired model position and presses the device button. Once all the landmarks are defined, the system automatically computes the cutting plane and segments the virtual model. The repositioning of these virtual bone segments can be made in all 6-DOF by means of the haptic device, the PC-mouse or the keyboard, as shown in Fig. 7.11(c). The position and orientation of each segment is feedback to the user in real time and stored automatically. An outstanding feature of this virtual model surgery is collision detection among the bone segments during the manipulation and repositioning tasks, which can be enabled or disabled by the user to avoid or allow, respectively, the overlapping among the bone fragments.

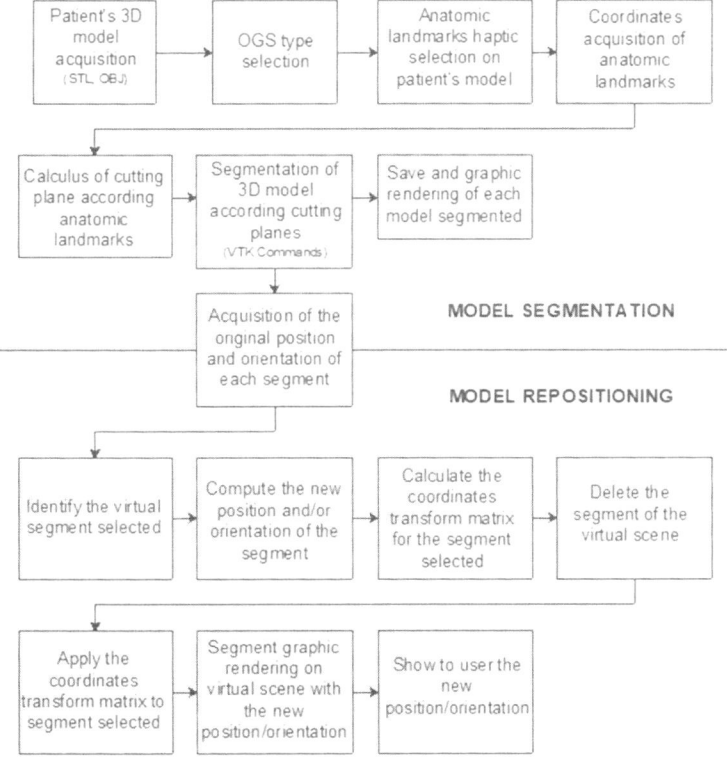

Fig. 7.10. Model segmentation and repositioning process.

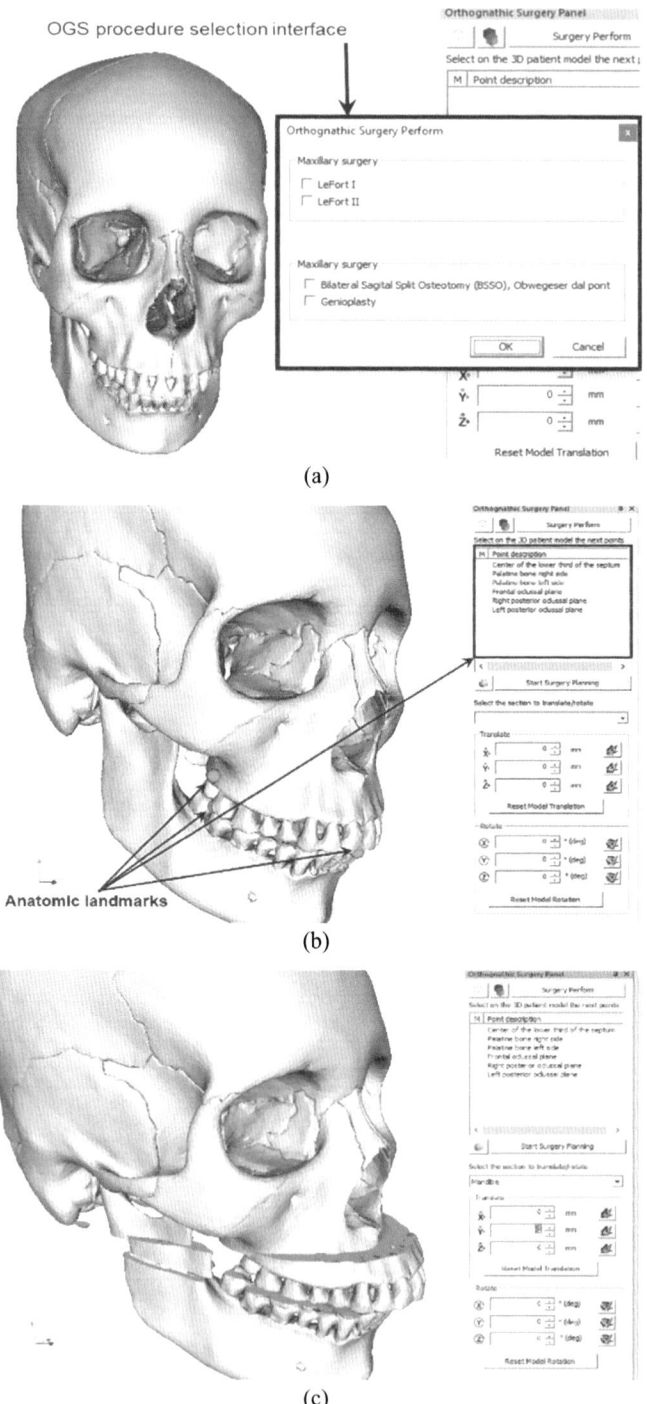

Fig. 7.11. Virtual model segmentation: (a) selection of the orthognathic procedure to be performed, (b) anatomic landmarks, (c) virtual repositioning, (d) real-time segment position.

7.4.2 *Virtual Design of Surgical Templates*

After the repositioning of the dental casts in the traditional model surgery process, a surgical template, also known as splint or intraoral wafer, is generated. On this surgical template, made of acrylic, the desired patient's occlusion information is engraved. In the virtual OGS planning system several CAD tools for the virtual design of intraoral templates have been incorporated. These CAD functionalities allow surgeons or specialists to generate the intraoral wafer without prior knowledge or experience in CAD systems. The virtual design process of the surgical template is shown in Fig. 7.12.

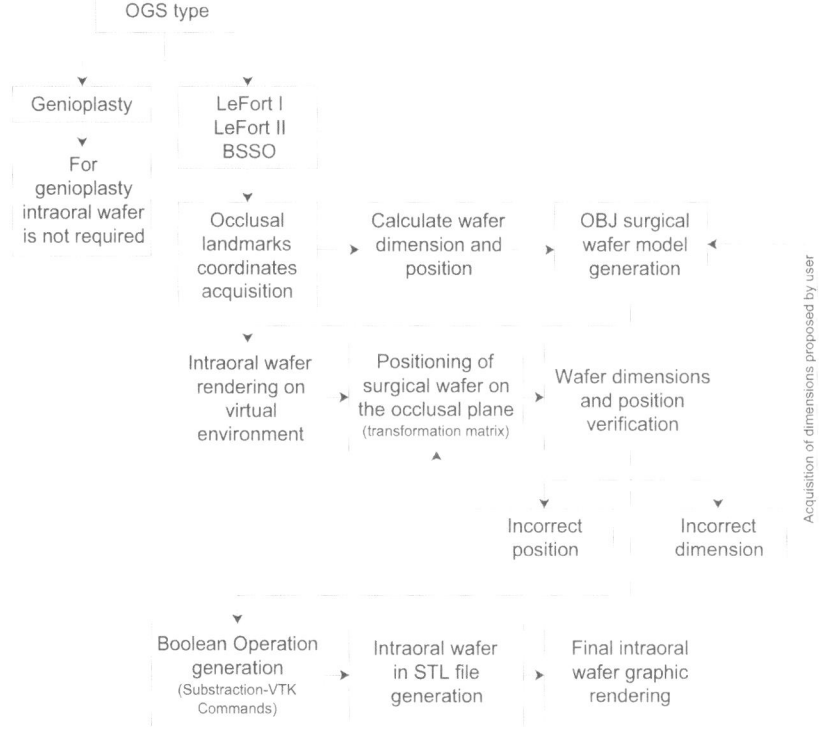

Fig. 7.12. Intraoral wafer virtual design process.

The design of the intraoral wafer is generated from a general parametrized 3D model as shown in Fig. 7.13(a). This parameterized 3D model has a similar shape to the maxillary arches and is created as an OBJ model made of a triangular mesh. The initial design parameters are automatically computed from the anatomic landmarks indicated by the user during the bone segmentation process. These design parameters are used by the system to automatically define the initial shape,

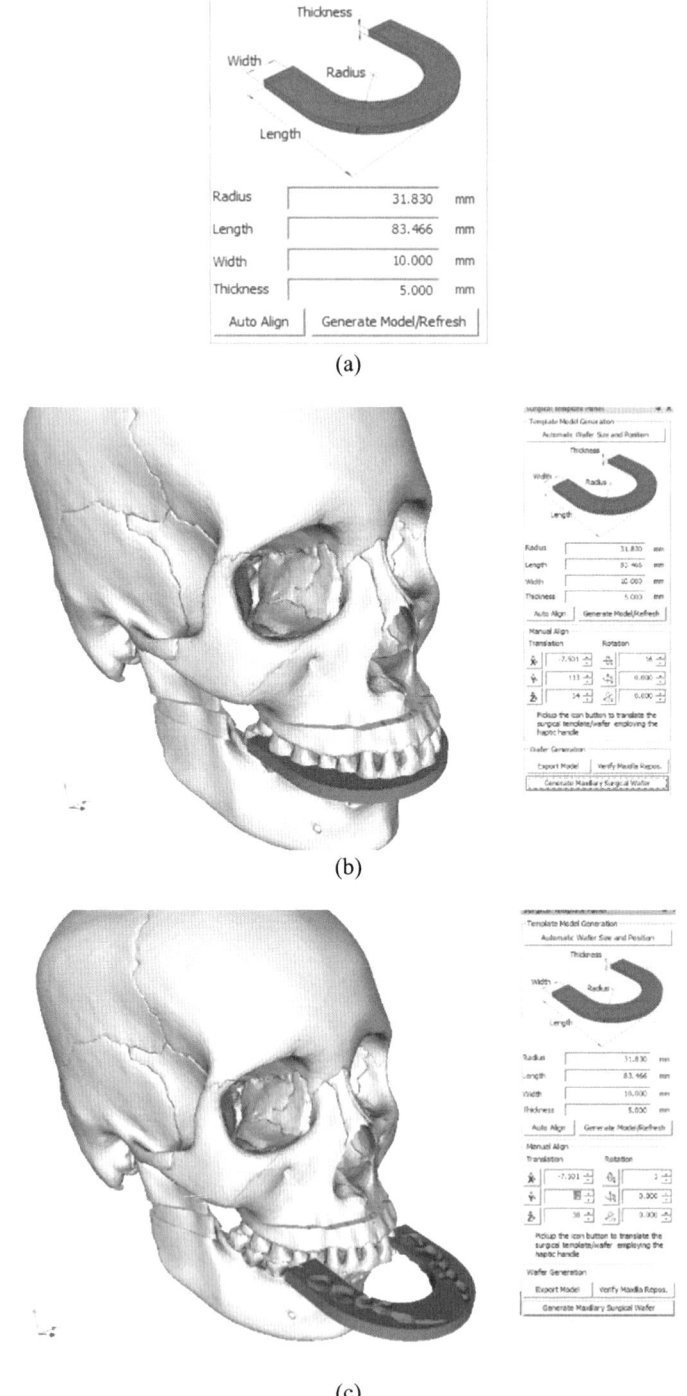

Fig. 7.13. Virtual intraoral wafer: (a) design parameters, (b) previsualization, (c) intraoral wafer generated.

dimensions, and position of the intraoral wafer. The wafer is rendered into the virtual scene as shown in Fig. 7.13(b). The specialist can then analyze and modify, if necessary, the design parameters and position prior to the occlusal engraving, which is executed once the design has been verified and accepted. The CAD tools that allow occlusal engraving are based on Boolean operations using the VTK commands. The result of the occlusal engraving on the wafer is rendered as shown in Fig. 7.13(c). The final design of the intraoral template can be saved or exported as an STL file in order to be used in the manufacturing process, such as CNC machining or additive manufacturing. A performance evaluation of the system has revealed that it takes an average time of 8 minutes for a surgeon to complete the design of the surgical template.

7.4.3   *Additive Manufacturing of Surgical Templates*

The incorporation of modern engineering design tools and advanced manufacturing technologies (such as Additive Manufacturing and Robotics) into the human healthcare area, can speed up the surgical planning process and the product development process of medical devices; leading to benefits in terms of risk, cost and time reduction. In the last years, Additive Manufacturing (AM) has been successfully used for medical applications.[105-108] AM technologies allows the rapid fabrication of prototypes or end-user parts corresponding to medical devices such as prostheses, ortheses, implants, surgical templates, surgical guides, surgical tools, etc. Moreover, medical devices are customized according to the end-user anthropometric characteristics and special needs. In the area of orthopedics and orthognathic surgery, numerous surgical tools have been developed using AM. These surgical tools have been used by the surgeons in the operating room: for instance, the bone repositioning guides.[109-111]

In orthognathic surgery the surgical splint or intraoral wafer is typically fabricated by hand. However, with the integration of CAD tools into the virtual OGS planning system, it is possible to fabricate this surgical guide using AM technologies. To do this, the system generates a three-dimensional model of the intraoral wafer as an STL format. A Creator Pro FDM system from FlashForge© was used to verify the design of the dental template. The material employed was PLA, and the selected FDM process parameters are shown in Table 7.3. The fabricated intraoral wafer is shown in Fig. 7.14. Based on a standard size of a dental template, it takes about one hour to fabricate it in a conventional AM system. Once the template is manufactured, a physical inspection must be performed to confirm that the basic aspects and dimensions are met. The sterilization of the implant is also necessary before its use in the real surgical procedure.

Table 7.3. Intraoral wafer fabrication parameters.

Parameter	Unit
Layer thickness	0.14 mm
Extrusion temperature	195 °C
Infill density	100 %
Infill pattern	Hexagon

Fig. 7.14. Intraoral wafer fabricated by additive manufacture.

Some research works have compared the surgical wafer obtained using the traditional approach and the surgical wafer fabricated from the virtual approach and AM technologies. These report that AM offers a good alternative as wafer-production-procedure, decreasing the shape errors produced by the acrylic shrinkage, and the time required by the surgeon to adapt the resin on the cast models in the traditional method.[109,112-114] Regarding the surgical wafer fabrication time, the results in the literature show that the production times corresponding to the traditional approach and the AM techniques are very similar. However, the time required in the traditional fabrication process corresponds to the time of a specialist, whereas in the virtual approach the production time corresponds to AM machine time, which is less expensive than the specialist labour time cost. AM systems have led to successful fabrication of surgical wafers because they include the use of biocompatible polymers for medical applications.[112]

Thus, the use of AM technologies to allow the rapid manufacture of surgical templates from its virtual model is possible by integrating CAD/CAM functionalities into the virtual environment.

7.5 Discussion

The proposed general methodology for the development of VR applications in medicine enables the incorporation of CAD and manufacturing tools in order to improve the surgical planning process and the development process of medical device. The integration of VR and haptic technologies allows specialists to interact with the patient's virtual anatomy in a more intuitive and natural way than in conventional CAD, CAE, and CAM systems. Using such an approach, this eliminates the need for a specialist in engineering tools and the practicality of the virtual approach is increased. By interacting in the virtual environment, medical professionals can easily accomplish the design of medical devices without the need of previous knowledge in CAD/CAE/CAM tools commonly used in engineering. Thus, the integration of design and manufacturing tools within VR systems opens up the possibility for new virtual applications in the medical field, the development of new surgical techniques and the improvement of current surgical and planning techniques.

The development of the haptic-enabled virtual system for orthognathic surgery planning has validated the proposed general methodology for the development of virtual medical applications. The virtual OGS system integrates manipulation tools for the segmentation and repositioning of 3D models and the design tools required for the generation of the intraoral template needed for actual maxillary surgery in the operating theatre. Thus, the system allows the virtual segmentation and repositioning of the patient's 3D model; this characteristic substitute the traditional process where the patient's cast models are cut and relocated manually. Consequently, leading to a reduction in errors related to the traditional mounting, cutting, and relocation of cast models.

Regarding the accuracy and precision of the haptic manipulation in the virtual environment, the authors have performed several evaluations of errors during the landmarking process.[33] The results have shown that errors associated to the haptic manipulation and landmarking in the virtual environment are significantly less than in the traditional approach. This large difference is due to the enhancement of landmark selection using haptics; this was also highlighted using verbal and questionnaire feedback from the users. It has been also observed that with the use of haptics the users can feel and touch the surface characteristics to identify the anatomical points more accurately, leading to less variation in the detection of these key landmarks. Therefore, the tracing and identification of 3D model landmarks is substantially improved by using haptic-enabled virtual manipulation.

Ongoing research work considers the use of VR and engineering technologies in the design of craniofacial implants and prosthesis with the proposed methodology shown in Fig. 7.15.[5] The functionality and usability of the proposed methodology has been evaluated by the development of a case study as shown in Fig. 7.16. The results have proved the effectiveness of the methodology to design and optimize customized craniofacial implants. The results have also proved that the time and risk of the surgical procedure is reduced by incorporating engineering technologies into traditional medical procedures.

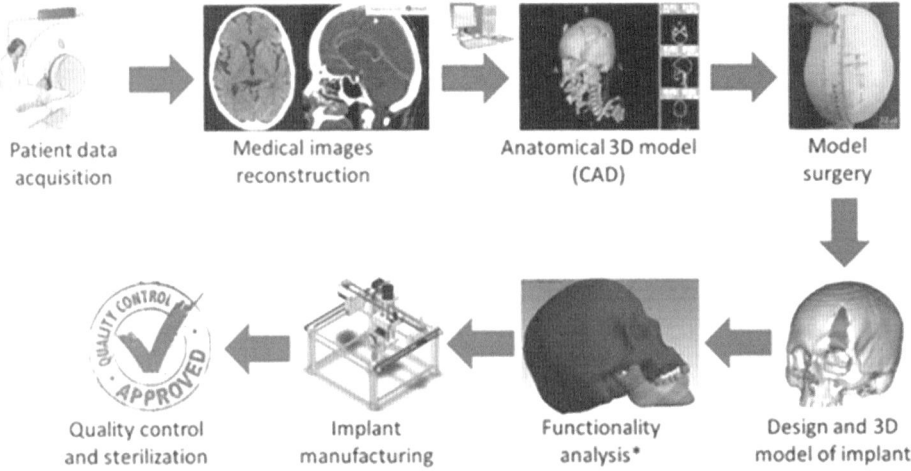

Patient data acquisition → Medical images reconstruction → Anatomical 3D model (CAD) → Model surgery

Quality control and sterilization ← Implant manufacturing ← Functionality analysis* ← Design and 3D model of implant

Fig. 7.15. Methodology for the design, optimization, and fabrication of craniofacial implants.

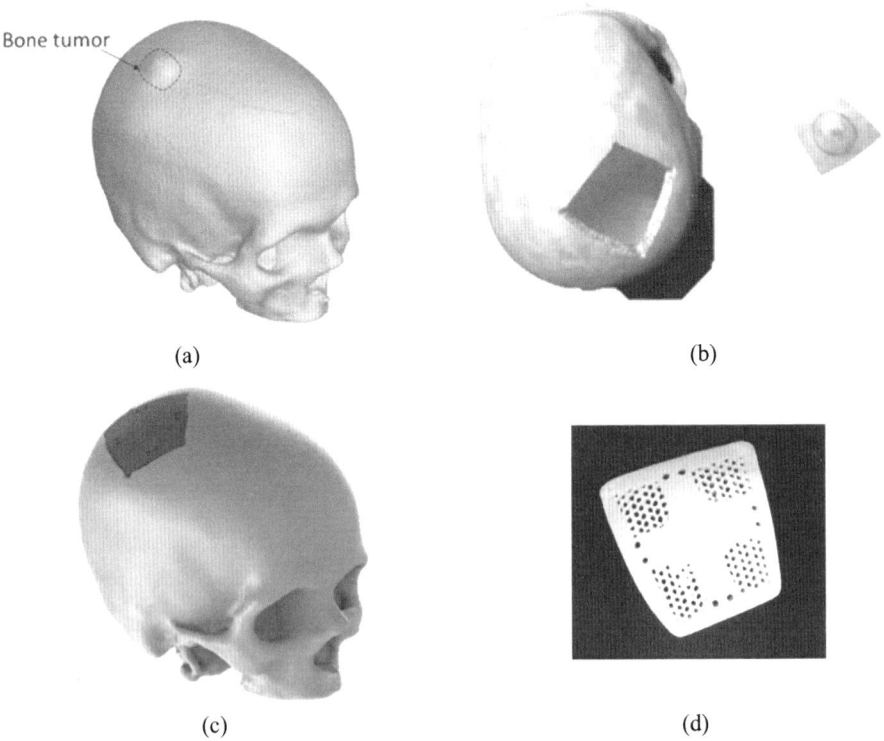

(a)   (b)

(c)   (d)

Fig. 7.16. Design, optimization, and fabrication of craniofacial implants: a) patient's skull model, b) AM skull model, c) model surgery, d) implant design, e) implant fabrication.

7.6 Conclusions

The use of VR and engineering technologies to enhance medical procedures is a reality new research area with high impact and benefits in human life. Using and extending approaches originally researched in the virtual manufacturing domain, it has been demonstrated that the integration of engineering tools into a virtual surgical planning system improves and speeds the design and fabrication process of orthognathic surgical templates. The system incorporates design- and manufacturing-assisted tools to enhance and ease the development process of surgical templates. The results have shown that the haptic manipulation of virtual objects during the segmentation and relocation of bone fragments increased the intuitiveness and realism of the virtual medical approach. Moreover, the integration of virtual design and manufacturing tools have reduced the need of specialized knowledge in CAD/CAE/CAM systems. Surgeons can design surgical templates in the virtual environment without needing specialized knowledge in engineering design tools. Additionally, the rapid fabrication of templates in additive manufacturing systems is possible.

Acknowledgments

This research was supported by CONACYT (National Science and Technology Council of Mexico), research grant CB-2010-01-154430. Acknowledgments are also given to the PRODEP and FAI programs from SEP and UASLP, respectively, for the supplementary financial support.

References

1. S. Lohfeld, P. McHugh, D. Serban, D. Boyle, G. O'Donnell, N. Peckitt, Engineering Assisted Surgery™: A route for digital design and manufacturing of customised maxillofacial implants, *Journal of Materials Processing Technology* **183**(2-3), 333–338 (2007).
2. G. R. Swennen, M. Gaboury, 3D Virtual Treatment Planning Transfer in the Operation Theatre, In *3D Virtual Treatment Planning of Orthognathic Surgery,* Gwen Swennen (ed). Springer (2017).
3. M. G. Bernal-Torres, H. I. Medellín-Castillo, J. C. Arellano-González, Design and Control of a New Biomimetic Transfemoral Knee Prosthesis Using an Echo-Control Scheme, *Journal of Healthcare Engineering* 1–16 (2018).
4. B. Z. Li Lei, Hao Sun, Jianbing Yuan, Steve Shen, Xudong Wang, A novel method of computer aided orthognathic surgery using individual CAD-CAM templates: A combination of osteotomy and repositioning guides, *British Journal of Oral and Maxillofacial Surgery* **51**, e239-e244 (2013). doi:0.1016/j.bjoms.2013.03.007.

5. C.A. Gómez Pérez, H.I. Medellín-Castillo, R. Espinosa-Castañeda, Computer Assisted Design and Structural Topology Optimization of Customized Craniofacial Implants. In *Proceedings of the ASME 2017 International Mechanical Engineering Congress and Exposition,* Tampa, Florida, USA (November 2017). doi:10.1115/IMECE2017-72219.

6. M. J. Zinser, R. A. Mischkowski, H. F. Sailer, J. E. Zoller, Computer-assisted orthognathic surgery: feasibility study using multiple CAD/CAM surgical splints, *Oral Surg Oral Med Oral Pathol Oral Radiol.* **113**(5), 673-687 (2012). doi:10.1016/j.oooo.2011.11.009.

7. X. Chen, X. Li, L. Xu, Y. Sun, C. Politis, J. Egger, Development of a computer-aided design software for dental splint in orthognathic surgery, *Scientific Reports* **6**, 38867 (2016).

8. J. Kraeima, J. Jansma, R. H. Schepers, Splintless surgery: Does patient-specific CAD-CAM osteosynthesis improve accuracy of Le Fort I osteotomy?, *Br J Oral Maxillofac Surg.* **54**(10), 1085–1089 (2016). doi:10.1016/j.bjoms.2016.07.007.

9. P. Scolozzi, Computer-aided design and computer-aided modeling (CAD/CAM) generated surgical splints, cutting guides and custom-made implants: which indications in orthognathic surgery?, *Revue de stomatologie, de chirurgie maxillo-faciale et de chirurgie orale* **116**(6), 343–349 (2015).

10. E. Shaheen, Y. Sun, R. Jacobs, C. Politis, Three-dimensional printed final occlusal splint for orthognathic surgery: Design and validation, *Int J Oral Maxillofac Surg.* **46**(1), 67–71 (2017). doi:10.1016/j.ijom.2016.10.002.

11. B. Li, S. Shen, W. Jiang, J. Li, T. Jiang, J. Xia, S.G. Shen, X. Wang, A new approach of splint-less orthognathic surgery using a personalized orthognathic surgical guide system: A preliminary study, *Int J Oral Maxillofac Surg.* **46**(10), 1298–1305 (2017).

12. S. Girod, E. Keeve, B. Girod, Advances in interactive craniofacial surgery planning by 3D simulation and visualization, *Int J Oral Maxillofac Surg.* **24**(1), 120–125 (1995). doi:https://doi.org/10.1016/S0901-5027(05)80872-0.

13. V. N. Palter, T. P. Grantcharov, Virtual reality in surgical skills training, *Surgical Clinics* **90**(3), 605-617 (2010). doi:https://doi.org/10.1016/j.suc.2010.02.005.

14. C. Ruiz, F. Montagut, J. Yeison, E. Heidenreich, Algorithm for virtual modeling of organs by medical images, *Vector* **4**, 14–26 (2009).

15. K. M. Stanney, K. S. Hale, *Handbook of Virtual Environments: Design, Implementation, and Applications.* CRC Press (2014).

16. D. A. Bowman, R. P. McMahan, Virtual reality: how much immersion is enough?, *Computer* **40**(7) (2007). doi:https://10.1109/MC.2007.257.

17. L. P. Berg, J. M. Vance, Industry use of virtual reality in product design and manufacturing: a survey, *Virtual Reality* **21**(1), 1–17 (2017). doi:https://doi.org/10.1007/s10055-016-0293-9.

18. T. S. Mujber, T. Szecsi, M. S. J. Hashmi, Virtual reality applications in manufacturing process simulation, *Journal of Materials Processing Technology* **155–156**, 1834–1838 (2004). doi:10.1016/j.jmatprotec.2004.04.401.

19. I. Kartiko, M. Kavakli, K. Cheng, Learning science in a virtual reality application: The impacts of animated-virtual actors' visual complexity, *Computers & Education* **55**(2), 881–891 (2010). doi.org/10.1016/j.compedu.2010.03.019.

20. O. Rübel, S. Ahern, E. W. Bethel, M. D. Biggin, H. Childs, E. Cormier-Michel, A. DePace, M.B. Eisen, C.C. Fowlkes, C.G.R. Geddes, H. Hagen, B. Hamann, M-Y. Huang, S.V.E. Keranen, D.W. Knowles, C.L. Luengo Hendriks, J. Malik, J. Meredith, P. Messmer, Prabhat, D. Ushizima, G.H. Weber, K. Wu, Coupling visualization and data analysis for knowledge

discovery from multi-dimensional scientific data, *Procedia Computer Science* **1**(1), 1757–1764 (2010). doi.org/10.1016/j.procs.2010.04.197.

21. G. Riva, Applications of virtual environments in medicine, *Methods of information in medicine* **42**(5), 524–534 (2003).
22. L. Sastry, D. R. Boyd, Virtual environments for engineering applications, *Virtual Reality* **3**(4), 235–244 (1998).
23. T. R. Coles, D. Meglan, N. W. John, The Role of Haptics in Medical Training Simulators: A Survey of the State of the Art, *IEEE Trans Haptics* **4**(1), 51–66 (2011). doi:10.1109/TOH.2010.19.
24. F. P. Vidal, F. Bello, K. W. Brodlie, N. W. John, D. Gould, R. Phillips, N. J. Avis, Principles and applications of computer graphics in medicine, *Computer Graphics Forum* **25**(1), 113–137 (2006). doi: 10.1111/j.1467-8659.2006.00822.x
25. P. Xia, A. M. Lopes, M. T. Restivo, Virtual reality and haptics for dental surgery: A personal review, *The Visual Computer* **29**(5), 433-447 (2012). doi:10.1007/s00371-012-0748-2
26. G. R. M. S. Székely, Virtual reality in medicine, *British Medical Journal* **319**(7220), 1305 (1999).
27. L. Panait, E. Akkary, R. L. Bell, K. E. Roberts, S. J. Dudrick, A. J. Duffy, The role of haptic feedback in laparoscopic simulation training, *Journal of Surgical Research* **156**(2), 312–316 (2009). doi:https://doi.org/10.1016/j.jss.2009.04.018.
28. R. Owens, J. M. Taekman, Virtual reality, haptic simulators, and virtual environments. In *The Comprehensive Textbook of Healthcare Simulation*, A.I. Levine, S. DeMaria Jr., A.D. Schwartz and A.J. Sim (eds). Springer (2013).
29. K. Salisbury, F. Conti, F. Barbagli, Haptic rendering: introductory concepts, *Computer Graphics and Applications* **24**(2), 24–32 (2004).
30. G. Vázquez-Mata, Realidad virtual y simulación en el entrenamiento de los estudiantes de medicina, *Educación Médica* **11**, 29–31 (2008).
31. G. Subhas, A. Gupta, V. K. Mittal, Necessity for improvement in endoscopy training during surgical residency, *The American Journal of Surgery* **199**(3), 331–335 (2010). doi:https://doi.org/10.1016/j.amjsurg.2009.09.013.
32. L. Hanna, Simulated surgery: the virtual reality of surgical training, *Surgery-Oxford International Edition* **28**(9), 463–468 (2010). doi:/10.1016/j.mpsur.2010.05.004.
33. H. I. Medellin-Castillo, E. H. Govea-Valladares, C. N. Perez-Guerrero, J. Gil-Valladares, T. Lim, J. M. Ritchie, The evaluation of a novel haptic-enabled virtual reality approach for computer-aided cephalometry, *Comput Methods Programs Biomed.* **130**, 46–53 (2016). doi:https://doi.org/10.1016/j.cmpb.2016.03.014.
34. M. Bozzetto, S. Rota, V. Vigo, F. Casucci, C. Lomonte, W. Morale, M. Senatore, L. Tazza, M. Lodi, G. Remuzzi, A. Remuzzi, Clinical use of computational modeling for surgical planning of arteriovenous fistula for hemodialysis, *BMC Medical Informatics and Decision Making* **17**(1), 26 (2017).
35. W. J. Greenleaf, Virtual reality applications in medicine, *Microelectronics Communications Technology Producing Quality Products Mobile and Portable Power Emerging Technologies: IEEE* (1995).
36. R. McCloy and R. Stone, Science, medicine, and the future: Virtual reality in surgery, *British Medical Journal* **323**(7318), 912 (2001).
37. 3D_Systems. GI Mentor (2017a). Available at http://simbionix.com/wp-content/pdf/Brochures/healthcare-gi-brochure-2017.9.en-web.pdf (Accessed January 19, 2017).

38. P. P. Banerjee, C. J. Luciano, Haptic augmented and virtual reality system for simulation of surgical procedures: *Google Patents* (2017).

39. 3D_Systems. URO-PERC Mentor (2017b). Available at http://simbionix.com/wp-content/pdf/Brochures/URO_PERC_Brochure_12_2016-Web.pdf (Accessed January 19, 2017).

40. T. Lange, D.J. Indelicato, J.M. Rosen, Virtual reality in surgical training, *Surgical Oncology Clinics of North America* **9**(1), 61–79 (2000). doi.org/10.1016/S1055-3207(18)30169-8.

41. P. Buń, F. Górski, R. Wichniarek, W. Kuczko, P. Zawadzki, Immersive educational simulation of medical ultrasound examination, *Procedia Computer Science* **75**, 186-194 (2015). https://doi.org/10.1016/j.procs.2015.12.237.

42. B. Preim, P. Saalfeld. A survey of virtual human anatomy education systems, *Computers & Graphics* **71**, 132–153 (2018). https://doi.org/10.1016/j.cag.2018.01.005.

43. G. Quero, A. Lapergola, L. Soler, M. Shabaz, A. Hostettler, T. Collins, J. Marescaux, D. Mutter, M. Diana, P. Pessaux, Virtual and augmented reality in oncologic liver surgery, *Surgical Oncology Clinics of North America* **28**(1), 31–44 (2019). https://doi.org/10.1016/j.soc.2018.08.002.

44. T-K. Huang, C.H. Yang, Y.H. Hsieh, J.C. Wang, C.C. Hung, Augmented reality (AR) and virtual reality (VR) applied in dentistry, *The Kaohsiung Journal of Medical Sciences* **34**(4), 243–248 (2018). https://doi.org/10.1016/j.kjms.2018.01.009.

45. K. Han, I.Y. Kim, J-H. Kim, Assessment of cognitive flexibility in real life using virtual reality: A comparison of healthy individuals and schizophrenia patients, *Computers in Biology and Medicine* **42**(8), 841–847 (2012). doi.org/10.1016/j.compbiomed.2012.06.007.

46. D. Lamargue-Hamel, M. Deloire, A. Saubusse, A. Ruet, J. Taillard, P. Philip, B. Brochet, Cognitive evaluation by tasks in a virtual reality environment in multiple sclerosis, *Journal of the Neurological Sciences* **359**(1–2), 94–99 (2015). https://doi.org/10.1016/j.jns.2015.10.039.

47. J.M.F. Montenegro, V. Argyriou, Cognitive evaluation for the diagnosis of Alzheimer's disease based on Turing test and virtual environments, *Physiology & Behavior* **173**, 42–51 (2017). https://doi.org/10.1016/j.physbeh.2017.01.034.

48. S. Cho, J. Ku, Y. K. Cho, I. Y. Kim, Y. J. Kang, D. P. Jang, S. I. Kim, Development of virtual reality proprioceptive rehabilitation system for stroke patients, *Computer Methods and Programs in Biomedicine* **113**(1), 258–265 (2014).

49. S.-Y. Hsu, T.-Y. Fang, S.-C. Yeh, M.-C. Su, P.-C. Wang, V. Y. Wang, Three-dimensional, virtual reality vestibular rehabilitation for chronic imbalance problem caused by Ménière's disease: a pilot study, *Disability and Rehabilitation* **39**(16), 1601–1606 (2017).

50. M. M. Kılıç, O. C. Muratlı, C. Catal, Virtual reality based rehabilitation system for Parkinson and multiple sclerosis patients, *2017 International Conference on Computer Science and Engineering (UBMK)*, pp. 328–331, Antalya, Turkey (2017).

51. R. Ludymila Borges, Felipe R. Martins, Eduardo L.M. Naves, Teodiano F. Bastos, Vicente F. Lucena, Multimodal System for Training at Distance in a Virtual or Augmented Reality Environment for Users of Electric-Powered Wheelchairs, *IFAC-Papers OnLine* **49**(30), 156–160 (2016). https://doi.org/10.1016/j.ifacol.2016.11.146.

52. P. Niederer, S. Weiss, R. Caduff, M. Bajka, G. Szekély, M. Harders, Uterus models for use in virtual reality hysteroscopy simulators, *European Journal of Obstetrics & Gynecology and Reproductive Biology* **144**(1), S90–S95 (2009). doi.org/10.1016/j.ejogrb.2009.02.009.

53. A. Hamrol, F. Górski, D. Grajewski, P. Zawadzki, Virtual 3D Atlas of a human body – development of an educational medical software application, *Procedia Computer Science* **25**, 302–314 (2013). https://doi.org/10.1016/j.procs.2013.11.036.

54. H.H. Biscaro, F.L.S Nunes, J. dS. Oliveira, G.R. Pereira, Comparing efficient data structures to represent geometric models for three-dimensional virtual medical training, *Journal of Biomedical Informatics* **63**, 195–211 (2016). doi.org/10.1016/j.jbi.2016.08.014.

55. D. C. Hon, Selectable instruments with homing devices for haptic virtual reality medical simulation: *Google Patents* (2000).

56. J. I. Efanov, A.-A. Roy, K. N. Huang, D. E. Borsuk, Virtual Surgical Planning: The Pearls and Pitfalls, *Plastic and Reconstructive Surgery Global Open* **6**(1), e1443 (2018).

57. J. L. McGrath, J. M. Taekman, P. Dev, D. R. Danforth, D. Mohan, N. Kman, A. Crichlow, W.F. Bond Using Virtual Reality Simulation Environments to Assess Competence for Emergency Medicine Learners, *Academic Emergency Medicine* **25**(2), 186–195 (2018).

58. V. N. Palter, T. P. Grantcharov, Individualized deliberate practice on a virtual reality simulator improves technical performance of surgical novices in the operating room: a randomized controlled trial, *Annals of Surgery* **259**(3), 443–448 (2014).

59. Y. Pulijala, M. Ma, M. Pears, D. Peebles, A. Ayoub, Effectiveness of immersive virtual reality in surgical training—A randomized control trial, *Journal of Oral and Maxillofacial Surgery* **76**(5), 1065–1072 (2017).

60. A. S. S. Thomsen, D. Bach-Holm, H. Kjærbo, K. Højgaard-Olsen, Y. Subhi, G. M. Saleh, L. Konge, Operating room performance improves after proficiency-based virtual reality cataract surgery training, *Ophthalmology* **124**(4), 524–531 (2017).

61. M. K. Wrzosek, Z. S. Peacock, A. Laviv, B. R. Goldwaser, R. Ortiz, C. M. Resnick, M.J. Troulis, L.B. Kaban, Comparison of time required for traditional versus virtual orthognathic surgery treatment planning, *Int J Oral Maxillofac Surg.* **45**(9), 1065–1069 (2016). doi:https://doi.org/10.1016/j.ijom.2016.03.012

62. M. Müller, S. Schirm, M. Teschner, Interactive blood simulation for virtual surgery based on smoothed particle hydrodynamics, *Technology and Health Care* **12**(1), 25–31 (2004).

63. B. Reitinger, A. Bornik, R. Beichel, D. Schmalstieg, Liver surgery planning using virtual reality, *IEEE Computer Graphics and Applications* **26**(6), 36–47 (2006).

64. MedicimNV. Mimics. (2008). Available at http://www.medicim.com/en/home (Accessed January 19, 2017).

65. N. Gélinas-Phaneuf, N. Choudhury, A. R. Al-Habib, A. Cabral, E. Nadeau, V. Mora, V. Pazos, P. Debergue, R. DiRaddo, R.F. Del Maestro, Assessing performance in brain tumor resection using a novel virtual reality simulator, *International Journal of Computer Assisted Radiology and Surgery* **9**(1), 1–9 (2014).

66. M. M. Tedesco, J. J. Pak, E. J. Harris, T. M. Krummel, R. L. Dalman, J. T. Lee, Simulation-based endovascular skills assessment: the future of credentialing? *Journal of Vascular Surgery* **47**(5), 1008–1014 (2008).

67. P. Rhienmora, P. Haddawy, P. Khanal, S. Suebnukarn, M. N. Dailey, A virtual reality simulator for teaching and evaluating dental procedures, *Methods of Information in Medicine* **49**(04), 396–405 (2010).

68. B. Tolsdorff, A. Pommert, K. H. Höhne, A. Petersik, B. Pflesser, U. Tiede, R. Leuwer, Virtual reality: a new paranasal sinus surgery simulator, *The Laryngoscope* **120**(2), 420–426 (2010).

69. M.Vankipuram, K. Kahol, A. McLaren, S. Panchanathan, A virtual reality simulator for orthopedic basic skills: a design and validation study, *Journal of Biomedical Informatics* **43**(5), 661–668 (2010).

70. D. Ni, W. Y. Chan, J. Qin, Y.-P. Chui, I. Qu, S. S. Ho, P.-A. Heng, A virtual reality simulator for ultrasound-guided biopsy training, *IEEE Computer Graphics and Applications* **31**(2), 36–48 (2011).

71. N. Iwata, M. Fujiwara, Y. Kodera, C. Tanaka, N. Ohashi, G. Nakayama, M. Koike, A. Nakao, Construct validity of the LapVR virtual-reality surgical simulator, *Surgical Endoscopy* **25**(2), 423–428 (2011).

72. S. Delorme, D. Laroche, R. DiRaddo, R. F. Del Maestro, NeuroTouch: a physics-based virtual simulator for cranial microneurosurgery training, *Operative Neurosurgery* **71**(suppl_1), ons32-ons42 (2012).

73. C. A. Linte, K. E. Augustine, J. J. Camp, R. A. Robb, D. R. Holmes III, Toward virtual modeling and templating for enhanced spine surgery planning. In *Spinal Imaging and Image Analysis,* Shuo Li and Jianhua Yao (eds). Springer (2015).

74. P. Korzeniowski, D. C. Brown, M. H. Sodergren, A. Barrow, F. Bello, Validation of NOViSE: A novel natural orifice virtual surgery simulator, *Surgical Innovation* **24**(1), 5–65 (2017).

75. O. L. Haas Jr., O. E. Becker, R. B. de Oliveira, Computer-aided planning in orthognathic surgery—systematic review, *Int J Oral Maxillofac Surg.* **44**(3), 329–342 (2015). https://doi.org/10.1016/j.ijom.2014.10.025.

76. J. Chapuis, P. Ryan, M. Blaeuer, F. Langlotz, W. Hallermann, A. Schramm, M. Caversaccio, A new approach for 3D computer-assisted orthognathic surgery—first clinical case, *International Congress Series* **1281**, 1217–1222 (2005).

77. S. Gelesko, M. R. Markiewicz, K. Weimer, R. B. Bell, Computer-aided orthognathic surgery, *Atlas Oral Maxillofac Surg Clin North Am.* **20**(1), 107–118 (2012).

78. BC Kim, CE Lee, W Park, M-K Kim, P Zhengguo, H-S Yu, CK Yi, S-H Lee, Clinical experiences of digital model surgery and the rapid-prototyped wafer for maxillary orthognathic surgery, *Oral Surgery, Oral Medicine, Oral Pathology, Oral Radiology, and Endodontology.* **111**(3), 278–285 (2011).

79. Li BZ, Lei; Sun, Hao; Yuan, Jianbing; Shen, Steve; Wang, Xudong, A novel method of computer aided orthognathic surgery using individual CAD-CAM templates: a combination of osteotomy and repositioning guides, *British Journal of Oral and Maxillofacial Surgery* **51**, e239–e244 (2013).

80. GR Swennen, W. Mollemans, F. Schutyser, Three-dimensional treatment planning of orthognathic surgery in the era of virtual imaging, *J Oral Maxillofac Surg.* **67**(10), 2080–2092 (2009).

81. GRJ. Swennen, 3D Virtual Treatment Planning of Orthognathic Surgery, In *3D Virtual Treatment Planning of Orthognathic Surgery: A Step-by-Step Approach for Orthodontists and Surgeons,* G Swennen (ed). Springer 217–277 (2017).

82. S Aboul-Hosn Centenero, F. Hernandez-Alfaro, 3D planning in orthognathic surgery: CAD/CAM surgical splints and prediction of the soft and hard tissues results - our experience in 16 cases, *J Craniomaxillofac Surg.* **40**(2), 162–168 (2012).

83. M. Agus, A. Giachetti, E. Gobbetti, G. Zanetti, A. Zorcolo, Adaptive techniques for real-time haptic and visual simulation of bone dissection, *IEEE Proceedings Virtual Reality*, 102–109, Los Angeles, CA, USA (2003).

84. P. Olsson, F. Nysjo, J.M. Hirsch, I.B. Carlbom, A haptics-assisted cranio-maxillofacial surgery planning system for restoring skeletal anatomy in complex trauma cases, *Int J Comput Assist Radiol Surg.* **8**(6), 887–894 (2013).

85. Slicer, B. a. D. 3D_Slicer. (2018). Available at https://www.slicer.org/ (Accessed November 12, 2020).

86. ITK-SNAP. (2018). Available at http://www.itksnap.org/pmwiki/pmwiki.php (Accessed November 12, 2020).

87. Oxipita_Inc. TurtleSeg: 3D image segmentation software (2010). Available at http://www.turtleseg.org/index.php?page=software (Accessed November 12, 2020).

88. PathersonDentalSupply. Dolphin Imaging (2017). Available at https://www.dolphinimaging.com (Accessed January 19, 2017).

89. M. Kedzierski, A. Fryskowska, Methods of laser scanning point clouds integration in precise 3D building modelling, *Measurement* **74**, 221–232 (2015).

90. F. Bernardini, H. Rushmeier, The 3D model acquisition pipeline. *Computer Graphics Forum* (2002).

91. E. Gobbetti, F. Marton, Far voxels: a multiresolution framework for interactive rendering of huge complex 3d models on commodity graphics platforms, *ACM Transactions on Graphics (TOG)* (2005).

92. F. Steinbrücker, J. Sturm, D. Cremers, Volumetric 3D mapping in real-time on a CPU, *IEEE International Conference on Robotics and Automation (ICRA)*, pp. 2021–2028, Hong Kong, (2014).

93. B. Hannaford, J. K. Barral, E. Rephaeli, C. D. Ching, V. S. Bajaj, Heads-up displays for augmented reality network in a medical environment: *Google Patents* (2017).

94. M. Mihelj, D. Novak, S. Beguš, *Virtual Reality Technology and Applications*. Springer (2014).

95. E. Govea, H. I. Medellín-Castillo, Design and development of virtual reality environments for biomedical and engineering applications. In *Proceedings of the ASME 2015 International Mechanical Engineering Congress and Exposition, Houston*, Texas, USA (November 2015). doi:10.1115/ IMECE2015-52817.

96. E. H. Govea-Valladares, H. I. Medellin-Castillo, J. Ballesteros, M. A. Rodriguez-Florido, On the development of virtual reality scenarios for computer-assisted biomedical applications, *Journal of Healthcare Engineering.* 13 pages (2018). doi.org/10.1155/2018/1930357.

97. Blender Foundation (2018). Available at https://www.blender.org/ (Accessed November 12, 2020).

98. Kitware_Inc. VTK The visualization toolkit. (2018). Available at https://www.vtk.org/ (Accessed November 12, 2020).

99. Python Software Foundation (2018). Available at https://www.python.org/ (Accessed November 12, 2020).

100. M. Harris, N. Hunt, *Fundamentals of Orthognathic Surgery*. Imperial College Press (2008).

101. D. M. Steinbacher, Orthognathic Surgery: Principles, Planning and Practice, *Plastic and Reconstructive Surgery* **140**(6), 1320 (2017).

102. H3DAPI. H3DAPI Open Source Haptics (2014). Available at http://www.h3dapi.org/ (Accessed November 12, 2020).

103. E. Coumans, Bullet Physics SDK (2017). Available at http://bulletphysics.org/ wordpress/ (Accessed January 19, 2017).

104. E. J. Liou, P.-H. Chen, Y.-C. Wang, C.-C. Yu, C. Huang, Y.-R. Chen, Surgery-first accelerated orthognathic surgery: orthodontic guidelines and setup for model surgery, *J Oral Maxillofac Surg.* **69**(3), 771–780 (2011).
105. L. Hieu, N. Zlatov, J. Vander Sloten, E. Bohez, L. Khanh, P. Binh, P. Oris, Y. Toshev, Medical rapid prototyping applications and methods, *Assembly Automation* **25**(4), 284–292 (2005).
106. I. Gibson, L. Cheung, S. Chow, W. Cheung, S. Beh, M. Savalani, S. Lee, The use of rapid prototyping to assist medical applications, *Rapid Prototyping Journal* **12**(1), 53–58 (2006).
107. P. Lopes, P. Flores, E. Seabra, Rapid prototyping technology in medical applications: A critical review, *Proceedings of the International Symposium CompIMAGE 2006, Computational Modelling of Objects Represented in Images*, Coimbra, Portugal (October 2006).
108. R. Bibb, D. Eggbeer, A. Paterson, *Medical Modelling: The Application of Advanced Design and Rapid Prototyping Techniques in Medicine*. Woodhead Publishing (2014).
109. A. Shqaidef, A. F. Ayoub, B. S. Khambay, How accurate are rapid prototyped (RP) final orthognathic surgical wafers? A pilot study, *Br J Oral Maxillofac Surg.* **52**(7), 609–614 (2014).
110. M. R. Mahfouz, Deformable articulating template (formerly: customized orthopaedic implants and related methods): *Google Patents* (2015).
111. I. Idram, J.-Y. Lai, T. Essomba, P.-Y. Lee, Study on Repositioning of Comminuted Fractured Bones for Computer-Aided Preoperative Planning, *Proceedings of the 2017 4th International Conference on Biomedical and Bioinformatics Engineering* (2017).
112. K.-G. Song, S.-H. Baek, Comparison of the accuracy of the three-dimensional virtual method and the conventional manual method for model surgery and intermediate wafer fabrication, *Oral Surgery, Oral Medicine, Oral Pathology, Oral Radiology and Endodontics* **107**(1), 13–21 (2009).
113. S. Bai, B. Bo, Y. Bi, B. Wang, J. Zhao, Y. Liu, Z. Feng, H. Shang, Y. Zhao, CAD/CAM surface templates as an alternative to the intermediate wafer in orthognathic surgery, *Oral Surgery, Oral Medicine, Oral Pathology, Oral Radiology and Endodontics* **110**(5), e1–e7 (2010).
114. B. C. Kim, C. E. Lee, W. Park, M.-K. Kim, P. Zhengguo, H.-S. Yu, C.K. Yi, S-H. Lee, Clinical experiences of digital model surgery and the rapid-prototyped wafer for maxillary orthognathic surgery, *Oral Surgery, Oral Medicine, Oral Pathology, Oral Radiology, and Endodontology* **111**(3), 278–285.e1 (2011).

Chapter 8

Augmented Reality Applications in Industrial Robots

Jingsong Chu, Ariyan Kabir, William Rose, Dennis Wang, Mingjun Yao, and Satyandra K. Gupta

8.1 Introduction

Industrial robots are widely used in mass production applications. However, currently, robots are not considered useful in small production volume operations. The following limitations are often cited as reasons:

- *High capital cost:* Previous generations of robots were expensive, so it was not possible to use robots unless utilization was extremely high.
- *Long programming time:* Currently, it takes a long time to program robots for performing complex tasks, so robots cannot be used high mix low volume applications where a task is repeated only for short durations (e.g., from few hours to few weeks).
- *Limited dexterity:* Current generation robots have limited dexterity. To use robots in the hybrid cells, products need to be designed or specialized tools need to be developed to ensure that manufacturing operations do not require a high level of dexterity.

As we move towards shorter product life cycles and customized products, automation will be crucial to remain cost-competitive in high-wage economies. However, setting up purely robotic cells is not a viable option for most high mix low volume manufacturing organizations.

Human workers offer the following benefits:

- *Versatility:* Humans can perform a wide range of manufacturing tasks and operate many different types of tools.
- *Dexterity:* They can perform complex coordinated motions in very tight spaces.

- *Ability to perform in-process inspection:* They can perform process inspection in real-time.
- *Ability to handle contingencies and recover from errors:* Humans are good at recovering from errors introduced in previous steps and handling unexpected situations.

However, human workers have the following limitations:

- *Inconsistency:* Humans lack consistency over long periods of time due to physical and mental fatigue.
- *Labor cost:* Developed countries have high wages and manufacturers there often find it difficult to compete with those in countries with low wages.
- *Size, weight, and speed limitations:* There are natural limitations on the size and weight of parts that can be manipulated, and the speed of manufacturing operations that can be achieved by human workers.

The previous generation of industrial robots imposed safety risks to humans, so physical separation had to be maintained between humans and robots. This was typically accomplished by putting the robot in a cage. In order for the robot to be operational, the cage door had to be locked and elaborate safety protocol had to be followed to ensure that no human operator was present in the cage. This made it very difficult to design work cells where humans and robots could collaborate effectively.

Recently several advances have been made in industrial robots that make them safer for humans, and hence presenting an opportunity for creating hybrid work cells, where humans and robots can collaborate in close physical proximities.[1,2] The underlying idea behind such cells is to decompose manufacturing operations into tasks such that humans and robots can collaborate by performing tasks that are especially suitable for them.

Several new low-cost robots have been introduced in the market over the last three years, making them cost-effective in many manufacturing applications where utilization may not be very high. This makes the idea of hybrid cells economically viable in small-volume production. Hybrid cells require new modalities for humans and robots to interact with each other.

Augmented Reality (AR) has emerged as a very important technology. Interest in AR is mainly driven by the gaming industry. However, AR technology is being evaluated by many different industries such as construction, education, manufacturing, health care, and service to improve human productivity. It can be used for training humans, offering them assistance during complex tasks, and preventing mistakes. It is emerging as a new mode of human interface.

The AR into modern manufacturing processes offers new ways for humans and machines to interact. One area where AR can contribute to significant improvements in manufacturing deals with Human-Robot Interactions (HRI), where AR is able to deliver information both to and from a robot to assist a human collaborator. This information can be used to increase safety, improve efficiency, or lessen the burden on the human when completing complex tasks. This chapter presents an overview of representative technologies that address the use of AR in the context of HRI. These technologies are creating new modalities for humans and robots to work together and improve safety and productivity in manufacturing operations.[3–24]

8.2   Background

ISO 10218-1 Clause	*Type of collaborative operation*	*Main means of risk reduction*
5.10.2	Safety-rated monitored stop (Example : manual loading-station)	No robot motion when operator is in collaborative workspace
5.10.3	Hand guiding (Example: Operation as assist device)	Robot motion only through direct input of operator
5.10.4	Speed and separation monitoring (Example: Replenishing pats containers)	Robot motion only when separation distance above minimum separation distance
5.10.5	Power and force limiting by inherent design or control (Example: ABB Dual-Arm Concept Robot collaborative assembly robot)	In contact events, robot can only impart limited static and dynamic forces

Fig. 8.1. Summary of HRI Tasks by ISO 10218-1, based on information in Matthias.[25]

8.2.1   *Collaborative Robots*

Collaborative robots are the heart of what has allowed robots to emerge from behind fenced areas and be used in new applications in the close proximity of human operators. These robots are designed to operate with human safety in mind and therefore can enhance manufacturing by enabling physical interaction with humans. These robots are being employed in areas where humans are required for some aspect of assembly such as welding[26] or when high dexterity and perception are required. Since the robots are built to be safe for humans, the space requirement and adaptability of the robots is also a major advantage of collaborative robots. A major attraction for collaborative robots has been to be able to operate robots without having to build new fences or safety barriers.

While collaborative robots have many advantages, there are also disadvantages to using these robots. One drawback is that collaborative robots must slow down or stop whenever a human is near. While this feature increases safety, it also can greatly impact efficiency. Consider the example of a human who completes an assembly operation started by a collaborative robot, but must reach across the path of the robot to retrieve the parts. In this case, the robot would slow down to avoid an unsafe condition while the human is in the way while the human may not realize the impact they are having on the production speed. AR can play an important role in alerting humans in such cases.

8.2.2   *Use of AR in Industry*

AR development has grown significantly in recent years, leading to many new applications.[27] The popularity of AR in the gaming and entertainment industry, by products such as Google Glass and Microsoft HoloLens, has led many to believe AR is mainly focused on head-mounted displays (HMD). However, a broader definition of AR suggests that it encompasses any technology which provides an overlay of digital information on the real world.[28] To this end, projector and screen-based methods of AR provide alternative approaches to the HMD. All of these approaches to realizing AR are useful in the context of HRI.

In general, AR serves to make humans and robots more efficient and safer when working together. AR can increase the efficiency of a process by providing inputs to either the robot or human that would otherwise not be available. For example, AR can display the path of a robot to a human that can be modified and updated in real-time to avoid certain working areas. For safety, AR provides the same function by making information available to both humans and robots. Humans can be more aware of the actions of the robot to avoid potential collisions and robots can use the inputs from humans to correct their actions.

8.2.3   *Safety Considerations in Robot Deployment*

Manufacturing can pose danger to human operators because of the existence of large machines, heavy loads, and high speeds. Therefore, the introduction of any new risk to this environment generates immense interest from stakeholders and is, subsequently, bound by strict regulations. As robots have begun to replace humans in the manufacturing process, the concern from a safety standpoint has been focused on ensuring the functions the robots are performing do not harm the humans that are working in the same environment (see Fig. 8.1). Traditionally, to ensure human safety, a series of physical barriers or controls were implemented to limit robots. However, with the emergence of collaborative robots and the increased need for HRI, new regulations have been introduced which guide the robot deployment and manage risks.

Prior to the development of advanced sensors and robots, the approach to ensuring safety with humans and robots was to create spatial separation during activities. One popular method of spatial separation is the use of fences or cages around the robot. These allow the robot to operate in an isolated environment where humans are not able to enter. This method further ensures human safety by using a cut-off switch which disables the robot's motion should a human open the fence or cage.[26] Since large cages and fences are costly and take up space, another method of separation was developed which utilizes sensors to detect a human presence relative to the robot's workspace. Should a human get within a predefined distance, the robot will slow its speed, eventually stopping altogether when the human gets too close. Typically, this method of separation is accomplished through a series of proximity sensors, cameras, or lasers (creating the term laser fence) as a substitute for a physical fence.[29] While these methods have been effective in reducing risks associate with robots, they eliminate any human-robot collaboration, necessitating the refinement of regulations when HRI is required.

A relevant regulation on HRI is ISO 10218-1 which details the kind of tasks a robot and human can accomplish together. These tasks and risk mitigation techniques are summarized in Fig. 8.1. One shortfall of ISO 10218-1/2 was the failure to provide special guidelines for power and force limiting robots. In response, ISO/TS 15066 was released and provided expanded definitions and regulations regarding the use of collaborative robots. Especially, the regulation highlights different use cases for collaborative robots and species limiting values for power and force in different applications.[30] The value in understanding the different safety regulations comes with the recognition of how the new technologies were developed to enhance the methods for meeting these regulations.

8.3 Overview of AR Technologies

8.3.1 *See-through AR*

The first technology that is relevant for robotics applications is see-through AR which provides a digital overlay of information directly to the observer through an overlay on a translucent material. These systems are normally worn like glasses and are either tethered to an external computer or have an internal computer linked to the existing system. A series of sensors embedded in the devices provide feedback to the computer about the spatial relation of objects in the field of view. From this input, the computer can determine what the user is looking at as well as decipher gestures of the user as inputs to the system. The applications reviewed in this section are potential uses of see-through AR to enhance HRI and can serve as a guide for further exploration.

8.3.1.1 *Robot visualization*

One of the simplest applications of AR is to gather information about the existing robotic infrastructure and provide this to the user in real-time. Possible use of this application would be in an environment where a user must interact with several different robots performing different functions. The user would be able to walk up to the robot and an overlay of relevant information would be available allowing them to make timely decisions about how to interact with the robot. Maly et al.[28] present an evaluation of see-through AR as a way for the user to gather this information as shown in Fig. 8.2. In their proposed solution, a user could evaluate the robot's joint angles, workspace, and future paths by observing a unique set of markers attached to the robot. This would then allow the user to make decisions that can create a safer or more efficient interaction. However, in their study, the researchers concluded that see-through AR provided a limited field of view and that the user's hand gestures, used to control the flow of virtual information, did not always work. Therefore, they suggested that the continued development of this technology would be needed before it can be applied in actual applications.

Fig. 8.2. An illustration of see-through AR used to determine information about robots (image provided by Ivo Maly based on work reported in Maly et al.[28]).

8.3.1.2 *User specific safe working areas*

See-through AR can also be used to enhance the safety of HRI by providing the user with a clear graphic of where a human is safe to operate. This technology would be especially useful in environments where the robot and human must work closely with shifting workspaces and complicated procedures. For example, a robot may bring several different parts from different angles to an assembly and require a human to complete the function of fastening the parts. In this scenario, without AR, the human is responsible for remembering where the robot is moving next and ensure they are in a safe area. Michalos et al.[31] provide a pilot case of the application of this technology in an automotive assembly operation where they suggest the AR system increases safety. Their application displays to the user a virtual red cube for unsafe areas and green cube for safe working zones. Additionally, the AR is enhanced with audio alerts and flashing messages when the robot is in motion, shown in Fig. 8.3.

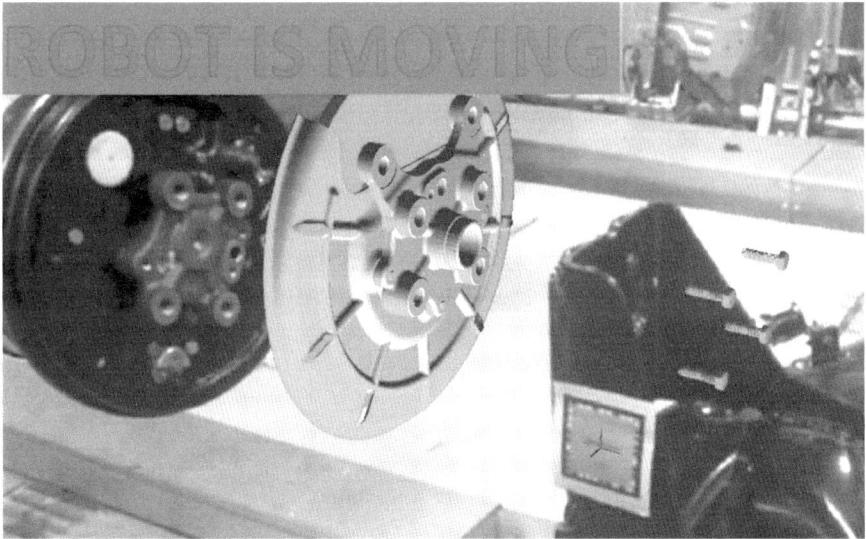

Fig. 8.3. An illustration of see-through AR displaying safe working spaces (image provided by George Chryssolourisa based on work reported in Michalos et al.[31]).

The use of see-through AR is advantageous over projector AR in this application because there is not the need for a medium to project the safe zone onto (such as a table) and there is less concern for distortion of the safe area due to a change in user perspective. Additionally, the technology is advantageous over screen AR because it allows the user to focus on the tasks being completed and enables them to use both hands for working. However, as the study notes, see-through AR hardware needs to become lighter and more agile for technology to be applied at manufacturing shop floors.

8.3.1.3   *Tasking of robots*

While see-through AR can improve safety, it can also be directly applied to the improvement of efficiency in certain processes. Huy et al.[32] studied the application of see-through AR to improve HRI with mobile robots that need user input to perform tasks. Especially, they suggest that the task of controlling a robot through manual entry on a pendant or controller is inefficient and can easily be adapted to see-through AR. In this instance, a user would be able to walk up to a robot, see what tasks it is currently performing, see what tasks it can perform, and provide necessary inputs. This information would be displayed to the user through see-through AR (see Fig. 8.4), and decisions could be input to the robot through a device attached to the user's hand. This would allow the user to interact with multiple robots quickly, rather than having to pick up each individual controller.

Additionally, the study provides an interesting insight into the advantage of see-through AR to increase the security of robots that require user input. In a large scale industrial setting, there may be hundreds or thousands of employees that must interact with robots and need to provide a wide variety of inputs. Since see-through AR is tied to the individual wearing the device, managers can select which users can direct the robot to perform specific functions. This eliminates the risk that anyone with a password to the controller can direct the robot to perform any function. While this level of security may seem excessive in today's environments, as robots become more prevalent in manufacturing one can see the benefits of regulating user inputs.

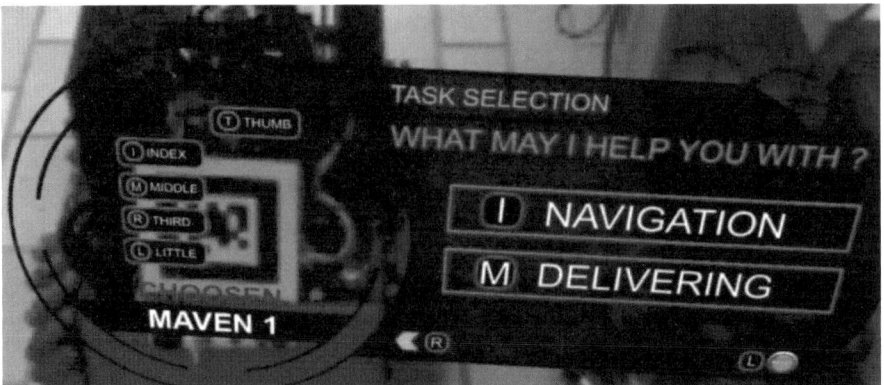

Fig. 8.4. An illustration of see-through AR used to provide input to robots (image provided by Gerald Seet Gim Lee based on work reported in Hui et al.[32]).

8.3.1.4 *Part classification*

Another use of see-through AR is to provide inputs to the robot by the user for part classification. Giseler et al.[33] suggest see-through AR could be used to combine the skills of a human to quickly classify parts and the robot's ability to quickly assemble the parts. Although this study was conducted in 2004, and sensor technology has developed significantly in that time, the premise still provides an interesting analysis of a way to improve HRI. The application uses a laser scanner to survey an environment which is then presented to the user for clarification. The user can see the scanned data overlaid on the real world and provide the input to identify the part required. For example, a process may involve assembling many parts that are delivered in a random configuration and are difficult for the robot system to properly identify. The user would be able to quickly identify the parts for the system, allowing the robot to complete the assembly. Although the obvious solution to this issue is to create a sensor or configuration which does not require the human to identify the parts, this application could be feasibly implemented where a sensor or better configuration is not available.

8.3.2 *Projector-Based AR*

A simple, yet effective, way to overlay digital information on the real world is using projector-based AR which utilizes common projectors to display information to users. This methodology has the same benefit as see-through AR of allowing the user to work with both hands without the additional burden of requiring a device to be worn. This means that anyone can walk up to a robot and interact with it without specialized training or equipment. However, projectors by themselves are simply passive systems that can only display information but not take user inputs. To address this concern, projector systems are often coupled with cameras sensors that can detect the location of specific items to provide feedback. Since all projector-based AR systems considered in this study utilize some form of sensor integration, the term projector AR will encompass both the physical project as well as the sensors and system.

8.3.2.1 *Safe area designation*

One of the primary ways to enable HRI is to stop robotic function whenever a human is within a certain distance creating certain safe and hazardous zones. While one way of displaying these zones was discussed previously with see-through AR, an alternative is also suggested which utilized projector AR. Vogel et al.[34] propose one method of projector-based AR which increases safety and efficiency. First, a series of sensors detect the part location and the system determines the robot's path to complete its task. Then a projector displays the hazardous area around this path so that users are aware of which areas to avoid. This hazardous area is continually updated based on the robot's location to enable greater utilization of the space than simply blocking o an entire area as shown in Fig. 8.5. The sensors of the system are also able to detect the user's location and stop the robot should the user pass into the hazard zone, as shown in Fig. 8.6, allowing for increased safety and efficiency.

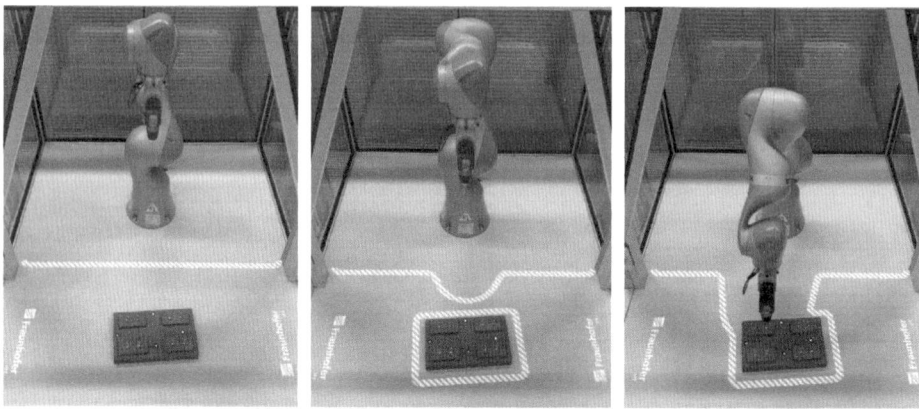

Fig. 8.5. An illustration of projector AR display of updating hazard areas as robot moves toward part (image provided by Christian Vogel based on work reported in Vogel et al.[34]).

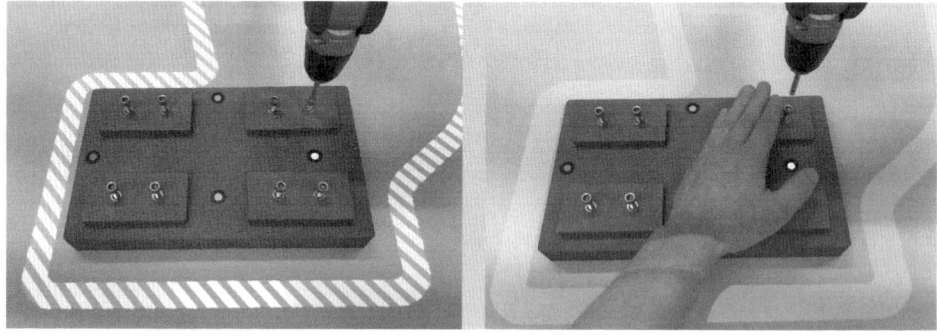

Fig. 8.6. An illustration of projector AR system displaying stop capability should user violate projected hazard areas (image provided by Christian Vogel based on work reported in Vogel et al.[34]).

A slight modification to this approach is proposed by Vogel et al.[35] in a different study designed for large robots and workspaces. A projector is still used to display the hazardous areas of a robot as it moves throughout its workspace. An illustrative example is shown in Fig. 8.7. However, instead of cameras to detect the human location, the workspace is covered with a specialized mat that can detect user location precisely and cease robot function should the human get in a hazard area. A factor of safety is built into the hazard areas to account for human behavior that cannot be detected by the mat, such as reaching or leaning into a hazard area. While both methodologies clearly demonstrate an improvement to safety, they can also be viewed as increasing efficiency by allowing the human to understand areas to avoid in order to not slow operations.

Fig. 8.7. An illustration of projector AR displaying hazard areas on a mat to provide warnings. In this figure, bottom right is danger zone, middle is warning zone, and upper left is safe zone.

8.3.2.2 *Display of current information*

In addition to displaying the safe operating areas for users, projector AR systems have also been proposed as methods for providing relevant data to humans about current robot actions. As far back as 1999, Terashima and Sakane[27] suggested that projectors could be used to display information to a human operator at a remote desk. The system would project a replicated robot and environment and prompt the user for necessary inputs through projected tools. Leutert et al.[36] expanded on this concept creating projections in a robot's workspace that a user can interact with. The system projects information such as the selected path for an operation and can be directly modified by the user in real-time, as shown in Fig. 8.8.

Further expansion on this concept involves the integration of a projection-based AR system onto mobile robots. With integrated projection units, mobile robots can project current information, such as their destination or upcoming actions, to allow

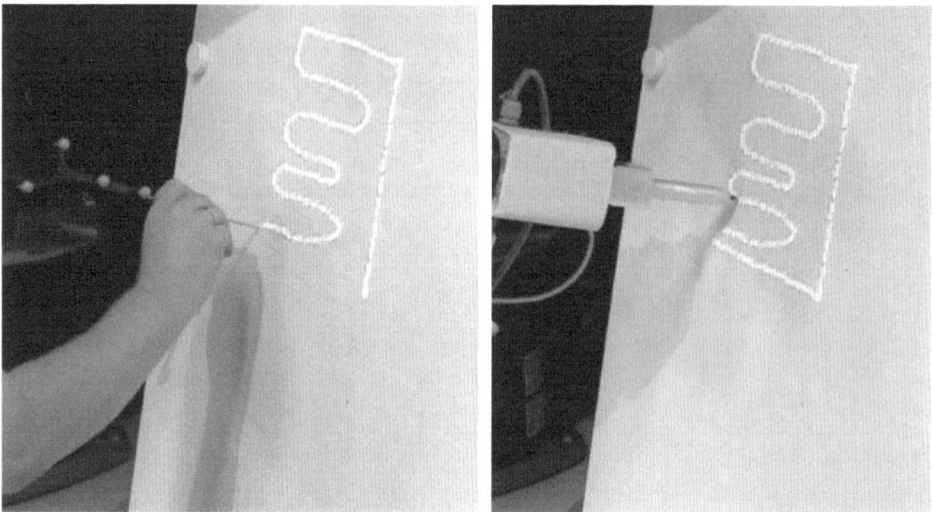

Fig. 8.8. Projection AR allowing a user to designate a path which followed by the robot (image provided by Klaus Schilling based on work reported in Leutert et al.[36]).

humans to better understand what they are doing. Costa and Arsenio[37] provide a methodology for ensuring the projected images from the robots can adapt to the changing perspective created by the robot movement. Their approach uses sensors to gather environmental data and alter the projector image to space for projection. An alternative methodology is demonstrated by Huy et al.[32] which uses a laser projector to create an image visible in outdoor or high-light environments.

8.3.2.3   *Projection for calibration*

Another application of projection AR is the use of projected information from a robot to allow a user to provide a calibration for the completion of tasks. Anderson et al.[38] propose that this method can be used when high precision is required from a robot and sensors are inadequate to detect spatial locations. Specifically, the study looked at welding studs on shipping hulls, requiring precise alignment of the robot and stud location. A projector on the robot end-effector creates a marker on the workpieces at the proposed weld location, then a human manual jogs the robot to align the maker with the correct location (Fig. 8.9(a)). Once this initial location is taught to the robot, it can then complete a series of subsequent tasks (Fig. 8.9(b)). The key advantage of this application over simply moving the robot by hand to the correct location is the ability for the operator to be in a remote location from the robot and still provide adequate calibration.

8.3.3 *Screen-based AR*

The final method of using AR for HRI investigated involves using a screen to display an overlay of digital information onto the real-world imagery. The screen can be a tablet connected to the system wireless or a monitor which is in a fixed position. The real-world imagery is generated through a camera that is either integrated into the screen itself (such as in a tablet) or positioned in known locations in the workspace. A key advantage to screen AR is the robustness of the technology which does not rely on a specialized headset and can display consistent information. For this reason, many technologies that are envisioned for use as see-through AR are first developed with screen-based systems as a trial. Therefore, the focus of this study will be on two key functional improvements screen AR provides without concentrating on unique applications of the technology.

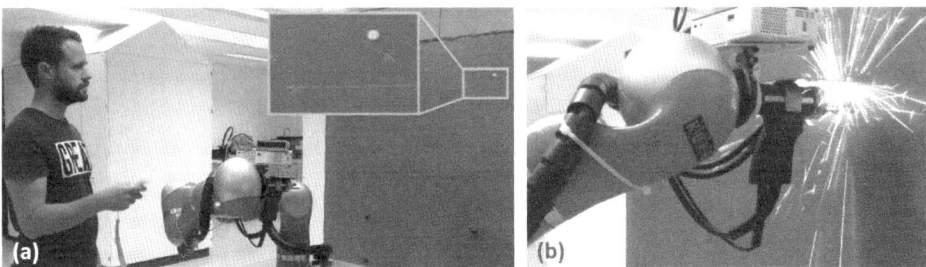

Fig. 8.9. Projector-based AR used for calibration of stud welding on ship hulls (a) operator adjusting stud position, (b) robot performing stud welding (images provided by Ole Madsen based on work reported in Andersen et al.[38]).

8.3.3.1 *Effective programming*

The methods for teaching robot collision avoidance and obstacle recognition are well studied. However, integrating screen-based AR into this process can allow for increased efficiency as the programmer is able to better visualize robot movements and configuration. The advantage of screen AR lies in the programmer's ability to visualize the suggested path in a simulation prior to execution and, subsequently, adjust the path if needed without having to waste time running the program with the robot. Gaschler et al.[39] provide one study where participants conducted a simple programming scenario with screen-based AR, demonstrating promising results. The participants of the study found the screen AR set up to be both intuitive and easy to use when surveyed after the experiment. While the time to complete the task was slightly longer, it can be inferred that the time to complete a more complicated task would be much less with the screen AR system than if conducted manually.

Other studies have found that the visual confirmation provided by screen AR can also be helpful in other robot planning applications. Ng et al.[40] provide a study involving laser and camera sensors to collect information about the workspace and relay the information to a screen with an overlay of proposed robot positions. In their analysis, the screen provided the user the ability to verify the tool path and end effector orientation on the workpiece prior to implementation. An illustrative example is shown in Fig. 8.10. A key feature in their study is the use of a laser sensor to provide exact positioning, negating the need for a hand marker from the user. This would allow the human to provide input to the screen from a distant area such as a control room or safe working area. For situations requiring closer observation by a human, Frank et al.[41] provide a similar study where user-designated objects for a robot to pick up through a screen AR system. Their analysis provided that the screen-based AR-enabled users to quickly adapt to changes in the workspace and could be advantageous when a robot must pick up a variety of different items that arrive in a random or unrecognizable pattern.

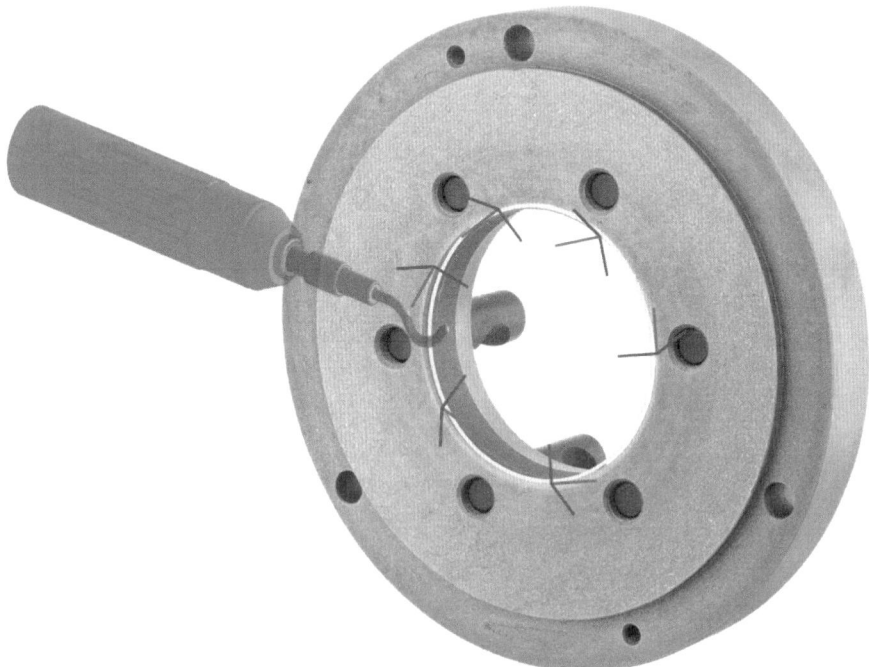

Fig. 8.10. An illustration of screen AR system for displaying tool orientation.

8.3.3.2 *New user interface*

In addition to increasing the efficiency of programmers, screen AR can provide new users with a simple way to interact with robots. Although an inexperienced programmer may not understand the complexities of collision avoidance or path selection, they will be able to intuitively understand the results of their decisions if displayed in a screen AR system. Fang et al.[42] suggest an entirely virtual robot can be used to teach complex robotics concepts to new users, increasing their efficiency when introduced to real robots (see Fig. 8.11). In this setup, a screen AR system allows users to place a virtual robot in a workspace, conduct a series of tasks and visualize the results. The obvious advantage of this system is the ability for multiple users to learn about robot programming without taking robots out of production for the instruction. Stadler et al.[43] provide an interesting comparison study for learning programming with screen AR where they suggest that the system may hinder long-term learning. The study suggests that the screen-based AR system does not require users to store information in short-term memory which translates to lower overall effectiveness as a programmer. This an example of the expertise reversal effect where effective techniques for learning a skill may decrease performance once a learner becomes an expert. However, the research shows that screen-based AR can provide interaction with users which might otherwise not have the ability, providing potential directions for further work in this area.

8.4   An Illustrative Case Study

8.4.1   *Overview*

Traditionally human operators program robot cells by using teach pendants. Most teach pendant does not have an intuitive interface. It takes human operators significant time to learn how to program robots using teach pendant. The motion being programmed is not easy to visualize. It takes significant time to program the robot to execute the complex motion. An error during robot programming can lead to the robot colliding with the objects in its work environment. This can lead to significant damage to the parts or the robots. Therefore, human operators proceed cautiously during robot programming.

   We believe that an AR-based user interface can be used to speed up robot programming and reduce the risk of damage during the robot programming. This will provide a safer way to let new users get used to controlling real robots before they had any experience in it. By seeing the gesture of the hologram, users can predict the behavior of the real robot. Also, with the ability to make the hologram perfectly align with the real robot, this AR user interface helps the user to actually prevent

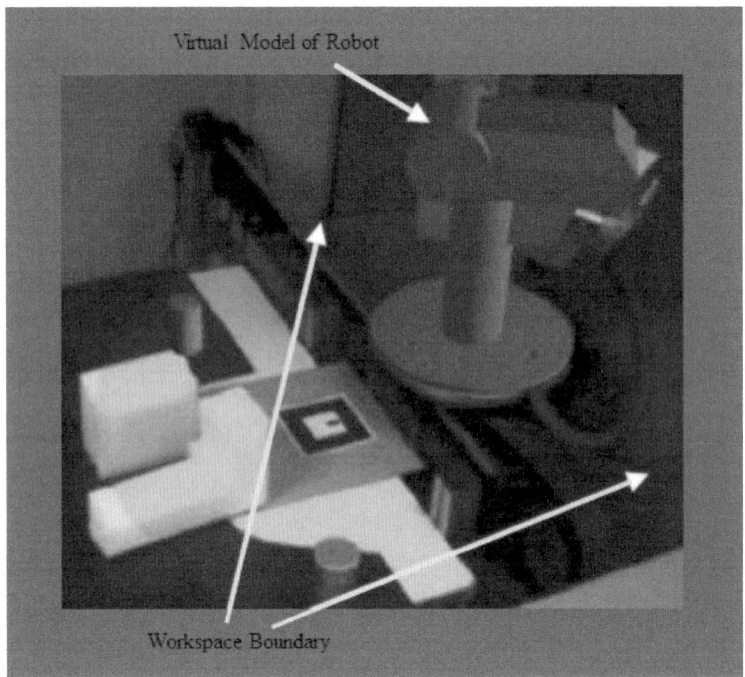

Fig. 8.11. An illustration of screen AR display of a virtual robot used for teaching robot programming (image provided by Ong Soh Khim based on work reported in Fang et al.[42]).

hitting obstacles before operating the real robot. This would help the operator speed up their manipulation to have more efficiency in their job.

We have developed a setup that enables humans to program robots using an augmented reality-based interface (see Fig. 8.12). This interface allows humans to move a virtual robot using a virtual teach pendant. Once the human is satisfied with the movement of the virtual robot, the motion command is transferred to the physical robot. We use Microsoft HoloLens as the platform to show the interface, and we use KUKA iiwa and Epson to be the robots controlled by HoloLens.

The interface is constructed by a hologram of the robot for visualization and some buttons for giving instructions to the hologram and communicating with the real robot.

The interface is displayed using Microsoft HoloLens. HoloLens is a pair of augmented reality smart glasses developed by Microsoft. Using an inertial measurement unit (IMU), a depth camera, and a video camera, HoloLens provides the ability for gaze and gesture recognition. HoloLens can make users see both the hologram of the robot and the real robot in the environment. In this way, people can visualize the behavior of the real robot because the hologram robot is on top of the real robot with the exact same size. Moreover, the system can use the gaze

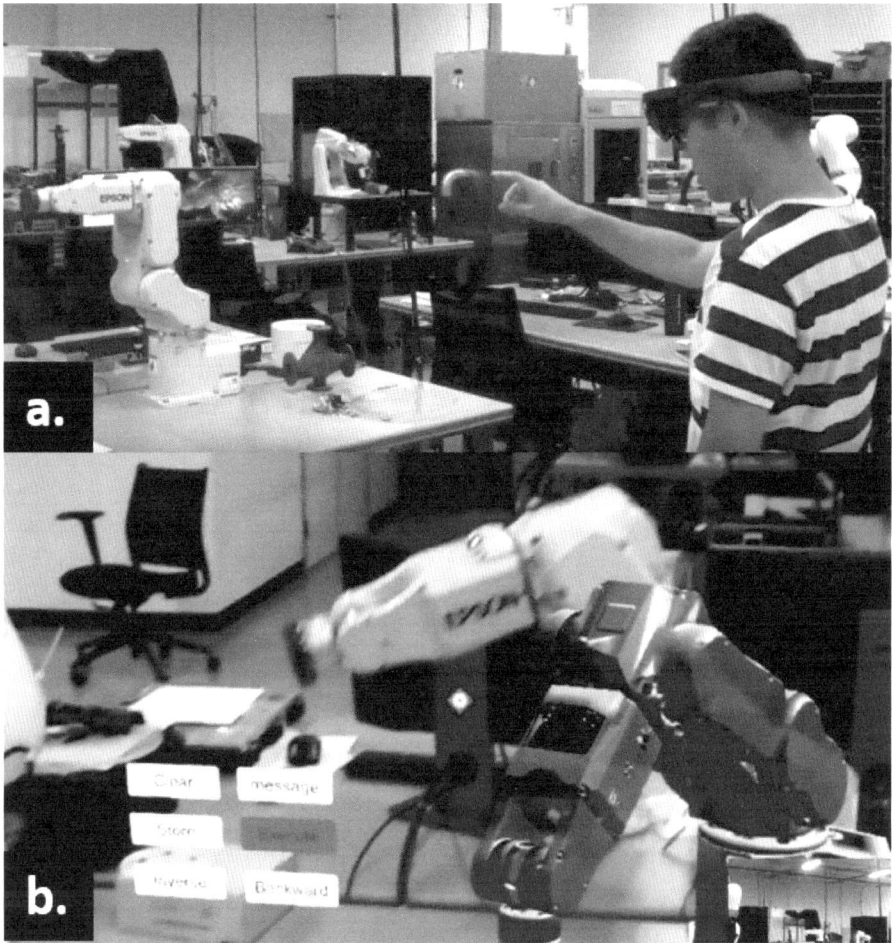

Fig. 8.12. Augmented Reality based interface for programming robots. (a) Human operator programming robot using augmented reality headset, (b) physical and virtual robot seen by the operator.

and gesture recognition to let users move the end-effector of the hologram robot to
achieve manipulation. Therefore, HoloLens is a good AR headset to implement an
augmented reality interface for controlling the robot.

We showed the hologram of the robot with the exact same size to align with the
real robot in order to predict the behavior and control the real robot. A symbol is
attached to the end-effector of the hologram for users to adjust the orientation and
position of the end-effector (see Fig. 8.13). Each joint of the hologram robot will
rotate in their own angles based on the inverse kinematics defined for the interface.
We used the CCD method to solve inverse kinematics.[44] Users can use the buttons
to choose if the current path is suitable for the situation to train the interface to come

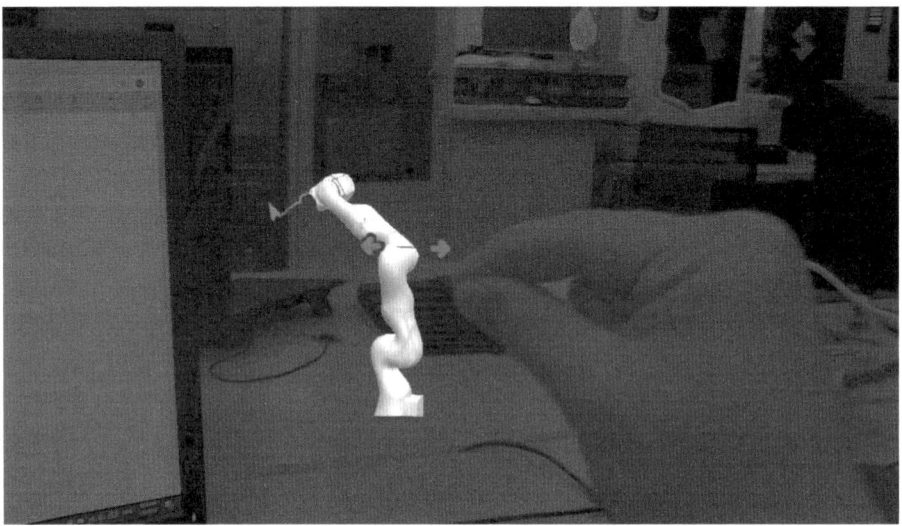

Fig. 8.13. KUKA iiwa robot hologram in HoloLens.

up with the best solution. After the gesture of the hologram, robot is determined by users, they can click the button to send joint angles to the real robot to achieve manipulation.

The interface contains the hologram of the robot, some buttons to give instructions to the robot. People can use this interface to control the gesture of the hologram by moving the end effector shown in HoloLens to where they want it to be. After making sure the gesture is the correct one, the user can click the communication button to make the real robot do the same behavior as its hologram displayed using HoloLens.

8.4.2 *Modeling Joints*

In order to deploy robot hologram into HoloLens, we used the Unity game engine as our development software to create our AR Interface. Unity is an easy-to-learn game engine. Moreover, it is the official software to develop an application in HoloLens. With the help of Unity, we successfully created our robot hologram and built an interface around it.

To create a robot hologram that can be manipulated by the user, the first thing is to import the 3D model of the robot into the Unity game engine. After importing the 3D model of the robot, we defined the inverse kinematics of the model so that the user can manipulate it with HoloLens. This process is divided into two parts, the first one is to create moving joints so that each part of the robot hologram can move based on the desired location. The second one is to introduce the CCD algorithm to solve the inverse kinematics problem.

For creating moving joints for the robot hologram, we defined several empty game objects, which is a base class for all entities in Unity scenes, to simulate servos for each joint. Then, we attached our scripts to the empty game objects to make each joint rotate based on the axis of the empty game objects. Moreover, we arranged the parts of the robot hologram in the hierarchy. In this way, we simulate the movement of the forward kinematics so that we can build the hologram of the robot.

8.4.3   *Using Gaze and Gesture-Based Interactions*

In order to interact with holograms in the virtual world, the gaze is a method to inform the application about the user's intent to focus on a particular hologram. The direction the user is looking at can be thought of as casting an imaginary beam of ray. The application can be developed such that when a beam hits a hologram, it will mark the hologram internally and prepare for further actions as the user performs a specific gesture. At the same time, a cursor will appear on top of the hologram to feedback to the user where he/she is looking at.

Holograms can also be set as non-responsive to gaze. This helps users to know which holograms will react to user commands. In order to do that, the hologram needs to have a rigid body, then it should be enclosed in a collider object. Finally, a callback function can be set up to react when a collision occurs. As the imaginary beam hits the hologram, a collision event is triggered and the callback function will be called.

A gesture is another method for the user to interact with holograms. It turns user intent into action. Air-tapping and sliding gestures will be utilized in our application. Air-tapping corresponds to selecting a hologram whereas sliding can correspond to either moving or rotating a hologram.

Holograms can be set up to listen and respond to gesture events. In Unity, there are two types of gesture events, navigation, and manipulation. Both events are triggered when the user performs a sliding gesture after an air-tap. Thus, it is recommended to listen to a single gesture event only. If a hologram is set up for a navigation event, users will be able to rotate the hologram with the sliding gesture. On the other hand, If a manipulation event is set up, users will be able to move the hologram in the virtual world.

With gesture control as the building blocks, we can successfully move or rotate a hologram. In the Unity game engine, for example, when a navigation gesture is recognized, the gesture displacement in x-y-z directions is computed. This displacement can then be applied as an input to move the target hologram. On the other hand, when a manipulation gesture is recognized, the change in x-y-z displacement is turned into rotation in alpha-beta-gamma Euler angles. This mechanism makes the users believe they are immersed in the virtual world and able to interact with holograms.

8.4.4 *Inverse Kinematics*

To do a task, we need the end-effector of the robot to follow a certain trajectory, with certain orientation and speed. Industrial robots are typically controlled by inputting desired joint parameters Thus, to control the robot, we need a way to calculate joint parameters from known end-effector position and orientation, and inverse kinematics is used for this computation.

There are several different types of numerical methods to solve inverse kinematics problems. An end-effector in 3-dimensional space has 6 degrees of freedom. Closed-form analytical methods can be used for solving robots that have 6 joints. Robots that have more than 6 joints are called redundant robots. In theory, infinitely many inverse kinematics solutions exist for redundant robots. Therefore, closed-form analytical methods do not exist for solving inverse kinematics for redundant robots. Numerical methods need to be used for solving inverse kinematics solutions for redundant robots. The basic idea behind numerical methods is to start with an initial guess of the join value and use forward kinematics to compute the end-effector position and orientations. These values are used to compute the error between the desired end-effector position and orientation and the current values. Joint values are changed by a small amount to see how the error in end-effector position and orientation changes. Joint values are updated to reduce the error. This process is repeated until the end-effector reaches close to the desired position and orientation.

We have used a method based on Cyclic Coordinate Descent (CCD). This method is able to handle robots that have more than six degrees of freedom. CCD is applied in many different fields, like biology, motion simulation, computer science, and robotics. We use Euclidean distance in three-dimensional space as the measure of position error between the desired and current end-effector position. We attach frames to the end-effector to track its orientation. The angles between the coordinate frames are used as a measure of the orientation axes. Cyclic Coordinate Descent methods do not simultaneously change all joint angles in a single iteration. Instead, it changes one angle at a time.

8.4.5 *Communication*

After users make sure both the posture of the robot hologram is what they want, they can click the button on the interface to send the joint angles of the hologram to the real robot. To achieve this goal, we used TCP/IP to build a connection between the robot and the HoloLens. However, because the robot used in this study can only be connected through Ethernet cable, it was a challenge for us to connect HoloLens directly to the robot. To solve this problem, a computer was utilized to be the server to connect both robots and HoloLens to make them communicate with each other. We created two server socket in the computer by using Python script, one for connecting HoloLens, and the other one for connecting the robot. After that, we made both HoloLens and robot as a client to exchange information with the computer. In this way, when users click the button to communicate with the real robot, HoloLens will send all the joint angles to the computer, and then the computer forwards the joint angles to the robot. This allows the real robot to imitate the behavior of the robot hologram by following the series of joint angles message.

8.5 Discussion

When reviewing the current research and technologies, the following trends are identified which provide insight into the application of AR for HRI.

- *Role of Regulations:* A primary driver for AR development in HRI appears to be a desire for increased safety of humans. This development is both aided and hindered by the regulations and perceived ambiguity in current requirements. On the one hand, the manufacturing community is interested technologies that can raise the awareness of the operators with robots and decrease the chance of injury. This leads to the development of many technologies that are demonstrated as a proof of concepts. However, since the regulations are still being developed and the wording in the existing regulations is not completely prescriptive. There appears to be a hesitance to invest too deeply in a technology that may not meet future requirements. For example, an organization may want to use the see-through AR method of visualizing safe zones, but are unlikely to employ it at scale with the risk of regulations coming out which impose stricter requirements. This issue leads to an inability to prove the technologies efficiency at scale, and thus a hindrance for the future development in unproven methods. Although easier proposed than implemented, a rapid expansion of current regulations is required further AR development. Additional regulation can pave the path for faster technology development and a willingness to invest.
- *Focus on Intuitive Implementation:* A common trend across the methods introduced is the prevalence of intuitive interaction. With a large concern in the manufacturing industry that low skills jobs may be lost with automa-

tion, a clear impetus for technological development that is accessible to low skill labor is clear. All three methods of AR outlined in this study rely on the user being able to quickly understand and act on the information that is being presented. The technology has been developed to work with existing knowledge sets such as gestures or pre-programmed commands. To this end, AR appears as a way to introduce humans to robotics without requiring advanced skills in coding or robotic analysis.

- *Technological Improvements:* The fundamental components of an AR HRI system are well developed, however, the systematic integration of the components still requires refinement. Robots have seen continued development inability, safety, and interface in the last several years. Similarly, sensors have also continued to develop, expedited in part from the rapid growth in autonomous vehicles. However, many of the systems studied need continued development in the integration of technologies to improve. Multiple studies suggested that if the existing design could be improved for increased comfort or ease of use, the application of the design would be a much more viable option.

8.6   Conclusions

This chapter provides a review of the current technologies which utilize AR to improve HRI. We also presented a case study on how to program a robot using an AR-based interface in a manufacturing application.

In order to further the field of research involving AR and HRI, the following areas of future work are suggested:

- *Integration of Additional Sensors:* Current methodologies commonly use static sensors in the workspace to provide inputs to the robot system. However, AR systems that are worn have built-in sensors which could be adapted for use with the robots. This would allow a user to re-position a robot quickly and efficiently without having to set up new cameras or sensors. While this proposal relies on continued sensor development in worn AR systems, this technology is developing quickly with the gaming and entertainment industry and could be adapted to a manufacturing environment.
- *AR for Training:* While several studies looked at training new users with AR technology, this area can still benefit from the continued study. As mentioned in the observed trends, AR technology will likely enable low skill workers to work in an increasingly complex and automated environment. Therefore, studies should focus on how AR can better train workers

to ensure there is a smooth transition to a new role.

- *Adaptation of Medical Techniques:* A large amount of research has published that is focused on using AR in medical procedures, allowing humans to perform complicated procedures with robots through AR. However, there was little crossover research to investigate how these procedures could be utilized in automated manufacturing. One can infer that manufacturing processes that require a high degree of skill and knowledge, such as precision welding or very detailed assembly can benefit from the lessons learned by the medical community.

References

1. F. Chen, K. Sekiyama, F. Cannella, and T. Fukuda, Optimal subtask allocation for human and robot collaboration within hybrid assembly system, *IEEE Transactions on Automation Science and Engineering* **11**(4), 1065–1075 (2014).
2. C. Morato, K. N. Kaipa, B. Zhao, and S. K. Gupta, Toward safe human robot collaboration by using multiple kinects based real-time human tracking, *Journal of Computing and Information Science in Engineering* **14**(1), 011006 (2014).
3. X. Wang, S. K. Ong, and A. Y. Nee, A comprehensive survey of augmented reality assembly research, *Advances in Manufacturing* **4**(1), 1–22 (2016).
4. L. F. de Souza Cardoso, F. C. M. Q. Mariano, and E. R. Zorzal, A survey of industrial augmented reality, *Computers & Industrial Engineering* **139**, 106159 (2020).
5. D. A. Vyas and D. Bhatt, Augmented reality (AR) applications: A survey on current trends, challenges, & future scope, *International Journal of Advanced Research in Computer Science* **8**(5) (2017).
6. S. K. Kim, S.-J. Kang, Y.-J. Choi, M.-H. Choi, and M. Hong, Augmented-reality survey: from concept to application, *KSII Transactions on Internet & Information Systems* **11**(2) (2017).
7. A. Benešová, M. Hirman, F. Steiner, and J. Tupa. Analysis of education requirements for electronics manufacturing within concept industry 4.0. In *2018 41st International Spring Seminar on Electronics Technology (ISSE)*, pp. 1–5 (2018).
8. P. Wang, S. Zhang, M. Billinghurst, X. Bai, W. He, S. Wang, M. Sun, and X. Zhang, A comprehensive survey of AR/MR-based co-design in manufacturing, *Engineering with Computers*. 1–24 (2019).
9. I. A. Sicaru, C. G. Ciocianu, and C.-A. Boiangiu, A survey on augmented reality, *Journal of Information Systems & Operations Management* **11**(2) (2017).
10. E. Bottani and G. Vignali, Augmented reality technology in the manufacturing industry: A review of the last decade, *IISE Transactions* **51**(3), 284–310 (2019).
11. S. Büttner, H. Mucha, M. Funk, T. Kosch, M. Aehnelt, S. Robert, and C. Röcker. The design space of augmented and virtual reality applications for assistive environments in manufacturing: a visual approach. In *Proceedings of the 10th International Conference on PErvasive Technologies Related to Assistive Environments*, pp. 433–440, (2017).
12. V. Mehta, H. Chugh, P. Banerjee, Devraj, Applications of augmented reality in emerging health diagnostics: A survey. In *2018 International Conference on Automation and Computational Engineering (ICACE)*, pp. 45–51 (2018).

13. T. Lindvall and Ö. Mirtchev. Survey of virtual and augmented reality implementations for development of prototype for practical technician training, Orebro University (2017).

14. A. Gallala, B. Hichri, and P. Plapper. Survey: The evolution of the usage of augmented reality in industry 4.0. In *IOP Conference Series: Materials Science and Engineering*, vol. 521, p. 012017 (2019).

15. D. Mourtzis, V. Zogopoulos, and E. Vlachou, Augmented reality application to support remote maintenance as a service in the robotics industry, *Procedia CIRP*. **63**(2017), 46–51, (2017).

16. O. Danielsson, M. Holm, and A. Syberfeldt. Augmented reality smart glasses for industrial assembly operators: A meta-analysis and categorization. In *Advances in Manufacturing Technology XXXIII: Proceedings of the 17th International Conference on Manufacturing Research*, p. 173, Belfast, Ireland (September 2019).

17. F. Zhou, X. Lin, C. Liu, Y. Zhao, P. Xu, L. Ren, T. Xue, and L. Ren, A survey of visualization for smart manufacturing, *Journal of Visualization* **22**(2), 419–435 (2019).

18. V. Elia, M. G. Gnoni, and A. Lanzilotto, Evaluating the application of augmented reality devices in manufacturing from a process point of view: An AHP based model, *Expert Systems with Applications* **63**, 187–197 (2016).

19. J. Boisvert, M.-A. Drouin, G. Godin, and M. Picard. Augmented reality, 3d measurement, and thermal imagery for computer-assisted manufacturing. In *Emerging Digital Micromirror Device Based Systems and Applications XII*, vol. 11294, p. 112940L. International Society for Optics and Photonics (2020).

20. A. Sanna and F. Manuri, A survey on applications of augmented reality, *Advances in Computer Science: An International Journal* **5**(1), 18–27 (2016).

21. I. F. del Amo, J. A. Erkoyuncu, R. Roy, and S. Wilding, Augmented reality in maintenance: An information-centred design framework, *Procedia Manufacturing* **19**, 148–155 (2018).

22. R. Alarcon, F. Wild, C. Perey, M. M. Genescà, J. G. Martínez, J. X. R. Martí, M. J. S. Olmos, and D. Dubert, Augmented reality for the enhancement of space product assurance and safety, *Acta Astronautica* **168**, 191–199 (2020).

23. V. Villani, F. Pini, F. Leali, C. Secchi, and C. Fantuzzi, Survey on human-robot interaction for robot programming in industrial applications, *IFAC-PapersOnLine* **51**(11), 66–71 (2018).

24. R. Palmarini, J. A. Erkoyuncu, R. Roy, and H. Torabmostaedi, A systematic review of augmented reality applications in maintenance, *Robotics and Computer-Integrated Manufacturing* **49**, 215–228 (2018).

25. B. Matthias, ISO/TS 15066 - Collaborative Robots - Present Status. In *European Robotics Forum 2016*, Vienna, Austria (March, 2015).

26. C.Thomas, F.Busch, B.Kuhlenkoetter, and J.Deuse, *Ensuring Human Safety with Offline Simulation and Real-time Workspace Surveillance to develop a Hybrid Robot Assitance System for Welding of Assemblies.* Springer (2012).

27. M. Terashima and S. Sakane. A human-robot interface using an extended digital desk. In *Proceedings 1999 IEEE International Conference on Robotics and Automation*, vol. 4, pp. 2874–2880 (1999).

28. I. Maly, D. Sedlek, and P. Leito. Augmented reality experiments with industrial robot in industry 4.0 environment. In *2016 IEEE 14th International Conference on Industrial Informatics (INDIN)*, pp. 176–181 (2016).

29. M. Vasic and A. Billard. Safety issues in human-robot interactions. In *International Conference on Robotics and Automation*, pp. 197–204 (2013).

30. B.Matthias and T.Reisinger. Example application of ISO/TS 15066 to a collaborative assembly scenario. In *Proceedings ISR 2016: 47th International Symposium on Robotics*, pp. 1–5 (2016).

31. G. Michalos, P. Karagiannis, S. Makris, O. Tokalar, and G. Chryssolouris. Augmented reality (AR) applications for supporting human-robot interactive cooperation. In *Research and Innovation in Manufacturing: Key Enabling Technologies for the Factories of the Future - Proceedings of the 48th CIRP Conference on Manufacturing Systems*, pp. 370–375 (2016).

32. D. Q. Huy, I. Vietcheslav, and G. S. G. Lee. See-through and spatial augmented reality - A novel framework for human-robot interaction. In *2017 3rd International Conference on Control, Automation and Robotics (ICCAR)*, pp. 719–726 (2017).

33. M. W. B. Giesler, P. Steinhaus and R. Dillmann. Sharing skills: Using augmented reality for human-robot collaboration. In *Stereoscopic Displays and Virtual Reality Systems XI (A. J. Woods, J. O. Merritt, S. A. Benton, and M. T. Bolas, eds.)*, pp. 446–453 (2004).

34. C. Vogel, C. Walter, and N. Elkmann. Safeguarding and supporting future human-robot co-operative manufacturing processes by a projection- and camera-based technology. In *Procedia Manufacturing, vol. 11, no. Supplement C*, pp. 39–46 (2017).

35. C. Vogel, M. Fritzsche, and N. Elkmann. Safe human-robot cooperation with high-payload robots in industrial applications. In *2016 11th ACM/IEEE International Conference on Human-Robot Interaction (HRI)*, pp. 529–530 (2016).

36. F. Leutert, C. Herrmann, and K. Schilling. A spatial augmented reality system for intuitive display of robotic data. In *2013 8th ACM/IEEE International Conference on Human-Robot Interaction (HRI)*, pp. 179–180 (2013).

37. N. Costa and A. Arsenio. Augmented reality behind the wheel-human interactive assistance by mobile robots. In *2015 6th International Conference on Automation, Robotics and Applications (ICARA)*, pp. 63–69 (2015).

38. R. S. Andersen, T. B. M. S. Bgh, and O. Madsen. Intuitive task programming of stud welding robots for ship construction. In *2015 IEEE International Conference on Industrial Technology (ICIT)*, pp. 3302–3307 (2015).

39. A. Gaschler, M. Springer, M. Rickert, and A. Knoll. Intuitive robot tasks with augmented reality and virtual obstacles. In *2014 IEEE International Conference on Robotics and Automation (ICRA)*, pp. 6026–6031 (2014).

40. C. L. Ng, T. C. Ng, T. A. N. Nguyen, G. Yang, and W. Chen. Intuitive robot tool path teaching using laser and camera in augmented reality environment. In *2010 11th International Conference on Control Automation Robotics Vision*, pp. 114–119 (2010).

41. J. A. Frank, M. Moorhead, and V. Kapila. Realizing mixed-reality environments with tablets for intuitive human-robot collaboration for object manipulation tasks. In *2016 25th IEEE International Symposium on Robot and Human Interactive Communication (RO-MAN)*, pp. 302–307 (2016).

42. H. C. Fang, S. K. Ong, and A. Y. C. Nee. Novel AR-based interface for human-robot interaction and visualization. In *Advances in Manufacturing, vol. 2*, pp. 275–288 (2014).

43. S. Stadler, K. Kain, M. Giuliani, and N. Mirnig. Augmented reality for industrial robot programmers: Workload analysis for task-based, augmented reality-supported robot control. In *2016 25th IEEE International Symposium on Robot and Human Interactive Communication (RO-MAN)*, pp. 179–184 (2016).

44. C. Welman. *Inverse Kinematics and Geometric Constraints for Articulated Figure Manipulation.* Simon Fraser University (1994).

Chapter 9

Anti-Fragility in Design Engineering Procedures Embedded in Hybrid Multiple Realms and Blended Environments — The Physical Real of Reality

Robert E. Wendrich

9.1 Introduction

Most design, engineering, and industrial processes (e.g. advanced manufacturing (AM), hyper technology, management, logistics, services, networks, systems, etc.) are determined and structured along provisional, preconceived, and consensual methods and/or methodologies outlined by agreed upon scientific and scholarly discourse, consensus and mutual understanding. Prevailing process structures and underlying frameworks are dominant organizational factors that somehow constrain, hinder, and obfuscate possible, alternative, and advanced methods, emergent and/or novel theoretical frameworks to protrude or make further progress over time. Papava states for example "...the type of economy that fosters the functioning of firms (i.e. retrofirms) that are relatively technologically backward (e.g. out-of-date equipment, processes, systems) in comparison to contemporary global achievements but where, nevertheless, the demand for their products still exists is referred to as a *retroeconomy*.[1]"

We assume that future making has become a social reality, a cultural fact, a globally extended process and becoming highly "real-world" and "globally-contextualized."[a] The fear of degeneration in the wake of technological change and possible future creative destruction (e.g. retroeconomics, monopolies, obsolescence) across domains and human pursuits, such as culture, health, biology,

---

[a] 'Four things are never far from you: underfoot, all around you, or away on the horizon, there they always are: the Forest, the Desert, the River, and the Hills' (Hindu Literature).

political systems, technology, urban organization, socioeconomic life and industry is set off (paradoxically) against the hope for future growth, prospect and progress.

Our present notion of "the future" has become a highly fragmented one.[2] For instance, the rapid and continuous growth, integration, application and progression of automatization, virtualization and artificial intelligence in production, manufacturing (i.e. advanced, green, cloud, sustainable and other) and in service industries lead to unavoidable change in belief-sets, socialization characteristics and directly impacts "labor", "laboring" and "laborers" living with machines, within machines and amongst machines. We present possible countenance of new (innovative) *anti-fragile* (i.e. the robust or resilient is neither harmed nor helped by volatility and disorder, while the anti-fragile benefits from them)[3] models of processes, imbued with well-tempered technologies, the embedment of hybrid realities (multiple convergence of analogue and digital) and multiplicity of context-aware networked situations, including volatility, complexity, ambiguity, uncertainty (VUCA).

9.1.1 *The World Around Us, Experience the VUCA World*

Everything is connected, as has been explained ambiguously and stated repeatedly. In literature, the use of the terminology error, uncertainty and variability is not unambiguous. Different researchers apply the same terminology, but the meaning attached to these is rather inconsistent.[4] Uncertainty is caused by incomplete information resulting from either vagueness, non-specificity or dissonance…bottlenecks are the mother of all squeezes.[3]

Uncertainty underpins "the wish to know" (predict) in order to be able to influence present and future. Complexity and asymmetry lead to explosive errors. At present, the future appears volatile and fragile.[2] The anti-fragile gains from prediction errors, in the long run.[3] Meanwhile, the world is getting less and less predictable. In fact, rethinking the "Enlightenment" (i.e. the generic denial of the cosmeticism and sucker-traps in the ideas of modernity)[3] entails an epistemological shift from a "local universalism" to a "global contextualism."[5] We have more and more nonlinearities-asymmetries, convexities-in today's VUCA-world.[6] We rely increasingly on technologies that have errors, are error prone, filter bubble (algorithms), and interactions that are harder to estimate, let alone predict. The very idea of anti-fragility in design engineering procedures (DEP) embedded in hybrid multiple realms and blended environments is to not only gain from anti-fragility in existing and current DEP, methods and methodologies, but also in realms of Advanced Manufacturing Systems and/or Technologies (AMS/AMT), production, service systems, logistics, supply-chain management, sustainable systems and design engineering services (e.g. green manufacturing, social manufacturing, service-oriented manufacturing) carried out throughout the product-life cycle (PLC). Technology is the result of antifragility, exploited by risk-takers in the form of tinkering and trial and error.[3]

According to Goldschmidt[7], designing is a purposeful and engaging activity with a goal in mind, possibly explicit and fully articulated from the onset or "vague", ill-defined and intertwined with ambiguity (i.e. ill-structured, rawshaping).[8] The combinatorial effect of cognition (i.e. meta-cognition, memory patterns), sensory affect, intuition, perception coupled with intention, experience and knowledge (i.e. domains) enables creative design idea generation (idea search) and conceptual design, see Refs. 9-11.

Tversky[12] stated, that in creating representations of space, real or metaphoric, inside or outside the mind, one requires abstraction, and consequent ambiguity. The creative thought process is founded on ambiguity to enable a multiplicity of interpretations. These mental representations of space (e.g. design space, ideation space, creative space) are constructed, however not from a single experience or from a distinct modality. We experience "space" from a specific viewpoint at a certain time but nevertheless time and space are perpetually changing. The mind is, among other things, a vast and changing data base.[12] Endsley[13] uses the following definition: "Situation awareness is the perception of the elements in the environment within a volume of time and space, the comprehension of their meaning, and the projection of their status in near future." Collected and stored information either specific or non-specific can be retrieved, applied, and structured to fit or suit a certain indirect purpose or direct goal. These established mental representations (abstractions) support our information processes during a task or activity. Furthermore, useful mental representations are stemming and are integrated from multiple experiences and modalities.[12] Goldschmidt[7] argues that requirements, information, data, and design methods (i.e. combined or separate) do not directly translate into design ideas, which must be sought differently, while keeping all the above in mind (i.e. mind's eye). Woodbury and Burrow[14] describe the ideation process as a search for ideas that occur in a design space that is as rich as the items that populate it. The use of intentional stance[15] in both computer science and animal psychology is ubiquitous, and intentional systems[16] theory explains why this is so[17] and applies to the human intuition, tools, and thinking with machines.

9.1.2 *Looking at Crafts, Craftsmanship, and Industry 4.0*

McCullough[18] stated: "We must look very closely at craft. As a part of developing more engaging technology, as well as developing a more receptive attitude toward opportunities raised by technology, we must understand what matters in traditional notions of practical, "form-giving" work." Wendrich[9-11] promotes the importance of bi-manual tangible interaction that relies on inbred skill sets and dexterity merged with the intuitive and imaginative qualities of analogue craftsmanship. Simultaneously and parallel to this, they incorporate and make use of assistive computational design tools to support this interaction. A broad spectrum of users are targeted, i.e. novice and expert designers, engineers, architects, artisans, craftsmen, and artists in the development of a hybrid methodology based on a holistic framework in conjunction with state-of-the-art and/or advanced technology.[9]

Domain shifts in design and /or engineering are the metamorphoses of fundamental change to evoke new or refreshingly different experiences. Metamorphosis can be orderly, disorderly, or chaotic. For example, a foundational craft is cooking rather than weaving, potting, or carpentry, but the logic of change applies to all crafts. Crafts is not design; however, design could become a craft and one could become a crafty designer and/or engineer in such. Levi-Strauss[19] presents change as a culinary triangle; "...a triangular semantic field whose three points correspond to the categories of the raw, the cooked, and the rotted." The raw is the realm of nature, as human beings find it: cooking creates the realm of culture, nature metamorphosed. It is always about culture, never about civilization. In cultural production food is both good to eat and good to think. Hence, from heating to sharing food, from eating to thinking instigating a domain shift. Metamorphosis provokes material consciousness in three ways: through internal evolution of type-form, in the judgment about mixture and synthesis, by the thinking involved in domain shift.[20] Flusser[21] connects "design" to all culture and states: "...that "design" deceives nature by means of technology, to replace what is natural with what is artificial and build a machine out of which there comes a 'god' who is ourselves."

Harari[22] follows in his footsteps and argues, "...that humans seek bliss and immortality but, are in fact trying to upgrade themselves into gods,...to acquire godlike control of their own biological substratum...to design and engineer our system in almost any manner we like..." In accordance and addition, the coming of Industry 4.0, which describes the fourth industrial revolution, possibly leads to intelligent, connected, and decentralized advanced production and manufacturing entailing a broad spectrum of dedicated, expert, and other heterogeneous users that should be able to connect, interact, and be supported and assisted with these technologies.[23] Tao et al.[24] state that, the manufacturing industry played a very important role in the evolution of "modern society." It has been suggested wittily, "…that humans have never been modern."[25] According to Tao et al.,[24] "…the sharing of manufacturing resources and capabilities, the value creation carriers, the value measuring criteria, the composition of the value chain and enterprise collaboration, and the user participation in manufacturing are all moving towards socialization…this also pertains to the evolution and adaptation of AMSs." In fact, globally more balanced and reciprocal conditions governing the political-societal economic relationships, should be sought more strongly and to maintain, strengthen and enhance prosperity, values and social-cultural models over the long run globally.

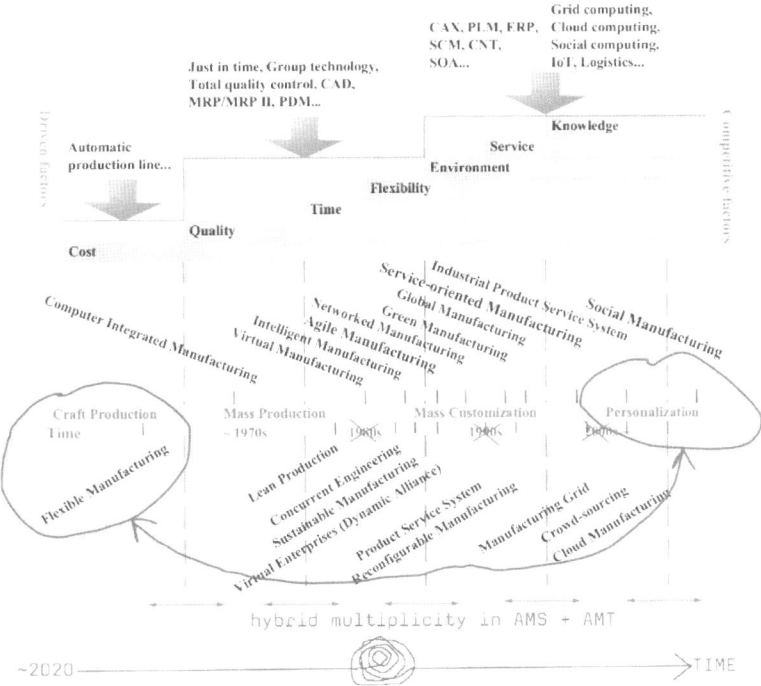

Fig. 9.1. Continual and evolving processes of flexible, agile and advancing manufacturing systems envisioned with the reappearance-loop of advanced flexible craft manufacturing (adapted).[24]

Still today, there are many "modern societies" that need to adapt to changing economic realities, challenges, socio-political frameworks (e.g. ideologies) to enable their own domestic policies, (e.g. human rights) and industrial base (e.g. AMSs). In their analysis and summary of AMSs, it is concluded that, the societal development requirements as well as the emergence and application of AMSs, including changes of user/market demand and economic factors in different periods (time construct), determine the developing and evolving directions of AMSs and their variable modalities and models (Fig. 9.1).[24]

The pursuit of progress, prosperity (e.g. fight emissions effectively), well-being, development (e.g. sustainability), and economic growth are stuck and become squeezed because of state-driven (state-owned) industrial and economic policies and lack of reciprocal markets access.[1] Development of more transparent, more balanced, and reciprocal relationships is therefore of great importance and a prerequisite for both success and failure. People (i.e. humanity), reality and processes (e.g. AMSs) are continuously changing and evolve and/or revolve over time, depending on a multiplicity of factors, issues, challenges, and constraints.

Reality removes the uncertainty, the imprecision, the vagueness, the self-serving biases that make us appear more intelligent. Mistakes are costly, no longer free, but being right brings actual rewards.[3] Therefore, tools such as hybrid machines for teaching, tinkering, design, thinking, engineering, interaction, and communication should be facilitated throughout, become available for a multitude and multiplicity of users in all layers of complexity, contextuality, and networks.

In effect, Industry 4.0 technologies not only support advanced manufacturers and/or producers to improve their production, including the underlying production systems in general and the production machines in particular.[26] In addition, the support and assist should and could be made available for the whole product-service development process (PSDP), circular economy, circular society and product-life cycle (PLC) (e.g. mfg.com). The evolving process of manufacturing paradigms from craft production, mass production to mass customization and personalization, AMSs have greatly promoted and influenced the related manufacturing technologies, management techniques, logistics, and economic advancements.[27] Since Industry 4.0 relies on intelligent-connected-decentralized technologies it will be and needs to be imbued with a multitude of additional and enhanced sensors, sensor systems and sensorial spaces for design-engineering, product-service-system development and advancement of production and manufacturing (Fig. 9.2).

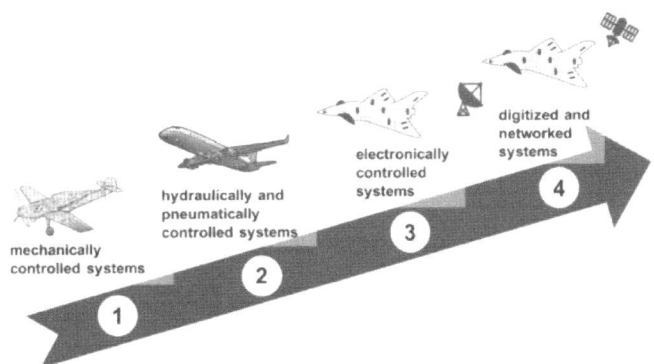

Fig. 9.2. Transformation towards Digitization and Networking.

Thereby, it entails and includes the opportunity to improve insight and understanding of these machined productions' and inherent processes. This will lead to further democratization for and through "production," "labor," "capital," "smart embedded systems," and "digitized and networked systems" for society, technology and science (STS)[28] on local, regional, provincial, national, international, and global advancement levels. Within Industry 4.0, smart embedded systems and the presence of volatile markets (i.e. VUCA) are key drivers of today's industrial companies and complexes. To meet the underlying and apparent challenges new and novel frameworks and transformations are needed and essentially built from a holistic and encompassing realism towards inclusiveness of existing, proven, optimized and preferred systems, networks, and/or machines.

Obviously, further and advanced upscale transformation and perfectionism is part of the ever increasing spiral of "innovation," "will to progress," and wish for "growth." However, in multiple areas of Industry 1.0 to 3.9 (entailing many areas and/or regions in the globalized economic system, production, manufacturing and process world) earlier and former state-of-the-art "technologies," quasi-innovative systems, are still doing the "thinking", "teaching," "machining" and "systemic production" on a quotidian fulfilment basis. In necro- and/or retroeconomies both make use of outdated technology; the difference is that under necroeconomic conditions, enterprises use equipment so out-of-date that the demand for products they manufacture is virtually non-existent and, therefore, these enterprises operate solely with government support while in a retroeconomy, the demand for such products does exist and enterprises enjoy only moderate support from government.[1] Both types, however, require government intervention, the former exists exclusively at the expense of the government, the latter requires government-sanctioned protection of the domestic market from international competition. This suggests that a mere "hybrid" approach in a "hybrid world" allows for more flexibility, multitudes of increased hybrid transformations and integral part of global economies, and advanced systems of production, manufacturing and services (Fig. 9.3).

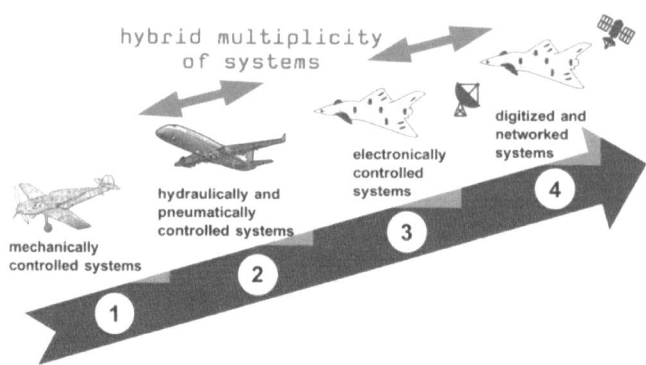

Fig. 9.3. Transformation and translation towards Digitization, Hybridization, and Networking.

Latour[29] states, "We do not know what is interconnected and woven together. We are feeling our way, experimenting, trying things out. Nobody knows of what an environment, system, process or network is capable." Industry 4.0 could be such an idea, to become real they must be made real. Other ideas must be prevented to "become something," and need to be transformed beyond recognition.[30] If others do not contribute, the idea of Industry 4.0 will remain nothing but an idea on paper or in the mind. For example, in developing countries (e.g. India, China) handicrafts and artisans[31] not only generate employment, but also play a significant and prominent role in the country's economy, social-cultural, and traditions.[32]

Crafts-industry is considered an informal sector characterized by certain features like, reliance on locally available resources, skills, family ownership, small-scale operations, labor intensity, traditional technology, skills generally acquired outside the formal school system, unregulated and competitive markets.[32] Artisans and craftsmen alike, mostly work in traditional and unorganized sectors in which they are vulnerable to exploitation and low wages.[33]

They fall into the lower strata of the hierarchy both socially and economically.[34] Most of these people are engaged in household or cottage industries, hard work but low to marginalized standard of living, subsistence, and livelihood.[31] One can imagine the multi-millions of people (laborers) that work "industrious lives" under these "conditions" in our global economies and markets today.

The traditional crafts have largely been marginalized by mass-produced consumer goods (import/export), which tend to be cheaper, of lesser quality, reduced meaning, due to the economies of scale associated with mechanization.[35] The nature of the crafts sector and challenges faced by artisans reduces their ability to compete effectively and efficiently with and against 'machine-made/automated' products-systems-networks.

9.1.3 *Low-Tech, High-Tech, Raw-Tech Realities*

To paraphrase Taleb[3], "…we have the illusion that the world functions thanks to programmed design, university research, and bureaucratic funding but there is compelling-very compelling- evidence to show that this is an illusion…, technology is the result of anti-fragility, exploited by risk-takers in the form of tinkering and trial and error, with nerd-driven design[36] confined to the backstage. Engineers and tinkerers develop things while history books are written by academics…' This ironic sample of perspective clarity illustrates our disavowal and blindness towards the "reality" and physicality of how the real raw world actually functions and works and manifests the manufactured consent and ideological constructs that determine the historic, present, and future time.

Economics is not the reality principle of technology; technology must be realized gradually, like the rest of the mechanisms for which it paves the way.[37] A technological project is *not* in a context; it gives itself a context or sometimes does not give itself one. What is required is not to "replace projects in their context," as the foolish expression goes, but to study the way the project is contextualized or decontextualized. To do that, the rigid, stuffy word "context" has to be replaced by the supple, friendly word "network." As such, our approach for DEP, advanced manufacturing technology (AMT) realms and/or environments follows to benefit from the added perspective of DEP, thinking in a collaborative research environment and to gain from an added design perspective that takes a holistic approach to addressing under-constrained problems. Immediately framing questions such as; "how designers can engage "wicked problems,"[8] 'raw notions of thought," "synthesize from raw data, information and matter"?

According to Cross[38] "design (*engineering*) knowledge resides in the people, process…and product," this notion is however not completely how "design" and/or "design engineering," for that matter, should be connoted or framed.

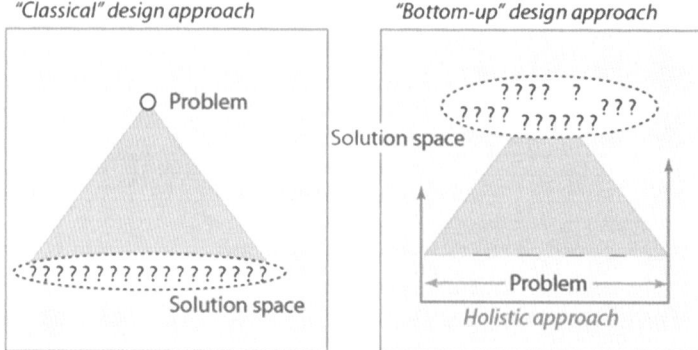

Fig. 9.4. Design engineering approach to problem-based multiples embedded in possible solution space.

For this, we need to reframe this notion to state that; 'design knowledge resides in the intended approach, creativity in process and networked reality[39] and follows through towards the targeted or possible (most effective?) outcome.' The rawshaping technology holistic approach[11] is based on this dynamic and agile development of human-machine-network-interaction (HMNI), along with the inclusion of meta-cognitive affordances, intuition, and bodily experiences (Fig. 9.4). Intuition comes in two types; either holistic hunches or automated expertise. A holistic hunch is a judgment or choice made through subconscious synthesis of information drawn from previous experience and knowledge.[40] Automated expertise happens when judgments or choices are made through a partial subconscious (i.e. autonomous, self-aware) process involving recognition of the situation. However, often it is the software alone that defines and determines how and what actions are possible within a virtual reality. As a result, 3D modelling tools (CAD), thinking machines[41] or any kind of digital *toolness* facilitated on a computer, are not unlike e.g. "hammers" and impose limitations to the solution space. These limitations have direct implications to the freedom of a designer-engineer, as well as the understanding of "form and shape" of virtual models.[42]

9.2 Hybrid Multiple Realms

Human experience and meaning depend in some way upon the body, for it is our contact with the entire spatio-temporal world that surrounds us. The key questions that must be asked are thus: Are embodied representations, our expressions developed from our bodily perceptions and imaginative systems of understanding, adequately shared to be thought of as appropriate to knowledge? Or, are they too subjective, unstructured, and unconstrained? To paraphrase Johnson[43], "...there is alleged to be no way to demonstrate the universal (shared) character of any representation of imagination."

9.3 Tools, Procedures, and Processes

Anti-fragile interaction design (AfxD) is therefore crucial to support the way designers and engineers (people) interact and exchange information and communicate throughout the design process. Rationalizing and externalizing the thought process that led to the insight is necessary to communicate the knowledge with others and make it plausible for them.[9-11] Brereton[44] uses the term 'distributed cognition' as "the process of designing and developing design understandings".

Distributed cognition during ideation and interaction with predetermined or loosely defined constraints is essential to manifest ideas, explore fuzzy-notions, and stimulate inventiveness.[45-46] Engineering design is the activity of design and development of technical products. A technical product is built to fulfill a well specified function under more or less well prescribed conditions of utilization. The complexity of modern technical products and systems tends to increase systematically, increasing the need for thorough design analysis[4] extended throughout the entire PLC.

9.3.1 *Creativity and Metacognitive Abilities*

Gestalt psychology has demonstrated that we recognize a familiar face by integrating our awareness of its elements, without being able to identify these particular elements. Gestalt psychology suggests that perception is transformed to a spontaneous equilibrium.[47] Polanyi suggests that Gestalt is the outcome of an active shaping of perception performed in the pursuit of knowledge. Metacognitive processes are responsible for this active shaping by which all knowledge is discovered, and once discovered, is held to be true. The structure of Gestalt, the result of actively shaped perception, is then recast into the logic of tacit thought.

"Cognition = Knowledge," the cognitive repertoire to sustain an illusion of reality. The highest forms of integration occur in the metacognitive skills of a scientific or artistic genius. "The art of an expert diagnostician may be listed next, as a somewhat impoverished form of discovery, and we may put in the same class the performance of skills, whether artistic, athletic, or technical." Perception, on which Gestalt psychology centered its attention, is the most impoverished form of tacit knowing. This does not imply that tacit knowing is not the opposite of explicit knowledge, it even cooperates with explicit knowledge. Grant[48] states "...tacitness is something personal, an ability or skill to do something or to resolve a problem that is based, in part, on one's own experiences in learning."

Polanyi[47] introduces awareness, which comprises a proximal and a distal term. Awareness in this sense has a focal point and subsidiary tacit awareness. The functional relationship between these terms is that the proximal term is only known by relying on the perception and our awareness of it for attending to the distal term.

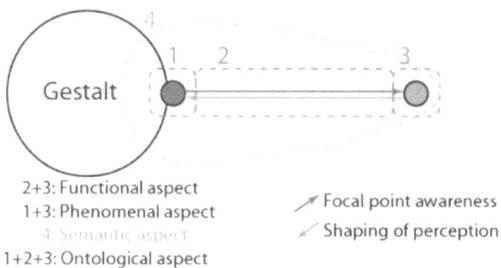

2+3: Functional aspect
1+3: Phenomenal aspect
4: Semantic aspect
1+2+3: Ontological aspect

Focal point awareness
Shaping of perception

Fig. 9.5. Awareness (2) of the proximal term (1) in the appearance of the distal term (3).

The relationship between these terms is described in four ways (Fig. 9.5):

- The functional structure of tacit knowledge: We are attending from elementary movements to the achievement of their joint purpose, and hence are usually unable to specify these elementary acts.
- The phenomenal structure of tacit knowledge: When performing a skill, we are aware of the proximal term in the appearance of its distal term.
- The semantic aspect of tacit knowledge: All meaning tends to be displaced from ourselves when we use a tool.
- The ontological aspect of tacit knowledge: The understanding of the comprehensive entity, which the two terms jointly constitute. The proximal term represents the particulars of this entity; we comprehend the entity by relying on our awareness of its particulars for attending to their joint meaning.

The human body as an instrument, the only instrument that we normally never experience as an object.[47] Because we experience our body in terms of the world to which we are attending from our body "…we feel it to be our body, and not a thing outside." However, when we use certain things for attending from them to other things, these other things appear to us in terms of the entities to which we are attending from them. In this sense we can say, that we can extend our body to include the distal term as proximal term, so that we come to dwell in it (see Fig. 9.6).

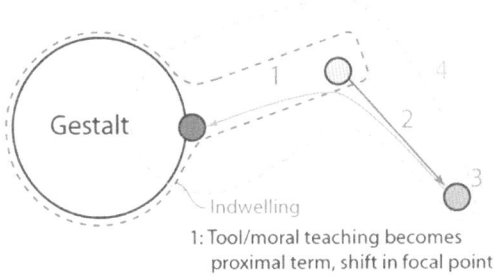

Fig. 9.6. The way we perceive a secondary distal term or entity (3) through the incorporation of the initial distal term (1).

The focal point of our awareness shifts from the initial distal term to a new distal term. Grant[48] explains this as achieving some wider objective using the proximate term such as a tool. His example is the use of a golf club and a ball, with the objective of putting the ball in a distant hole. "Skillful individuals can focus on the overall objective; less skilled ones pay more attention to the proximate device (the subsidiary awareness)." Another type of indwelling is aesthetic appreciation.

By representing "aesthetic appreciation as an entering into the work of art and thus dwelling in the mind of its creator."[47] The main conclusion in 'the tacit dimension' is, that tacit knowing is shown to account for:

(1) A valid knowledge of a problem.
(2) The scientist's capacity to pursue a solution, guided by his sense of approaching the solution.
(3) A valid anticipation of the yet indeterminate implications of the discovery arrived at in the end.

9.3.2 *Creative Investment*

Creative people have the habit to "respond to problems in fresh and novel ways, rather than allowing themselves to respond mindlessly and automatically."[49] In Sternberg and Lubart[50] it is proposed as an "investment theory of creativity". According to this theory, creative people are the ones willing to pursue ideas that are unknown or out of favor but have growth potential. As the "raw" idea is larger in the mind of the creator, initially the idea might encounter resistance.

Furthermore, according to investment theory creativity requires a confluence of six distinct, but interrelated, resources: intellectual abilities, knowledge, thinking styles, personality, motivation, and environment. Regarding the intellectual abilities, three skills are particularly important:

(a) The synthetic ability to see problems in new ways and to escape the bounds of conventional thinking;

(b) The analytic ability to recognize which of one's ideas are worth pursuing and which are not; and

(c) The practical–contextual ability to know how to persuade others of—to sell other people on—the value of one's ideas.

When we compare these to Polanyi[47] main conclusion, tacit knowing seems to account for these three intellectual abilities. Furthermore, tacit knowing cooperates with knowledge, thinking styles, personality, motivation, and the perception of an environment. Beyond the distinct interrelated resources of creativity, the tacit dimension has a large influence on creativity. Besides these intellectual abilities, the following resources of creativity are of interest:

Knowledge, is the knowledge a creative person has on the field in which he or she wants to be creative.[49-50] On one hand knowledge is necessary to move beyond existing knowledge, on the other hand it can result in an entrenched perspective, hindering creativity. Thinking styles are someone's preferred ways of approaching problems. In case of a creative person, the approach is global as well as local, "distinguishing the forest from the trees and thereby recognizing which questions are important and which ones are not."

Personality attributes are important for creative functioning, although the type of attributes is not fixed. According to Sternberg and Lubart[49] "these attributes include, but are not limited to, willingness to overcomes obstacles, willingness to take sensible risks, willingness to tolerate ambiguity and self-efficacy." Motivation is something inherent to a person. People rarely do creative work in an area when they do not love what they are doing and focus on the potential rewards, rather than on their work. Finally, creativity is enhanced in a supportive environment that is rewarding of creative ideas.

The confluence of these resources for creativity is limited to the extent that there may be a threshold for some components, below which creativity is not possible. However, partial compensation may occur when strength in one component counteracts a weakness in another. Finally, interaction between components may occur, enhancing creativity.

9.4 Conceptual Design Through Ideation Procedures

During the conceptual design and engineering stage, the dreamed-up ideas, fuzzy thoughts and notions are changing frequently, constantly evolving.[51] In creativity it is crucial that you produce as many ideas as possible, produce ideas as raw and wild as possible, build upon each other's ideas and avoid passing judgment.[52]

In early-phase design (i.e. fuzzy-front end) the actual focus on detail is not particularly needed as the need to generate, transform, and manipulate ideas quickly.[53] It has been stated that computers still demand special skills from users and distract them with secondary tasks, like configuration of settings. Instead they should offer immediate access to affordances "so that we are freed to use them without thinking and "mental gymnastics" and to focus beyond computers on new goals."[54] They draw on the concept of conceptual integration to explain why computers can be very difficult to use. Computers are difficult to use because they require too many steps of conceptual integration and do not make enough use of simple concepts that most people have learned through interaction with the physical world and their social context.[53]

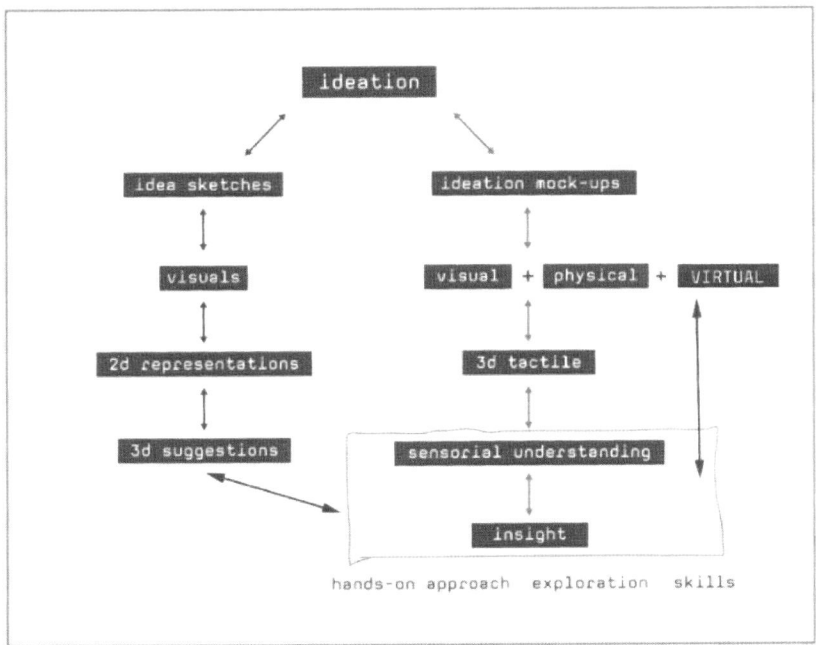

Fig. 9.7. The mixed ideation representation diagram for analogue, digital, and virtual conceptualization.

Conceptual integration is the idea that humans learn complex concepts like "shame" or "happiness" through integration of other less complex concepts. This means that basic concepts that can be learned through perception like 'up' and 'down' are connected to complex concepts through many steps of integration.[55] This relates to theory on tacit knowledge, because one is mostly unconsciously using these concepts to carry out tasks. This also means that the mind must be viewed as inherently embodied, because even the most abstract tasks are built on bodily experiences.[43] Designers create initial solutions, then modify or combine them and create concept variants to match the design requirements, placed on the product by either customers or the context of the artefacts or products being designed or created.[56-57] As sketching, modelling, and prototyping (physical, virtual, hybrid) are quintessential conceptual design activities, a number of computer aided design (CAD) and computer aided engineering design (CAED) systems have attempted to adapt it to the digital environment.[58] Even where sketching, modelling, and prototyping (physical, virtual, hybrid) may not be necessary for the generation of ideas and/or designs, externalizing an idea is crucial and serves a communicative purpose.[53,57,59]

Sketching and drawing are just one of the possible forms of representation to choose from to externalize ideation processes. Of course, there are numerous ways thinkable of externalization possible ideas or insights next to sketching. Pen and paper are easy to acquire, the affordance is simple, easy, and fluid. And most people can create a decent "sketch" to illustrate, convey or represent what they think or mean, see Fig. 9.7. However, to open-up the scope of conceptual representation, whereby not only the two-dimensional and three-dimensional aspects of visualization of ideas are considered through sketching, we have to consider all the other multiple modalities and mixed representational techniques available to address this externalization and communication of ideas within ideation processes. Early-phase design is "structured" around a blend of approaches.

9.4.1 *Idea Generation, Blind Spots, and Early-Phase Design Processes*

By allowing randomness in DEP the geometry will be jagged but with a logic of its own and one that is easy to understand and identifies the idiosyncratic value of the object. In design ideation and conceptualization, the support and look for unintentional change in processing, unpredictability in shaping and forming, being oblivious to *blind spots*, create variable contexts, resonate intentions of design interactions and allow adversaries creating stories. Inadvertently, we all inherit the same shortcomings, perceptive and sensorial problems and issues that come to the design workbench or computational design workstation in multitudes of multiples where the need for ways of thinking on design and design science about design *blind spots* are sheer necessity and imminent. In general, one could say that there seems to be a pre-dominance in visual abstract representation over material representation.[46] This could be partially instigated by proximity and the abundance of digital technologies within the realm of design education. Emphasis on sensory perception was far greater than the implementation of sensory feeling within the design solution space. Apparently learning in design is enabled through continually challenging abstract representations against material representations.

The comparison shows voids that inspired us to further investigate design processing, design representation, raw approaches on design, ways of thinking, creative intelligence and raw tinkering in design articulation. In sensory perception we rely on our visual system, tracking, and parsing, dodging, spotting, guiding, predicting and sometimes seeing things before they happen. Naturally, we have blind spots that allow us to create visual illusions and allow for disembodiment. *Blind spots* are unexpected, unseen, unknown, unforeseen and/or ignored areas of knowledge or gaps in understanding and experience in the world around you. They are a combination of low predictability and large impact once they become apparent.[46] The sense of touch allows us to do more than explore the world around us, it makes us like or loath material sensations. Touch receptors in our skin give us control, power of expectation, creates highly focused attention and physical relaxation.

9.4.2 *Synthesis, Analysis, and Iterative Step-Change Modeling*

Design and creativity are not solely about making digital virtual illusions in multiple-dimensional representations and simulate these in virtual or synthetic environments. More importantly current and future design tools facilitate interaction, imagination, and communication in such that the user(s) feels as comfortable working the digital tool as in their physical realm (mimetic).[59] It is a priority to make more adaptive learning environments in, for example, educational institutions based on pleasurable engagement, enjoyment, serious gaming, and play to ignite and foster creativity. The same goes for bringing these "blended spaces," "virtual environments" and/or "mixed reality spaces" in industry, society, and scientific contextual networks. It is stated that some topics (i.e. design, creativity, and ideation) need the human touch and a sense of context and personal voice more than others.[3] How is such possible, when most of our technology is based on standardization, uniformity and conformity of ideation, presentation and representation? Colwell[60] states, "if engineers only had to follow a set of directions, we wouldn't need engineers; computers and robots can do that much." In the physical realm the use of tools shows a variety and diversity in use and outcome when used by a plethora of different users. This is often due to or a direct consequence of (intrinsic) skill set, experience, knowledge, understanding and insight in tool use and its prospective usefulness.

The idiosyncratic qualities and capacity will become visible directly and without any hidden surprise.[45] This phenomenon is not only in the process activity but especially in the iterative quality and effectiveness of the chosen tool solution. In digital technology these aspects, of making use of the deep meaning of personhood, are often completely diffuse, consequently reducing the human capacity by illusions of bits; people degrade themselves in order to make machines seem smart all the time.[3] Consequently, the use of tools is no guarantee for success, as "a fool with a tool is still a fool."[61]

9.5 Anti-Fragility, Expectation, Intention, and Promise

Complex systems are full of interdependencies, risks and externalities – these are hard to detect – and have non-linear responses. In effect the odds of rare and peculiar events are not computable or predictable. The anti-fragile gains from prediction errors and gets better over time, whilst going beyond resilience and robustness for that matter. Hidden non-linearities means, that the response is not straight-forward and should not or never be a straight line.[3] Asymmetrical or eccentric positionality entails the possibility to take or view from a different angle or position in order to acquire a new field of vision. "More is thought than people think", Plessner[62] wittily remarked. There is no one in your head who does the thinking.

Material a priori[62] makes the emergence of self-awareness from how life organizes itself formally clear and goes on to demonstrate that material mediation is a necessary condition of human self-articulation.[63] It has been stated that, "we know more than we can tell," pointing towards the vast realm of human tacit knowledge and skills.[47] Each of us has his or her own representation of the outside world in the head, depending on our standpoint in perspectival space. If we move our bodies through space to one another's positions, we can assume one another's standpoints in turns.

Knowledge is thus based on reciprocally compared and corroborated representations of the world, that we perceive somewhere outside ourselves, but that is duplicated inside us in words and images.[63] Human ex-centricity inevitably leads to a division into inner world, outer world, and shared world. This is followed by the famous three primary laws of the ex-centric life form: mediated immediacy, artificiality by nature, and the utopian standpoint. Taken as a whole, this means that the boundaries between inside and outside are not fixed, but that they must be drawn afresh in each historical period, depending on the negotiations between people and their mediatory instances.[62] Kockelkoren[63] states that, "the notion of self has also undergone drastic changes in our everyday experience.

The modern notion of self is relatively recent but has nevertheless become firmly anchored in the popular imagination. We believe that each of us has a highly particular influence on his or her own destiny. We behave as though we are free to organize our lives as we choose. Moreover, we like to believe that our lives form a constant entity that we direct with the aid of the media at our disposal today, such as all kinds of photographic, video and audio technologies plus distribution social networks such as, Facebook, YouTube, WhatsApp, Twitter, Instagram, LinkedIn etc." From Kockelkoren[63] one can deduce that,"… there is little individual about the inner worlds that we put on show. Our cherished interiors are furnished with the clichés of our era. The outside world of trendy brands and status symbols is internalized via the media, arranged to appeal to its target group, and then put on display as a highly individual creation. At most, the self appears as a consistent collage of consumer choices that combine to define a lifestyle. It is no wonder that there are fears of the death of the authentic self today."

9.6 Balance the Interfaces in Virtuality Naturally

Hormesis, is the slight stressor of episodic deprivation. Computer, systems and machine interfaces can activate this "stressor" in users. Furthermore, if windows, icons, menus and pointers (WIMP) interfaces are already 'difficult to use,' because they are too abstract, complex and "unnatural", how can we design virtual environments (VE) that are perceived to be natural? See Refs. 64-68 for more details. When VE interaction is closer to interaction in the "real" physical world (i.e. hybrids, blends, mixed), it becomes easier for users to understand and use digital technologies. Valli[69] clearly sees the necessity of hybrid interaction tools and virtual representation of artefacts that can be manipulated similarly to physical artefacts.

The development of VEs that support natural interaction is proposed by many; "Natural interaction is defined in terms of experience: people naturally communicate through gestures, expressions, movements, and discover the world by looking around and manipulating physical stuff."[68,69] To achieve spontaneous interaction through simplicity and physical interaction the representation of content, organization of information and the interactive device more and more simple and invisible. See Refs. 65, 68 and 69 for more details.

As interactive technologies become more and more embedded and behave more like physical entities, users become less aware of the mediation taking place and the interaction becomes more fluid and natural. The interface should allow the user to think aloud, explore patterns, and experience multi-sensory synaesthesia (*ideasthesia*) that can induce sensations in parts of the body, evoke spatial awareness, and nudge users to explore uncommon sounds by introducing randomness into the process. In addition, it should and could spur improvement on some of the usability deficits of existing design and engineering production tools (i.e. CAD, CAED, etc.). Guidelines derived from Ref. 9, 10 and 68, could be applied and used for design and development of hybrid design tools, systems, and networks:

- Mediate between physical and virtual representations
- Support untethered bi-manual tangible interactions
- Facilitate tinkering and exploration of vision, sound, tangibles, olfactory
- Facilitate a process of iteration, synthesis, and morphing
- Allow for immediate natural interaction
- Allow for intuitive expressiveness of the user
- Be intuitively usable and give the user a sense of being in control
- Facilitate enter flow state
- Support thinking processes and decision making in design ideation
- Support collaboration, conversation, and back and forth signaling between multiple users using multiple tools
- Support ambiguity and randomness
- Support play, fun, and enjoyment

Ishii et al.[70,71] coined the term tangible bits, digital data that can be accessed through interaction with tangible objects. They established three ways of bridging the gap between virtual environments (VE) and physical environments (PE):

- Interactive surfaces in an architectural environment that allow immediate access to a VE
- Hybrid artefacts that allow access to and manipulation of digital data belonging to a physical artefact
- Ambient media such as sound, light, olfactory and temperature that influence and are influenced by users

9.6.1 *Malleable and Shape Changing Interaction Modalities*

Jamming user interfaces (JUI) are malleable and shape changing and perceived to be more organic than traditional interaction modalities, like mouse and keyboard or touchscreens. There are two types of high-resolution shape sensing methods:

Index-matched particles and fluids, and capacitive and electric field sensing. They propose the development of interfaces that are not only deformable and stay in form but can also be computationally actuated to change their material properties like stiffness. They see that so far there have been more advances in shape sensing and mechanical actuation than in particle jamming, which is the computational actuation of material properties.[72]

The Tunable Clay JUI for example is characteristic, it uses a hydraulic system to change the material properties and structured light depth sensing to measure deformation of the interface. Other interfaces that allow for haptic feedback provide information for the user through shape-changing capabilities. Haptic feedback can be categorized into active and passive forms of feedback. Passive feedback is the feedback a matcrial provides because of its properties, for example; foams, springs, and rubbers return to their original state, if deformed to a certain degree. Active feedback, or actuation, is when an active mechanism changes the form of an interface. In mechanical actuation this is often done using electrical motors, as shown in 'Who is Stewart', a tactile interface based on the Stewart platform that can move in six degrees of freedom (DoF), using six servomotors.[73]

It can also be used for haptic input, allowing for tactile communication between the user and the machine.[74] Mechanical actuation and particle jamming provide new ways of providing feedback to users, mostly neglected in traditional UIs. Even though in many buttons' springs are used to provide passive haptic feedback, the full potential of passive feedback modalities has not been explored in traditional UIs. Furthermore, passive feedback is easier to implement in interfaces, since no motors or pumps are needed.

9.7 Design Engineers Engineering Designs

Engineers do not play "war games," in fact they do not play at all; they work. They are not sent to the "negotiating table" (i.e. no doctrines of merchandising and compromise); the perfect and most effective technology possible. In fact, they do not negotiate at all; they calculate.[37]

Design engineers (*designeers*) are much differently "wired" and "trained"; they are thought to play (i.e. thinking, sensorial, imagination), be creatively inclined, use their imagination and act on their "gut feelings." However, the dominant view was that designers focused solely on the surface structure or the visual aesthetics of software and hardware artifacts. This idea of design and designers as having a focus on "*decoration*" is a commonly held belief of design by most people.[75]

Adventurous and unruly (*raw*) "thinking" is dead, the fun and play in thinking is being suppressed or even oppressed, the enchantment of thinking freely, uninhibited disappeared. Most of our current thinking is "geological,'" sort of a hierarchy of layered thoughts, patterns and recurrences. In this, all layers could be explored layer-by layer, ordered, selected, sorted and classified.

Sometimes, we find ourselves in an unsettling unruly, raw, unstructured and highly chaotic realm of thinking (*unconsciously?*). This correction in space and time allows us to create and form new realms, spaces and voids that allow for new concepts, ideas and/or conceptualizations (*consciously?*). In such thinking could be a "*rhizome*" (network) of various bifurcations, ramifications, knots, hubs, connections, openings, and hidden treasure caves. Extended this could lead to renewed creative illusions, novel unexplored realities, and apertures of the thinking-system (ibid).[76] The "rhizome" is *a map and not a tracing*. Make a map, not a tracing. What distinguishes the map from the tracing is that it is entirely oriented toward an experimentation in contact with the real.

The map does not reproduce and unconsciously closed in upon itself; it constructs the unconscious. It fosters connections between variety and diversity of fields and objects (heterogeneity), creates multiplicity in spaces and/or realms, allows a-signifying ruptures to re-stratify everything continuously and, last but not least, it is not amenable to any structural or generative model (decalcomania, cartography). Latour[77] describes these connections (sociology of associations) as always, a matter of *new* connections-and, thereby, concerns a collective that is undergoing constant movement and change. This becomes necessary whenever 'things' accelerate; innovations proliferate; boundaries between groups are blurred; and the number of new entities in the collective multiply. Our present-day, nearby future, and futuristic science-dominated, high-tech society—with its rapid expansion of hybrids—is marked precisely by just such an unstable state of movement and change. Where we previously "*modernized*," we must now "*ecologize*"; where previously we interrupted "*the flow of water*" for purely human purposes, we must now show greater (and humbled) respect for the water's own *finality*.[25]

9.7.1 *The Design Engineering Approach in Education*

In general, design and design engineering graduates are not conscious of user requirements, experiences or attitudes and of their importance in design and engineering. Design and engineering curricula do not typically encourage or reward risk taking, non-linear approaches and experimentation, all of which are reported to develop creativity and innovation. Design and engineering education generally lack encouragement of cycles of divergent and convergent thinking, reflection and incubation that are cited as promoting and developing creativity.

Within the design and engineering curriculum design has been highlighted as the key area providing opportunity for developing creativity. See Refs. 78, 79 and 80 for more detail. The use of open-ended problem scenarios in design teaching is highlighted as important in developing creativity and providing authenticity to the design experience. See Refs. 81, 82 and 83 for more detail. Teamwork/groupwork (collaborative) activities are also cited as important in the development of creativity[80,82,84] and these have been shown to lead to enhanced academic achievement.[85]

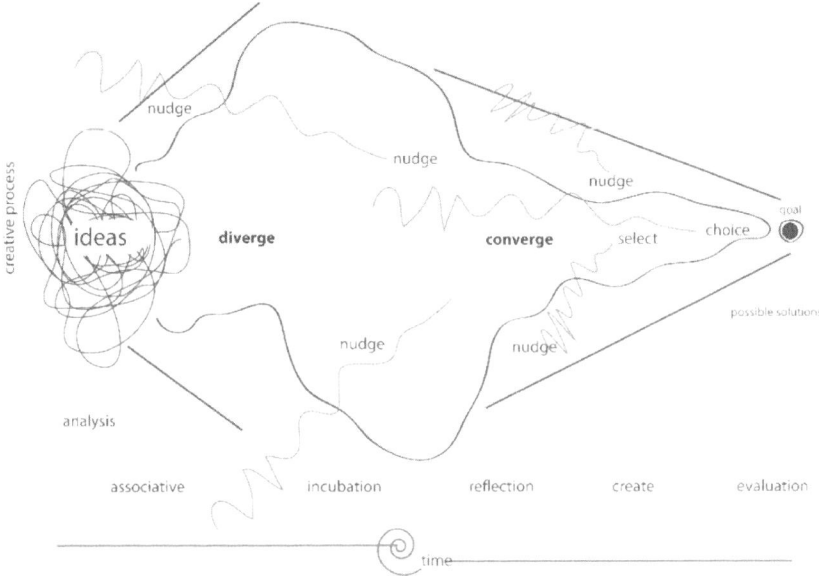

Fig. 9.8. The divergent – convergent design engineering conceptualization process and progressions.

Development of creative and innovative potential has been linked to exposure to, and development of, attitude towards risk taking.[86,87] The development of both divergent and convergent thinking at points within the design process has been linked with creative engineering design[79] and it has been noted that divergent thinking is not particularly encouraged within engineering education.[88] Ref. 89 highlight the importance of awareness of user-requirements and attitudes within design teaching.

Divergent thinking processes are linked with developing creativity, and yet Tornkvist[88] indicates that engineering education does not generally encourage divergent thinking. Many research refers to fostering of creativity using both divergent and convergent thinking, with these happening at key stages of the design process.[80] Other research point and direct the focus on tool use. See Refs. 9, 10, 68 and 90 for more details. They refer to "generation tools" such as creative analysis tools, creative thinking tools, and creative stimuli tools, (Fig. 9.8).

9.8   Tools and Procedures Embedded in Hybrid Multiple Realms and Blended Environments

Kruijff[91] describes that the input and output possibilities are often seen as "system," leading to the notion of a human I/O system (the "human processing unit"), thereby confronting many system-centered design approaches (conventionally user-centered). This way of thinking (-forward) or directing does not mean that humans are seen as "machines", even when sometimes the boundaries between both get very close or "uncanny."

In effect human capacity often reveals incentives to develop conventional, novel, and/or unconventional interfaces, systems and/or tools (IST). "Unconventional" is to describe ISTs that deal with experimental psycho-physiological ways of performing (general) tasks, performing tasks with experimental devices, or experimental tasks. Figure 9.9 illustrate several possible axes (directions) of unconventional (right) and more conventional approaches (left).

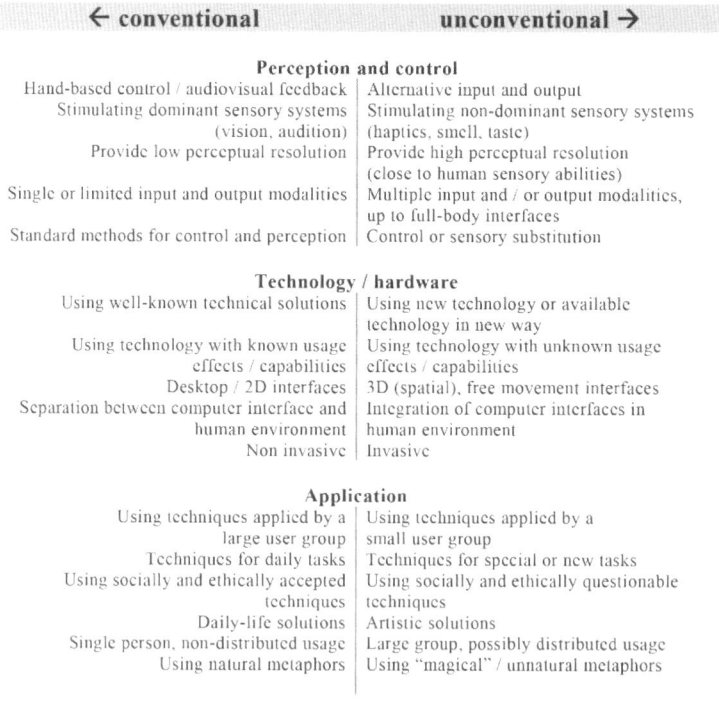

← conventional	unconventional →
Perception and control	
Hand-based control / audiovisual feedback	Alternative input and output
Stimulating dominant sensory systems (vision, audition)	Stimulating non-dominant sensory systems (haptics, smell, taste)
Provide low perceptual resolution	Provide high perceptual resolution (close to human sensory abilities)
Single or limited input and output modalities	Multiple input and / or output modalities, up to full-body interfaces
Standard methods for control and perception	Control or sensory substitution
Technology / hardware	
Using well-known technical solutions	Using new technology or available technology in new way
Using technology with known usage effects / capabilities	Using technology with unknown usage effects / capabilities
Desktop / 2D interfaces	3D (spatial), free movement interfaces
Separation between computer interface and human environment	Integration of computer interfaces in human environment
Non invasive	Invasive
Application	
Using techniques applied by a large user group	Using techniques applied by a small user group
Techniques for daily tasks	Techniques for special or new tasks
Using socially and ethically accepted techniques	Using socially and ethically questionable techniques
Daily-life solutions	Artistic solutions
Single person, non-distributed usage	Large group, possibly distributed usage
Using natural metaphors	Using "magical" / unnatural metaphors

Fig. 9.9. Possible axis of unconventionalism in systems embedded multiple networks or spaces.

In fact, earlier research related the effects of such interfaces to the quality of motor activities, where he defines epistemic or pragmatic actions for classifying designers' motor activities.[92] Epistemic actions to reveal hidden information are difficult for humans to compute mentally. Physical activities help people perform easier, faster, reliably and more on internal cognitive computation. Epistemic actions can improve cognition by:

(i)   decreasing the involvement of memory in mental computation (termed space complexity);

(ii) decreasing the number of mental computation steps (termed time complexity);

(iii) decreasing the rate of mental computation error (termed unreliability).[92]

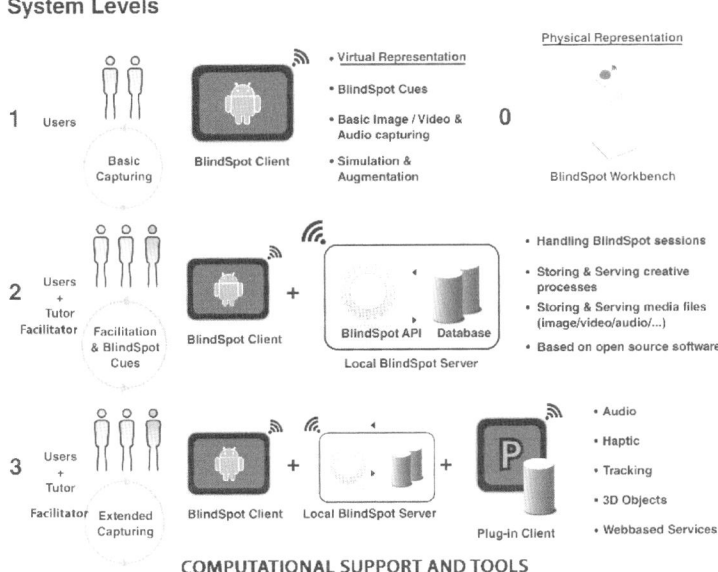

Fig. 9.10. Mobility, lightweight computational support tools, system architecture and variable levels.

Blending realities was already present during the initial wake of the computer-revolution; the idea of "disembodied cognition" became very popular.[93,94] The trouble here is that being "disembodied" created great challenges, frustrations, and problems to solve in human interaction with computers or cyber-physical systems.

The HDTs, for example, in which the user intuition/intention-experience-knowledge (IEK) and human-interaction play an important role are developed congruous with the aspects of quiescence and ambiguous computational tool interaction. Focus and direction of our latest research is on mobility, lightweight, and ease-of-use tools to be part of the crowd and the cloud (Fig. 9.10). See Refs. 9-11, 57-59, 68-72 and 91 for more details.

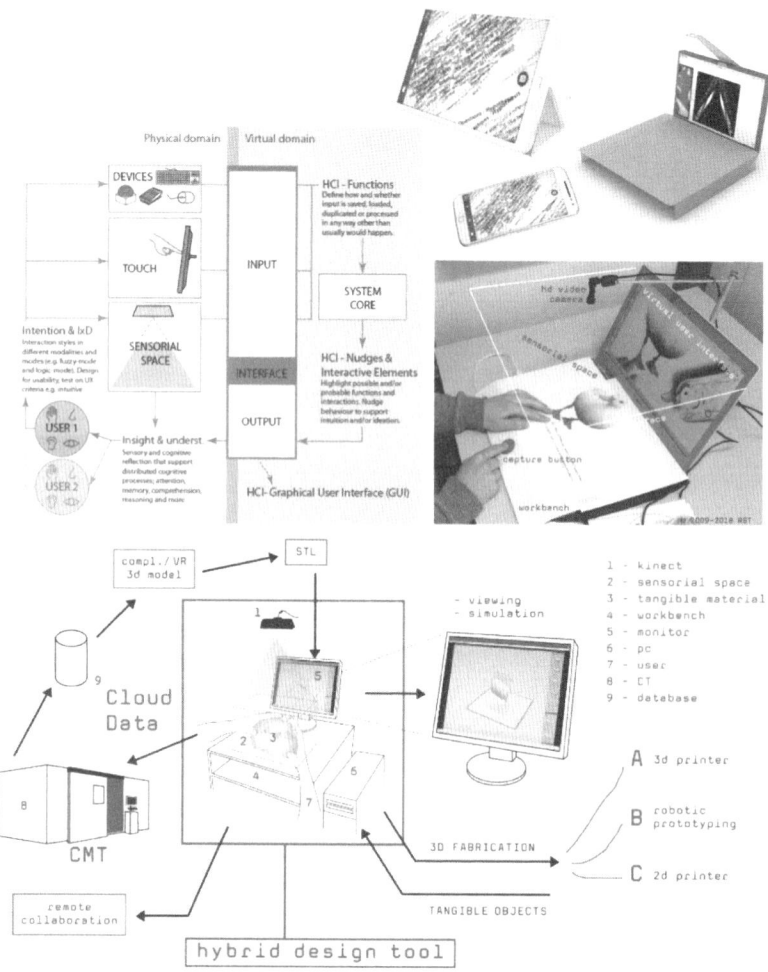

Fig. 9.11. Hybrid design tools, virtual environments and cyber-physical systems.

We need to enable and engage people (society in general) "creatively" (i.e. designers, architects and engineers), to work and explore their ideas, represent fuzzy notions, and express their mental pictures without predefined boundaries and fixed constraints either inside or outside their work environment (e.g. industry, research, workplace, office, studio, garage). The emerging technologies and possibilities of AMS/AMT to be a "free-agent" within the interconnected society change the role of the creative agent. The exterior real world merged with multiple virtual realms (mixed reality) aided with computational tools helps to address this change. For example, the workplace environment is changing; office buildings no longer have a desk for everyone, people work from different places at different times, people become tacit workers, people work more individualistic and work life and home life start blending (Fig. 9.11).

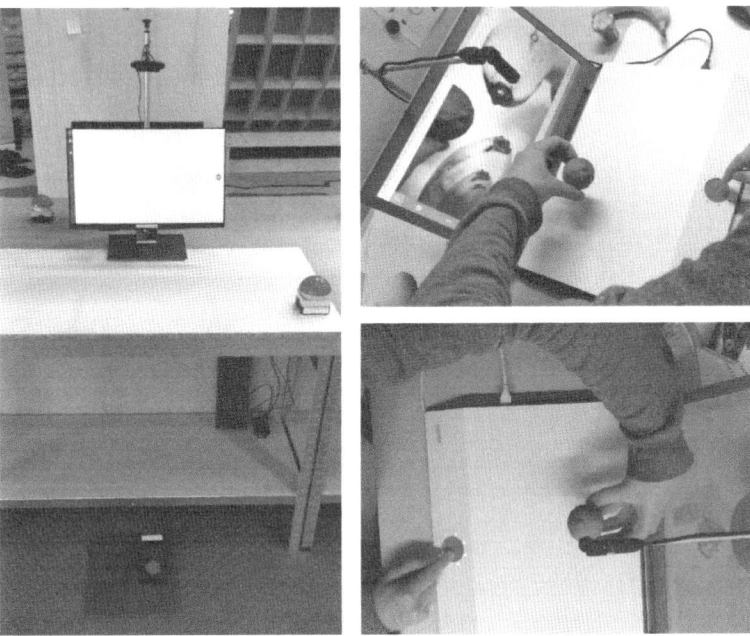

Fig. 9.12. Hybrid design tools – lightweight, mobility, flexible usability, and natural user interactive.

The challenges are to understand more about the nature and value of informal and spontaneous communicative activity and seeing whether technology could be fruitfully employed to aid it.[95] Exploration, representation, and externalization combined with user in-the-loop, user-out-the-loop, or on-the-loop mobility will extend the horizon and trigger imagination to support creativity and innovative activities. User feedback, trackback, automatic synthesis, and workflow greatly influences the performance, fidelity, and usability of the apps, tools, and/or devices' functionality, interaction, and communication (Fig. 9.12).

We postulate that indeed a high-level of visual literacy is needed, whilst an abundance in tactile and tangible materials, objects, tools and artefacts at-hand, on-hand and in-hand are equally important to enhance creativity and foster learning. Congruously hybrid tools, environments and spaces to support and assist people (e.g. designers, engineers) to exploit, explore, and externalize their ideas, even if it stems from ludic fallacy or illusions-of-bits,[96] serve to increase their potential skills, augment their creativity,[97,98] improve human capacity, boost their motivation[99] and conceivably trigger the discovery of raw serendipity.[7,9]

References

1. V. Papava, Technological backwardness — global reality and expected challenges for the world's economy. *Georgian Foundation for Strategic and International Studies*, Expert Opinion 70, (2016).
2. H. Nowotny, *The Cunning of Uncertainty*. John Wiley & Sons (2015).
3. N. N. Taleb, *Antifragile: How to Live in a World We Don't Understand* (Vol. 3). London, Allen Lane (2012).
4. D. Vandepitte and D. Moens, Quantification of uncertain and variable model parameters in non-deterministic analysis. In *IUTAM Symposium on the Vibration Analysis of Structures with Uncertainties,* pp. 15–28 (2011).
5. Y. Elkana and H. Klöpper, *The University in the 21st Century: Teaching the New Enlightenment in the Digital Age*. Central European University Press, Budapest (2012, Transl. 2016).
6. H. F. Barber, Developing strategic leadership: The US army war college experience, *Journal of Management Development* 11(6), 4–12 (1992).
7. G. Goldschmidt, Ubiquitous serendipity: Potential visual design stimuli are everywhere. In *Studying Visual and Spatial Reasoning for Design Creativity*, John S. Gero (ed.), Springer (2015).
8. H. A. Simon, The structure of ill structured problems, *Artificial Intelligence* 4(3–4), 81–201 (1973).
9. R. E. Wendrich, Hybrid design tools for conceptual design and design engineering processes: bridging the design gap: towards an intuitive design tool. PhD Thesis, University of Twente (2016).
10. R. E. Wendrich, and R. Kruiper, Keep IT real: On tools, emotion, cognition and intentionality in design. In DS 84: *Proceedings of the DESIGN 2016 14th International Design Conference* (2016).
11. R. E. Wendrich, Blended spaces for integrated creativity and play in design and engineering processes, *Journal of Computer Information Science Engineering*, 16(3), 031005 (2016).
12. B. Tversky, On abstraction and ambiguity. In *Studying Visual and Spatial Reasoning for Design Creativity*, John S. Gero (ed.). Springer (2015).
13. M. R. Endsley, Measurement of situation awareness in dynamic systems. *Human Factors* 37(1), 65–84 (1995).
14. R. F. Woodbury and A. L. Burrow, Whither design space, *AI Edam* 20(2), 63–82 (2006).
15. D. C. Dennett, *The Intentional Stance*. MIT Press (1989).
16. D. C. Dennett, Intentional systems. *The Journal of Philosophy* 68(4), 87–106 (1971).
17. D. C. Dennett, *Intuition Pumps and Other Tools for Thinking*. WW Norton & Company (2013).
18. M. McCullough, *Abstracting Craft*. The MIT Press (1996).
19. C. Lévi-Strauss, Culinary triangle. *New Society* 8(221), 937–940 (1966).
20. R. Sennett, *The Craftsman*. Yale University Press (2008).
21. V. Flusser, *The Shape of Things: A Philosophy of Design*. Reaktion Books (1999).
22. Y. N. Harari, *Homo Deus: A Brief History of Tomorrow*. Random House (2016).
23. H. Lasi, P. Fettke, H. G. Kemper, T. Feld, and M. Hoffmann, Industry 4.0. *Business & Information Systems Engineering* 6(4), 239–242 (2014).

24. F. Tao, Y. Cheng, L. Zhang, and A. Y. Nee, Advanced manufacturing systems: socialization characteristics and trends. *Journal of Intelligent Manufacturing* **28**(5), 1079–1094 (2017).

25. B. Latour, *We Have Never Been Modern.* Harvard University Press (1993).

26. T. Stürmlinger, B. Gladysz, M. Strauch, and A. Albers, Design with Industry 4.0 - Priorization of sensor data for a smart data driven product development process. In *Proceedings of the Twelfth International Symposium on Tools and Methods of Competitive Engineering*, Gran Canaria, Spain (2018).

27. S. J. Hu, Evolving paradigms of manufacturing: From mass production to mass customization and personalization. *Procedia CIRP* **7**, 3–8 (2013).

28. B. Latour, *Pandora's Hope: Essays on the Reality of Science Studies.* Harvard University Press (1999).

29. B. Latour, From the world of science to the world of research? *Science* **280**(5361), 208–209 (1998).

30. B. Latour, *Science in Action: How to Follow Scientists and Engineers Through Society.* Harvard University Press (1987).

31. A. Shah, and R. Patel, Problems and challenges faced by handicraft artisans. *Voice of Research* **6**(1), 57–61 (2017).

32. K. K. Mahato, P. C. Kalita, and A. K. Das, Design intervention for productivity improvement in glass bangles manufacturing unit. In *Proceedings of the Twelfth International Symposium on Tools and Methods of Competitive Engineering*, Gran Canaria, Spain (2018).

33. M. L. Meena, G. S. Dangayach, and A. Bhardwaj, Measuring quality of work life among workers in handicraft industries of Jaipur. *International Journal of Industrial and Systems Engineering* **17**(3), 376–390 (2014).

34. S. M. Ghouse, INDIAN Handicraft Industry: Problems and Strategies. *International Journal of Management Research and Reviews* **2**(7), 1183 (2012).

35. S. K. Hashmi, Market for indian handicrafts. *International Journal of Engineering Technology and Management Science* **1**(1), 1–7 (2012).

36. L. Gabora, Revenge of the "neurds": Characterizing creative thought in terms of the structure and dynamics of memory. *Creativity Research Journal* **22**(1), 1–13 (2010).

37. B. Latour and C. Porter, *Aramis, or, The Love of Technology.* Harvard University Press (1996).

38. N. Cross, Design research: A disciplined conversation. *Design Issues* **15**(2), 5–10 (1999).

39. A. N. Whitehead and D. W. Sherburne, *Process and Reality.* Macmillan (1957).

40. C. C. Miller and R. D. Ireland, Intuition in strategic decision making: Friend or foe in the fast-paced 21st Century? *Academy of Management Perspectives* **19**(1), 19–30 (2005).

41. M. Maruyama, The second cybernetics: Deviation-amplifying mutual causal processes. *American Scientist* **51**(2), 164–179 (1963).

42. R. Kruiper, Enhanced hybrid design tool environment, MsC Thesis, University of Twente, (2015).

43. M. Johnson, *The Body in the Mind: The Bodily Basis of Meaning, Imagination, and Reason.* University of Chicago Press (1987).

44. M. Brereton Distributed cognition in engineering design: Negotiating between abstract and material representations. In *Design Representation*, Gabriela Goldschmidt and W. L. Porter (eds.) Springer (2004).

45. R. E. Wendrich, A novel approach for collaborative interaction with mixed reality in value engineering. In *ASME 2011 World Conference on Innovative Virtual Reality,* pp. 103–111, (January 2011).

46. R. E. Wendrich and M. D'Cruz, *Blind Spots: Scenarios for Nurturing Creativity and Creative Potential in Design and Engineering Education.* University of Twente, The Netherlands & University of Nottingham, UK, (2011). Available at: https://research.utwente.nl/en/publications/hybrid-design-tools-for-conceptual-design-and-design-engineering-processes(917e19ae-f865-4110-ae36-ec6aa571f3d4).html (Accessed December 1, 2019).

47. M. Polanyi, *The Tacit Dimension.* The University of Chicago Press (1964).

48. K. Grant, Tacit knowledge revisited — We can still learn from Polanyi. *The Electronic Journal of Knowledge Management* **5**(2), 173–180 (2011).

49. R. J. Sternberg and T. I. Lubart, An investment theory of creativity and its development. *Human Development* **34**(1), 1–31 (1991).

50. R. J. Sternberg and T. I. Lubart, *Defying the Crowd: Cultivating Creativity in a Culture of Conformity.* Free Press (1995).

51. J. Kang, K. Zhong, S. Qin, H. Wang, and D. Wright, Instant 3D design concept generation and visualization by real-time hand gesture recognition. *Computers in Industry* **64**(7), 785–797 (2013).

52. A. F. Osborn, *Applied Imagination: Principles and Procedures of Creative Thinking.* Iyer Press (1953).

53. R. E. Wendrich, H. Tragter, F. G. M. Kokkeler, and F. J. A. M. van Houten, Bridging the design gap: Towards an intuitive design tool. In *Proceedings of the ICSID World Design Conference* (2009).

54. H. C. Jetter, H. Reiterer, and F. Geyer, Blended interaction: Understanding natural human computer interaction in post-WIMP interactive spaces, *Personal and Ubiquitous Computing* **18**, 1139–1158 (2014).

55. G. Lakoff and M. Johnson, *Metaphors We Live By. University* of Chicago Press (1980).

56. F. Müller, M. Pache, and U. Lindemann, Digital free-hand sketching in 3D-a tool for early design phases. In *DS 31: Proceedings of ICED 03, the 14th International Conference on Engineering Design*, pp. 129–130, Stockholm, Sweden (2003).

57. R. E. Wendrich, The creative act is done on the hybrid machine. In *DS 75-1: Proceedings of the 19th International Conference on Engineering Design (ICED13)*, Design for Harmonies, Vol. 1: Design Processes, pp. 399–408, Seoul, Korea, (August 2013).

58. Z. Kosmadoudi, T. Lim, J. M. Ritchie, Y. Liu, R. Sung, J. B. Hauge, S. Garbaya, R. E. Wendrich, and I. A. Stanescu, Harmonizing interoperability–emergent serious gaming in playful stochastic CAD environments. In *International Conference on Games and Learning Alliance*, pp. 390–399 (October, 2013).

59. R. E. Wendrich, Hybrid design tools for design and engineering processing. In *Advances in Computers and Information in Engineering Research, Volume 1*, John G. Michopoulos, Christiaan J.J. Paredis, David W. Rosen, Judy M. Vance (eds). ASME Press (2014).

60. B. Colwell, Complexity in design, *Computer* **38**(10), 10–12 (2005).

61. O. Gassmann and F. Schweitzer, Managing the unmanageable: The fuzzy front end of innovation. In *Management of the Fuzzy Front End of Innovation,* Oliver Gassmann and Fiona Schweitzer (eds.). Springer (2014).

62. H. Plessner, *Die Stufen des Organischen und der Mensch: Einleitung in die philosophische Anthropologie* (Vol. 2200). Walter de Gruyter (1975).

63. P. Kockelkoren, The quest for the sources of the self, seen from the vantage point of Plessner's material a priori. In *Plessner's Philosophical Anthropology*, Jos de Mul (ed). Amsterdam University Press (2014).

64. M. Beaudouin-Lafon, Instrumental interaction: an interaction model for designing post-WIMP user interfaces. In *Proceedings of the SIGCHI conference on Human Factors in Computing Systems,* pp. 446–453 (2000).

65. M. Weiser, The computer for the 21st century. *Scientific American* **265**(3), 94–105 (1991).

66. A. Van Dam, Post-WIMP user interfaces. *Communications of the ACM* **40**(2), 63–67 (1997).

67. M. Billinghurst, Crossing the chasm. In *International Conference on Augmented Tele-Existence (ICAT 2001),* pp. 5–7, Tokyo, Japan (2001).

68. R. E. Wendrich, Rawshaping formfinding: Tacit tangible CAD. *Computer Aided Design and Applications* **7**(4), 505–531 (2010).

69. A. Valli, The design of natural interaction, *Multimedia Tools and Applications* **38**(3), 295–305 (2006).

70. H. Ishii and B. Ullmer, Tangible bits: towards seamless interfaces between people, bits and atoms. In *Proceedings of the ACM SIGCHI Conference on Human Factors in Computing Systems,* pp. 234–241 (March 1997).

71. H. Ishii, C. Ratti, B. Piper, Y. Wang, A. Biderman, and E. Ben-Joseph, Bringing clay and sand into digital design—Continuous tangible user interfaces, *BT Technology Journal* **22**(4), 287–299 (2004).

72. S. Follmer, D. Leithinger, A. Olwal, N. Cheng, and H. Ishii, Jamming user interfaces: programmable particle stiffness and sensing for malleable and shape-changing devices. In *Proceedings of the 25th Annual ACM Symposium on User Interface Software and Technology,* pp. 519–528 (October 2012).

73. F. Ros, http://felixros.com/stewart.html (Online). (Accessed July 2018).

74. J. Terken, P. Levy, C. Wang, J. Karjanto, N. M. Yusof, F. Ros, and S. Zwaan, Gesture-based and haptic interfaces for connected and autonomous driving. In *Advances in Human Factors and System Interactors,* Isabel L. Nunes (ed). Springer (2017).

75. J. Zimmerman, J. Forlizzi and S. Evenson, Research through design as a method for interaction design research in HCI. In *Proceedings of the SIGCHI Conference on Human Factors in Computing Systems*, pp. 493–502 (2007).

76. G. Deleuze and F. Guattari, *A Thousand Plateaus: Capitalism and Schizophrenia.* Bloomsbury Publishing (1988).

77. B. Latour, Network theory|networks, societies, spheres: Reflections of an actor-network theorist, *International Journal of Communication* **5**, 15 (2011).

78. E. Petty, Engineering curricula for encouraging creativity and innovation, *European Journal of Engineering Education* **8**(1), 29–43 (1983).

79. C. Charyton, R.J. Jagacinski, and J.A. Merrill, CEDA: A research instrument for creative engineering design assessment, *Psychology of Aesthetics, Creativity and the Arts* **2**(3), 147–154 (2008).

80. Y. L. Wong and K. W. M. Siu, A model of creative design process for fostering creativity of students in design education, *International Journal of Technology and Design Education* **22**, 437–450 (2012).

81. A. Rugarcia, R. M. Felder, D. R. Woods, and J. E. Stice, The future of engineering education I. A vision for a new century, *Chemical Engineering Education* **34**(1), 16–25 (2000).

82. A. Silva, E. Henriques, and A. Carvalho, Creativity enhancement in a product development course through entrepreneurship learning and intellectual property awareness, *European Journal of Engineering Education* **34**(1), 63–75 (2009).

83. N. W. Page and D. N. P. Murthy, A programme to integrate engineering, creativity and management in undergraduate teaching, *European Journal of Engineering Education* **15**(4), 369–381 (1990).

84. C.K. Chan, B.C., Jiang, and K.Y. Hsu, An empirical study of industrial engineering and management curriculum reform in fostering students' creativity, *European Journal of Engineering Education* **30**(2), 191–202 (2005).

85. L. Springer, M. E. Stanne, and S. S. Donovan,   Effects of small-group learning on undergraduates in science, mathematics, engineering and technology: A meta-analysis, *Review of Educational Research* **69**(1), 21–25 (1999).

86. T. N. Garavan and B. O'Cinneide, Entrepreneurship education and training programmes: A review and evaluation – Part 1, *Journal of European Industrial Training* **18**(8), 3–12 (1994).

87. E. McWilliams and S. Haukka, Educating the creative workforce; new directions for twenty-first century schooling, *British Educational Research Journal* **34**(5), 651–666 (2008).

88. S. Törnkvist, Creativity: Can it be taught? The case of engineering education, *European Journal of Engineering Education* **23**(1), 5–12 (1990).

89. J. Murray and R. Renton, Creativity and technology; Industrial design education for manufacturing industry — the Napier Experience, *European Journal of Engineering* **13**(2), 161–166 (1988).

90. T. J. Howard, S. J. Culley, and E. A. Dekoninck, Describing the creative design process by the integration of engineering design and cognitive psychology literature, *Design Studies*, **29**(2), 160–180 (2008).

91. E. Kruijff, Unconventional 3-D user interfaces for virtual environments. PhD Thesis, University of Hamburg (2006).

92. G. Fitzmaurice, Graspable user interfaces. PhD Thesis, University of Toronto (1996).

93. B. Tversky and B. M. Hard, Embodied and disembodied cognition: Spatial perspective-taking, *Cognition*, **110**(1), 124–129 (2009).

94. B. Z. Mahon and A. Caramazza, A critical look at the embodied cognition hypothesis and a new proposal for grounding conceptual content, *Journal of Physiology-Paris*, **102**(1), 59–70 (2008).

95. F. Hickmann, Serendipity at the workplace for future tacit workers. PhD Thesis, Delft University of Technology (2009).

96. J. Lanier, *You Are Not A Gadget.* Penguin (2010).

97. M. Billinghurst, H. Kato, and I. Poupyrev, Tangible augmented reality, *ACM SIGGRAPH ASIA*, 7, (2008).

98. T. J. Howard, S. J. Culley, and E. A. Dekoninck, Reuse of ideas and concepts for creative stimuli in engineering design, *Journal of Engineering Design*, **22**(8), 565–581 (2010).

99. E. Petty, Engineering curricula for encouraging creativity and innovation, *European Journal of Engineering Education*, **8**(1), 29–43 (1983).